NATIONAL CURRICULUM MATHEMATICS
Level 7

K.M. VICKERS

Authors
K.M. VICKERS
M.J. TIPLER
H.L. van HIELE

Copyright ©
K.M. VICKERS
H.L. van HIELE

First Published March 1992
Reprinted twice in 1992
Reprinted four times in 1993
Reprinted February 1994

ISBN 1-873941-01-3

Published by
Canterbury Educational Ltd
Canterbury House
1 Sheffield Road
Southborough, Tunbridge Wells
Kent TN4 0PD

Printed at
Printed at Alden Press Limited
Oxford and Northampton, Great Britain

Preface

"National Curriculum Mathematics" by K.M. Vickers, M.J. Tipler and H.L. van Hiele is a complete course of six books for pupils aged from 11 to 16. This is the fifth of the seven books. It covers all the material in Level 7 of the National Curriculum. This book i arranged in four separate sections: Number, Algebra, Shape and Space, Data Handling. Using and Applying Mathematics is integrated throughout each chapter of these sections. The material is presented in this order to enable a pupil, or a group of pupils, to work across different areas of mathematics at different levels, as required by the National Curriculum.

Each section begins with revision from Levels 1 to 6, printed on pink paper for ease of identification and to distinguish it from Level 7 material. Each section ends with a review chapter which contains revision questions on the Level 7 material. In each of the other chapters, every skill developing exercise finishes with review questions.

This book does not replace the teacher. Rather, it is a resource for both the pupil and the teacher. The teacher can be flexible about what is taught and when.

Throughout the book there is a variety of activities: skill developing exercises, investigations, practical work, problem solving activities, discussion exercises, puzzles and games. All the activities are related to the topic being studied. Whenever possible, activities and exercises have been written as open rather than closed tasks.

There is a good balance between tasks which develop knowledge, skills and understanding, and those which develop the ability to tackle and solve problems. Many activities do both. There is a thorough and careful development of each topic. Questions within each exercise or activity are carefully graded to build pupil confidence.

This book takes into consideration:
> pupils' needs
> pupils' interests
> pupils' experiences
> the need for pupils to explore mathematics
> the use of technology
> both independent and co-operative work habits

This book encourages pupils to:
> use a wide range of mathematics
> discuss mathematical ideas
> undertake investigations
> participate in practical activities
> use reference material
> relate mathematics to everyday life
> select appropriate methods for a task
> analyse and communicate information

2

discuss difficulties
ask questions

It is hoped that the pupil who uses this book will:
    develop a real interest in mathematics
    become well motivated
    gain much enjoyment from mathematics
    develop a fascination with mathematics
    develop an ability to use mathematics in other subjects
    become confident in the use of the calculator and computer
    gain a firm foundation for further study
    become proficient at applying mathematics to everyday life
    develop both independent and co-operative work habits
    become aware of the power and purpose of mathematics
    develop an ability to communicate mathematics
    develop an appreciation of the relevance of mathematics
    develop an ability to think precisely, logically and creatively
    become confident at mathematics
    gain a sense of satisfaction

Calculator keying sequences are for the Casio FX82C and FX82D calculators. Some slight variation may be needed for other makes and models.
The programming language used is BBC BASIC.

K.M. Vickers

Note for this printing

A supplement has been added to this printing so that this book covers **all** the material in the December 1991 syllabus for Level 7.
The only differences between the 1989 and 1991 Programmes of Study are:

No longer in: solving inequalities on the number line
Now in: measurement degree of accuracy; compound measures

With the exception of the Programme of Study and Statements of Attainment on pages 8 and 9, all the pages in this book are identical with those of earlier printings. The publishers have deliberately placed the supplement at the end of the book rather than integrating it in the book, to enable teachers to use copies from this printing alongside copies from earlier printings with pupils in the same class. If a pupil is referred to any particular page the contents on that page will be the same in all printings.

K.M. Vickers

Contents

NUMBER

ALGEBRA

SHAPE and SPACE

DATA HANDLING

LEVEL 7

PROGRAMME of STUDY	STATEMENTS of ATTAINMENT

AT1

- following new lines of investigation using alternative methods to overcome difficulties; devising a mathematical task; working methodically within an agreed structure; using judgement in the use of given information, using 'trial and improvement' methods and reviewing progress.

    (a) Follow new lines of enquiry when investigating within mathematics itself or when using mathematics to solve a real-life problem.

- following a chain of mathematical reasoning; spotting inconsistencies.

    (b) Examine and comment constructively on generalisations or solutions.

AT2

- multiplying and dividing mentally single-digit multiples of any power of 10, realising that with a number less than one, multiplication has a decreasing effect and division has an increasing effect.

    (a) Multiply and divide mentally single-digit multiples of any power of 10.

- solving problems and using multiplication and division with numbers of any size.

    (b) Use a calculator efficiently when solving problems.

- expressing positive integers as a product of primes.

- using the memory and bracket facilities of a calculator to plan a calculation and evaluate expressions.

- recognising that measurement is approximate; and choosing the degree of accuracy appropriate for a particular purpose.

    (c) Recognise that measurement is approximate and choose the degree of accuracy appropriate for a particular purpose.

- recognising that a measurement expressed to a given unit is in possible error of half a unit.

- understanding and using compound measures, e.g. speed, density.

AT3

- using symbolic notation to express the rules of sequences.

    (a) Use symbolic notation to express the rules of sequences.

- exploring complex number patterns generated by a computer.

- using the rules of indices for positive integer values.

- understanding the meaning of reciprocals and exploring relationships.

- solving a range of polynomial equations by 'trial and improvement' methods.

    (b) Solve equations or simple inequalities.

- using algebraic and graphical methods to solve simultaneous equations in two variables.

8

- drawing and interpreting the graphs of linear functions.

- generating various types of graph on a computer or calculator and interpreting them.

- constructing and interpreting flow diagrams with and without loops.

AT4
- using co-ordinates to locate position in 3-D.

- determining the locus of an object moving subject to a rule.

- understanding and applying Pythagoras' theorem.

- using knowledge and skills in length, area and volume to carry out calculations in plane and solid shapes.

- enlarging a shape by a fractional scale factor.

(a) Use co-ordinates (x, y, z) to locate position in 3-D.

(b) Determine the locus of an object which is moving subject to a rule.

(c) Use Pythagoras' theorem.

(d) Carry out calculations in plane and solid shapes.

AT5
- specifying a simple hypothesis; designing and using an appropriate questionnaire or method to test it; collecting and analysing results to see whether a hypothesis is valid.

- using and recording grouped data with class intervals suitably defined; producing a frequency table; calculating the mean using a calculator.

- comparing the mean, median, mode and range of a frequency distribution, where appropriate, for given sets of data, and interpreting the results.

- drawing a frequency polygon as a line graph from a frequency distribution for grouped data; making comparisons between two frequency distributions.

- constructing and interpreting flow diagrams with and without loops.

- drawing a line of 'best fit' by inspection on a scatter diagram.

- understanding and using relative frequency as an estimate of probability.

- appreciating, when assigning probabilities, that relative frequency and equally likely considerations may not be appropriate and 'subjective' estimates of probability have to be made.

- understanding and applying the addition of probabilities for mutually exclusive events.

(a) Organise and analyse data.

(b) Understand and use relative frequency as an estimate of probability.

(c) Given the probability of exclusive events, calculate the probability of a combined event.

9

Acknowledgements

The author wishes to thank all those firms and enterprises who have so kindly given permission to reproduce tables and other material. A special thanks to S.M. Bennett, S.P.R. Coxon, J.A. Ogilvie and S. Napier for their valuable contributions and to F. Tunnicliffe for the illustrations.

Photographs on pages 24, 30, 44, 62, 72, 82, 92, 102, 144, 150, 164, 178, 202, 232, 238, 258, 266, 284 and 294 by kind permission of Dr P.M. van Hiele.

NUMBER

Number from Previous Levels

Calculation

The scientific calculator does operations in the correct order. An expression such as $14 - 2 (5 + 1)$ is keyed in as 14 $\boxed{-}$ 2 $\boxed{\times}$ $\boxed{[}$ 5 $\boxed{+}$ 1 $\boxed{]}$ $\boxed{=}$ to get the correct answer of 2. (Some calculators do not need the $\times$ pressed before the [sign.)

If an expression such as $14 - 2 (5 + 1)$ is worked out without the calculator we must
  1. work out the brackets first
  2. then do $\times$ and $\div$
  3. finally do $+$ and $-$

For instance, $14 - 2 (5 + 1) = 14 - 2 \times 6$
$$= 14 - 12$$
$$= 2$$

The word "of", used in calculation, means "multiply".

For instance, $\frac{5}{6}$ of 42 means $\frac{5}{6} \times 42$. That is, $\frac{5}{6}$ of $42 = 35$.

3^4 is read as "three to the power of four" and means $3 \times 3 \times 3 \times 3$. That is, $3^4 = 81$.

To multiply 23×90, without using the calculator, first multiply 23 by 10 to get 230; then multiply 230 by 9 to get 2070.

To divide 3600 by 400, without using the calculator, first divide 3600 by 100 to get 36; then divide 36 by 4 to get 9.

Methods for **long multiplication** and **long division,** without using the calculator, are shown below.

$895 \div 41$

```
                41
                         895
     10  | 410  |  -  410
                         485
     10  | 410  |  -  410
                          75
      1  |  41  |  -   41
     ─────        ────────
      21                34
       ↑                 ↑
    answer           remainder
```

895 × 41		800	90	5
	40	32000	3600	200
	1	800	90	5

$$895 \times 41 = 32000 + 3600 + 200 + 800 + 90 + 5$$
$$= 36695$$

Decimals

The number 76·48 is read as "seventy six point four eight".
Digits after the decimal point are read separately but digits before the point are not.

Place value is given by the following.

100000	10000	1000	100	10	1	$\frac{1}{10}$	$\frac{1}{100}$	$\frac{1}{1000}$

For instance, the number 4809·203 consists of four thousands
eight hundreds
nine ones (or units)
two tenths
and three thousandths

A decimal such as 0·166666, in which the digit 6 repeats, is called a **recurring decimal**; it is written as 0·1$\dot{6}$.

Approximation and Estimation

To approximate (round) to d.p. (**decimal places**), decide how many figures are wanted after the decimal point. Omit all the following figures with the proviso that, if the first figure omitted is 5 or larger, increase the last figure kept by 1.
For instance, 34·548 rounded to 1d.p. is 34·5, 34·548 rounded to 2d.p. is 34·55.

To approximate to s.f. (**significant figures**), count from the first non-zero figure. Zeros may need to be inserted so the size of the number is unchanged.
For instance, 34·548 rounded to 3 s.f. is 34·5; 34·548 rounded to 1s.f. is 30; 0·03458 rounded to 2 s.f. is 0·035.

Finding a rough answer to a calculation is called **estimating** an answer. To estimate an answer proceed as follows.
Step 1   Round each number in the calculation to one (or perhaps two) significant figures.
Step 2   Use these rounded figures in the calculation to get an estimate of the answer.
For instance, an estimate of the answer to 212·4 × 9·8 is 200 × 10 = 2000.

Always estimate the answer when using the calculator for a calculation.

Number Lines. Negative Numbers

< means "is less than"   > means "is greater than"
On a number line, the smaller a number the further to the left it is placed.
For instance, since 2·1 < 2·8, 2·1 is to the left of 2·8 on a number line ;
since $\frac{4}{5}$ > $\frac{2}{5}$, $\frac{4}{5}$ is to the right of $\frac{2}{5}$ on a number line.

The $\boxed{\pm/-}$ key on the calculator is pressed to display a negative number.
Positive numbers, such as +2, may be written without any sign.
Negative numbers, such as –2, are always written with the negative sign.
The negative numbers are shown on a number line, or scale, as numbers that are less than zero.

Problem Solving

The **"trial and improvement"** method of finding an answer to a problem consists of the following steps.
  Step 1   Guess a likely answer.
  Step 2   Check to see this answer fits the given facts (the trial).
  Step 3   Make a better guess (the improvement).
Repeat from Step 2 until the actual answer is found.

Fractions and Ratio

In the fraction $\frac{4}{9}$, 4 is called the **numerator** ; 9 is called the **denominator**.
The numerator is the number on top ; the denominator is the number on the bottom.

$\frac{4}{9}$ is read as "four-ninths" and means 4 divided by 9. It also means 4 parts out of every 9.
$\frac{4}{9}$ may also be written as the **ratio** 4 : 9.

The ratio of two quantities x and y is written as x : y and is read as "the ratio of x to y".
A ratio compares quantities of the same kind.
For instance, if A = 3cm and B = 7mm then the ratio A : B is 3cm : 7mm which is 30mm : 7mm or simply 30 : 7.

Equivalent fractions (equal fractions) may be formed by multiplying (or dividing) both the numerator and denominator by the same number.

For instance, since $\frac{16}{24} = \frac{32}{48}$ (multiplying top and bottom by 2)

and $\frac{16}{24} = \frac{2}{3}$ (dividing top and bottom by 8)

then $\frac{2}{3}, \frac{16}{24}, \frac{32}{48}$ are equivalent fractions.

Equivalent ratios (equal ratios) may be formed by multiplying (or dividing) both parts of a ratio by the same number.
For instance, the ratios $2 : 3$, $16 : 24$ and $32 : 48$ are equivalent ratios.

A fraction (or a ratio) is written as the **simplest fraction** (or **simplest ratio**) if the numbers in the fraction (or ratio) are the smallest possible whole numbers. A fraction written in its simplest form is said to be written in its **lowest terms**.

For instance, since $\frac{16}{24} = \frac{2}{3}$ we say that, in its lowest terms the fraction $\frac{16}{24}$ is $\frac{2}{3}$.

For instance, since $1 \cdot 2 : 3 = 12 : 30 = 2 : 5$, we say that $1 \cdot 2 : 3$ written as the simplest ratio is $2 : 5$.

To **increase** (or decrease) a quantity **by a given fraction** firstly work out the actual increase (or decrease).

For instance, to decrease 720cm by $\frac{1}{3}$ proceed as follows:

Step 1 $\frac{1}{3}$ of 720cm = 240cm

Step 2   Decrease 720cm by 240cm to get the answer of 480cm.

To **increase** (or **decrease**) a quantity **in a given ratio** firstly rewrite the ratio as a fraction.
For instance, to increase 100g in the ratio $5 : 4$ proceed as follows:

Step 1   Rewrite $5 : 4$ as $\frac{5}{4}$

Step 2   Find $\frac{5}{4} \times 100$g = 125g

To **share in a given ratio** proceed as shown in the following example.
Example   To share £600 between two people in the ratio $2 : 3$ take the following
steps:

Step 1   For every £2 that the first person gets, the second person gets £3. That is, from every £5 the first person gets £2 and the second person gets £3. Hence the first person gets $\frac{2}{5}$ of the money ; the second person gets $\frac{3}{5}$.

Step 2 $\frac{2}{5}$ of £600 = £240 ; $\frac{3}{5}$ of £600 = £360.
Hence one person gets £240 and the other gets £360.

Percentages

7% means 7 parts in every 100. That is, 7% means $\frac{7}{100}$.

Any percentage, decimal, fraction or ratio may be written in one of the other forms.

For instance, 7% may be rewritten as $\frac{7}{100}$ or 0·07 or 7 : 100.

For instance, $\frac{2}{5}$ may be rewritten as 0·4 or 40% or 2 : 5.

For instance, 0·61 may be rewritten as $\frac{61}{100}$ or 61% or 61 : 100.

For instance, 3 : 4 may be rewritten as $\frac{3}{4}$ or 0·75 or 75%.

In **percentage calculations** we usually rewrite the percentage as either a fraction or a decimal.

For instance, to find 15% of £5 we may begin with $\frac{15}{100} \times £5$ or 0·15 × £5 to get answer of 75p.

To **write a given quantity as a percentage of another quantity** proceed as follows:

 Step 1   Write the given quantity as a fraction of the other quantity.
 Step 2   Rewrite this fraction as a percentage.

For instance, £5 as a fraction of £8 is $\frac{5}{8} = \frac{5}{8} \times 100\%$
$$= 62\cdot5\%$$

Time Measure

$$1 \text{ minute} = 60 \text{ seconds}$$
$$1 \text{ hour} = 60 \text{ minutes}$$
$$1 \text{ day} = 24 \text{ hours}$$
$$1 \text{ year} = 365 \text{ days (or 366 days in a leap year)}$$

April, June, September, November have 30 days.
January, March, May, July, August, October, December have 31 days.
February has 28 days except in a leap year when it has 29 days.

All years that are divisible by 4 are **leap years** except centuries which are leap years only if they are divisible by 400. For instance, 1600 and 1988 were leap years; 1900 and 1986 were not.

a.m. time is from midnight until noon; p.m. time is from noon until midnight. For instance, 1100 hours is 11a.m., 2300 hours is 11p.m.

Metric Measure

length	km	hm	Dm	**m**	dm	cm	mm
capacity	k*l*	h*l*	D*l*	***l***	d*l*	c*l*	m*l*
mass	kg	hg	Dg	**g**	dg	cg	mg

Each unit on the table is 10 times as large as the unit immediately to its right. The relationships between the metric units in common use are as follows.

Length
1km = 1000m
1m = 1000mm
1m = 100cm
1cm = 10mm

Capacity
1*l* = 1000m*l*
1m*l* = 1cm^3

Mass
1kg   = 1000g
1g   = 1000mg
1 tonne = 1000kg

Imperial Measure and Metric Measure

Some **imperial units** still in common use and the relationships between these units are as follows.

Length
1 mile = 1760 yards
1 yard = 3 feet
1 foot = 12 inches

Capacity
1 gallon = 8 pints

Mass
1 ton   = 160 stone
1 stone = 14lb
1 lb   = 16oz

Rough approximations between imperial and metric units are:

1kg is about 2lb (a better approximation is: 1kg is about $2\frac{1}{4}$ lb)

1 litre is about $1\frac{3}{4}$ pints

1 inch is about $2\frac{1}{2}$ cm

5 miles is about 8km

1m is a little longer than 3 feet

Compound Measures

average speed = $\dfrac{\text{distance travelled}}{\text{time taken}}$ Units for speed are km/h, m/s, mph.

density = $\dfrac{\text{mass}}{\text{volume}}$ Units for density are g/cm^3, kg/m^3.

17

REVISION EXERCISE

1.

| km | m | mm | t | kg | g | mg | *l* | m*l* |

State which unit of measurement the following are most likely to be measured in. (Choose from the units in the box.)

(a) the depth of water in a bath   (b) the length of a sports ground
(c) the amount of water in a bath   (d) the weight of a ship
(e) the mass of a feather   (f) the distance between two villages

2. Fifty thousand and four =
       A. 5004   B. 500004   C. 50004   D. 504

3. In a sports stadium, 58 people can be seated in each row.
  (a) **Estimate** the minimum number of rows needed to seat a crowd of 3142.
  (b) **Calculate** the minimum number of rows needed.

4.
  I am equivalent to $\frac{3}{8}$.
  The sum of my numerator and denominator is 55.
  What fraction am I?

5. Write down two things that would be measured to each of the following degrees of accuracy.
  (a) to the nearest mm   (b) to the nearest *l*   (c) to the nearest kg

6.

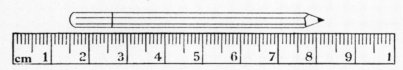

To the nearest mm, how long is this pencil?

7. Write the following as decimals.
  (a) eighty seven and two tenths
  (b) seven and three hundredths
  (c) two tenths and five thousandths

8. Which digit is the tenths digit in each of the following?
  (a) 0·361   (b) 0·046   (c) 24·059   (d) 3·98

9. Round each of the numbers in **question 8** to 1 significant figure.

10. Find the missing numbers.
    (a) $2 \cdot 5l = \cdots ml$
    (b) $5\text{cm} = \cdots \text{mm}$
    (c) $2841\text{cm} = \cdots \text{m}$
    (d) $13 \cdot 4\text{kg} = \cdots \text{g}$
    (e) $345\text{kg} = \cdots \text{tonne}$
    (f) $34ml = \cdots l$
    (g) $0 \cdot 23\text{km} = \cdots \text{m}$

11.

$\frac{2}{3}$	$\frac{3}{4}$	$\frac{5}{9}$	$\frac{6}{7}$	$\frac{1}{2}$	$\frac{4}{5}$

Write the fractions given in the box in order, from smallest to largest.

12.

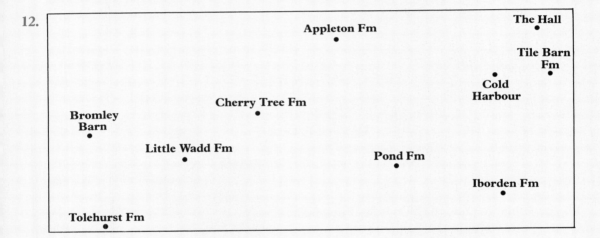

Scale 1 : 50000

(a) Use the scale given on the map to find the missing numbers.
    Map distance of 1mm represents actual distance of $\cdots$ mm = $\cdots$ m.
(b) To the nearest 50m, how far is it from Tolehurst Farm to Bromley Barn?
(c) To the nearest kilometre, how far is it from Appleton Farm to Ibornden Farm?
(d) To the nearest kilometre, how far is it from Tile Barn Farm to Cherry Tree Farm?
(e) Shona's farm is approximately 5km from The Hall. What is the name of Shona's farm?

13. Without using the calculator find:
    (a) $9 + 2 \times 4$
    (b) 28×600
    (c) $34 + 6(3 + 7)$
    (d) 4^3
    (e) 348×56
    (f) $962 \div 37$
    (g) $\frac{3}{8}$ of 72

19

14.

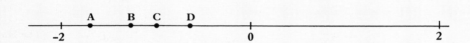

| 2·6 | 2·614 | 2·09 | 3·46 | 2·146 | 3·61 | 3·064 | 2·64 | 2·4 | 3·6 |

Place the numbers given in the box in order, from smallest to largest.

15. A cycle manufacturer makes tricycles and bicycles. Last week, 101 wheels were used to make a total of 44 cycles (both tricycles and bicycles). Use "trial and improvement" to find the number of tricycles and the number of bicycles made by this manufacturer last week.

16. Which of the following are recurring decimals?

(a) $\frac{1}{6}$ (b) 33%   (c) $\frac{3}{20}$ (d) $\frac{2}{3}$ (e) $\frac{6}{7}$ (f) 7·9%

17.

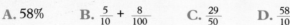

One of the integers −1, −1·3, −0·6, −1·8 is at A, another is at B, another is at C and the other at D. Which of these integers is at each of A, B, C and D?

18. Which of the following is *not* the same as 0·58?

A. 58%   B. $\frac{5}{10} + \frac{8}{100}$ C. $\frac{29}{50}$ D. $\frac{58}{10}$

19. (a) Write the ratio of the length of this photo to its width in the simplest form.
    (b) This photo is to be enlarged in the ratio 5 : 2. How long will the enlargement be?

20. Write these as the simplest possible fraction.
    (a) 0·6   (b) 0·16   (c) 0·07   (d) 0·048

21. Peter picked 35 buckets of strawberries. The average number of strawberries in each of these buckets was 97. From the buckets, the strawberries were packed into punnets which each contained 14. These punnets were sold for 98p each.
    How much were the strawberries that Peter picked sold for?

22. Write these ratios in their simplest form.
    (a) 40 min : 2 hours   (b) 64cm : 3m   (c) £2·60 : 70p

23.

| 1800 | 1840 | 1882 | 1895 | 1900 | 1916 | 1939 | 1992 | 2000 | 2050 |

Which of these years were (or will be) leap years?

24. Janine bought a shirt that was originally priced at £8·25 and a dress that was originally priced at £24. How much change does Janine get from £40?

> **STOCKTAKING SPECIALS**
> All shirts reduced by $\frac{1}{3}$
> All dresses reduced by 25%.

25. Paula measured the school hockey field. Her sketch is shown below.

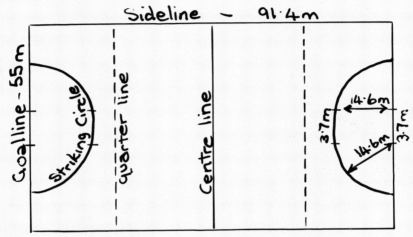

Make a scale drawing of this sketch, using the scale 1 : 500.

26. A concentrated liquid weed killer needs to be mixed with water in the ratio 1 : 20. How many litres of water are used with 60m*l* of the concentrated weed killer?

27. Are these statements true or false?

(a) $\frac{5}{8} < \frac{3}{4}$ (b) $\frac{9}{20} > 0·4$ (c) $\frac{5}{9} > 0·59$

28. At a Secondary Schools' athletics competition, a cup is awarded to the school with the best overall results in 20 events. The system of points used is shown.
This year, Harrowdale School won the cup. They gained 29 points in the 20 events. How many 1st, 2nd and 3rd placings did this school have?
Is there more than one answer to this problem?

> **1st   3 points**
> **2nd 2 points**
> **3rd   1 point**

29. Which of the following is *not* the same as $\frac{6}{15}$?

A. $\frac{12}{30}$ B. $\frac{2}{5}$ C. 0·4   D. 6 : 15   E. 40%

30. A video recorder is set to begin and finish recording as shown. If a 180 minute tape is used, would there be enough room on this tape to also record another programme which runs for 55 minutes?

> Start   22 : 40
> Finish   01 : 15

31. Before Paul got a 5% increase his salary was £12000. What was Paul's salary after the increase?

32. Find the value of x in each of the following.

   (a) $\frac{x}{5} = \frac{9}{15}$ (b) $\frac{12}{x} = \frac{4}{3}$ (c) $\frac{3}{4} = \frac{x}{20}$ (d) $x : 2 = 6 : 8$

33.

Quality of popular coastal bathing waters : by Water Authority area
England, Wales and Northern Ireland   Numbers

Water Authority area	1986		1987	
	Number tested	Numbers failing to comply with EEC Bathing Water Directive coliform standards [2]	Number tested	Number failing to comply with EEC Bathing Water Directive coliform standards [2]
Northumbrian	19	10	19	10
Yorkshire	21	3	22	2
Anglian	28	8	28	10
Thames	2	1	2	2
Southern	65	24	65	27
Wessex (South Coast)	27	3	27	1
South West	103	25	109	13
Wessex (Bristol Channel)	11	4	11	5
Welsh	47	24	47	19
North West	30	26	30	20
England & Wales total	353	128	360	109
Northern Ireland	5	2	14	3

[2] Failure to meet standards does not necessarily imply a danger to health.

Source: Key Data 1989/90

Source: Water Authorities and Department of Environment (N).

From: Social Trends 1989, Table 9.20

Where rounding is necessary give the answers to 1 decimal place.

   (a) What total number of waters were tested in England, Wales and Northern Ireland in 1987?
   (b) What percentage of waters tested in 1987 were in the South West area?
   (c) What percentage of waters tested in the Southern area in 1987 failed to comply with the EEC Bathing Water Directive?
   (d) How many more waters were tested in 1987 than in 1986?
       What percentage increase was this?
   (e) In the 10 areas in England and Wales, what was the average number of waters tested in 1986?

34. Andrew began his run along the beach at 0900 hours. He ran for 30 minutes at an average speed of 10km/h. After a 20 minute stop, he jogged for another 2km at an average speed of 8km/h.
   At what time did Andrew stop jogging?

35. The ratio of boys to girls in a school is 8 : 9. The school roll is 952. How many girls are there in this school?

36. Deborah's car uses oil at the rate of 1 litre per 1600km.
    (a) How much oil does this car use on an 80km journey? (Answer in m*l*.)
    (b) About how many pints is 1000m*l*?
    (c) About how many miles is 1600km?
    (d) To the nearest half of a pint, how many pints of oil will Deborah's car use in 5000 miles of motoring?
    (e) What does 1 litre of oil weigh if its density is 1·8g/cm³?

Two techniques for problem solving are "Making a Table" and "Drawing a Diagram". Worked examples, illustrating each, are given below. These are followed by a selection of problems, all of which may be solved by one or other of these techniques.

MAKING a TABLE

Worked Example   When Jane, Emma and Hien went to the disco they decided to swap earrings and watches. Each of them wore someone else's earrings and the watch that belonged to yet another. If Hien wore Emma's earrings, whose watch did Emma wear?

Answer   The following steps show how a table is completed from the given information.

Step 1

	Earrings	Watch
Hien	Emma	
Jane		
Emma		

We are told that Hien wore Emma's earrings.

Step 2

	Earrings	Watch
Hien	Emma	
Jane	Hien	
Emma		

Since Emma's earrings are worn by Hien and Jane doesn't wear her own, Jane must wear Hien's earrings.

Step 3

	Earrings	Watch
Hien	Emma	
Jane	Hien	
Emma	Jane	

Emma must wear Jane's earrings since these are the only ones left.

Step 4

	Earrings	Watch
Hien	Emma	Jane
Jane	Hien	Emma
Emma	Jane	Hien

The watch column can now be filled in since each girl must wear the watch of a friend whose earrings she doesn't wear.

Step 4 shows the completed table. From this table, we see that Emma wore Hien's watch.

Worked Example   Shalome, Victoria, Elizabeth and Jenny each have one brother, Bryan or Ian or John or Neil.

Shalome is neither Ian's nor John's sister.
Victoria is neither Bryan's nor Neil's sister.
Elizabeth is neither Ian's nor Neil's sister.
Bryan is not Jenny's brother.

If John is Elizabeth's brother, whose brother is Neil?

Answer   *Step 1*   Place the given information on a table. Use a $\sqrt{}$ to show people are in the same family; use a $\times$ to show they are not.

	Bryan	Ian	John	Neil
Shalome		×	×	
Victoria	×			×
Elizabeth		×	$\sqrt{}$	×
Jenny	×			

Step 2   Fill in the gaps in the table, using deduction, until Neil's sister is found. In the table below each $\times$ or $\sqrt{}$ has been numbered in the order these were deduced. Notes on these follow the table. Notice that there must be no more than one $\sqrt{}$ in any row or column.

	Bryan	Ian	John	Neil
Shalome	$\sqrt{}_2$	×	×	$\times_3$
Victoria	×			×
Elizabeth	$\times_1$	×	$\sqrt{}$	×
Jenny	×			$\sqrt{}_4$

Notes $\times_1$ – Bryan cannot be Elizabeth's brother since John is.
$\sqrt{}_2$ – Bryan must be Shalome's brother since he isn't Victoria's or Elizabeth's or Jenny's brother.
$\times_3$ – Neil cannot be Shalome's brother since Bryan is.
$\sqrt{}_4$ – Neil is not Shalome's or Victoria's or Elizabeth's brother so he must be Jenny's brother.

Step 3   Write down the answer to the problem. The answer is: Neil is Jenny's brother.

26

DRAWING a DIAGRAM

Worked Example Jamie runs up the stairs, three at a time, starting with his right foot. Annie runs up, two at a time, starting with her left foot. If Annie begins on the second stair and Jamie begins on the first stair, which stair will be the first one on which both Annie and Jamie put their left foot?

Answer Let J_R represent Jamie's right foot, J_L represent Jamie's left foot, A_R represent Annie's right foot and A_L represent Annie's left foot.
Draw a diagram of a staircase. Place J_R on the 1st stair, J_L on the 4th stair, J_R on the 7th stair and so on. Place A_L on the 2nd stair, A_R on the 4th stair, A_L on the 6th stair and so on.

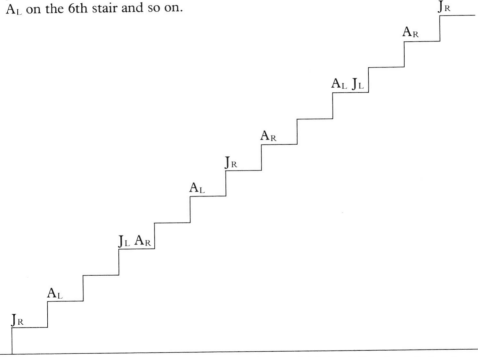

From the diagram, we see that the first stair on which both Jamie and Annie place their left foot is the 10th stair.

EXERCISE 1:1

Solve these problems, using one of the previous techniques or some other technique. If you make little progress using a particular technique, begin again using another.

1. Anna planted daffodil bulbs, 20cm apart, in a straight row. The row was 2m long. How many bulbs did Anna plant?

2. Circular bracelets are made by threading 3 red beads and 3 black beads onto nylon thread. How many different colour combinations could there be?

3. In Hurstfield, there are three sets of twins ; the Smiths, the Eades and the Holdens. In each of these sets of twins there is a boy and a girl. On a date, each of these twins dated another of these twins.
   If the Smith boy dated the Holden girl, who dated the Smith girl?

4. Sophie sets out in her boat to row to her friend's place, a distance of 6km by river. She is in no hurry to get there and takes a book to read. Sophie rows upstream for 2km, then reads. While she reads, she drifts back downstream 1km. Sophie continues her journey in this way, alternately rowing for 2km and drifting back 1km.
   If every kilometre she travels (either rowing upstream or drifting downstream) takes 15 minutes, find how long it takes Sophie to reach her friend's place.

5. One evening, Hari visited Mrs. Uren in hospital. On the way to the hospital, he bought flowers at the florists and grapes at the greengrocers. On the way home, he played squash at the gym.
   The florist is open during the evening on Tuesday, Friday and Saturday. The gym. is open every evening except Saturday. The greengrocers is open every evening except Thursday and Friday. What evening did Hari visit Mrs. Uren in hospital?

6. Square paving slabs are to be placed around a square garden to form a continuous border of uniform width.
   Show how exactly 84 paving slabs can be used.
   Is there more than one solution to this problem?

7. The Andersons, Coopers and Taylors are neighbours who live at 17, 19 and 21 Joyce Crescent.
   > The Coopers live next door to the Andersons.
   > Kate Cooper and Anna Taylor go to the same school.
   > The labrador and terrier are not neighbours.
   > There are no children at Number 19.
   > Kate's labrador is very old.
   > The terrier does not live at Number 17.
   Who lives at which address?

8. A sheet of stamps is 4 stamps long and 3 stamps wide. In how many ways could you cut out four stamps which are all attached to each other?

9.

 Rebecca, Annabel, Megan, Lisa and Heather stand in a row to have their photo taken. No two of them are the same height. They stand with the tallest at one end and the rest of them arranged in order of their heights, as shown in the photo. Use the following clues to find who is who in the photo.

 Rebecca is taller than Annabel.
 Annabel is not the shortest.
 Rebecca is not the tallest.
 Only one girl is shorter than Heather.
 Megan is taller than Annabel.
 More than one girl is taller than Annabel.

10. A mountaineer sets out from base camp. He can carry a maximum of 5 days supplies. A number of porters go with him. Each porter can also carry a maximum of 5 days supplies. It will be 8 days before the mountaineer reaches the next camp where fresh supplies and more porters will be flown in.
 How many porters must go with the mountaineer to ensure that he reaches the next camp and that all the porters return safely to base camp?

Review 1 In Avis Close there are four dogs, Churchill, Jake, Millie and Paz. These dogs are all different breeds; one is a collie, one is a terrier, one is a labrador and the other is a spaniel.
 Jake is neither a terrier nor a spaniel.
 Paz is neither a spaniel nor a collie.
 Churchill is neither a collie nor a terrier.
 Millie is not a collie or a terrier or a labrador.
 Which dog is which breed?

Review 2 A rectangular garden, which measures 16m × 14m, is to have a fence built right around the perimeter. The fence posts are to be spaced one metre apart. If there must be a post at each of the four corners of the garden, how many posts will be needed altogether?

MENTALLY MULTIPLYING and DIVIDING by DECIMALS

DISCUSSION EXERCISE 2:1

$$40 \times 5 = 200$$
$$40 \times 50 = 2000$$
$$40 \times 500 = 20000$$
$$40 \times 5000 = 200000$$
$$40 \times 50000 = 2000000$$
$$40 \times 500000 = 20000000$$

Discuss how to use the number pattern above to find the answer to the following multiplications.

$$40 \times 0{\cdot}5 \qquad 40 \times 0{\cdot}05 \qquad 40 \times 0{\cdot}005$$

"Multiplying a given number by a number that is greater than 1, increases the given number." Make a similar statement about multiplying by a number that is less than 1. **Discuss.**

$$\frac{8000}{4000} = 2$$

$$\frac{8000}{400} = 20$$

$$\frac{8000}{40} = 200$$

$$\frac{8000}{4} = 2000$$

Discuss how to use the number pattern above to find the answer to the following divisions.

$$\frac{8000}{0{\cdot}4} \qquad \frac{8000}{0{\cdot}04} \qquad \frac{8000}{0{\cdot}004}$$

"Dividing a given number by a number that is greater than 1, decreases the given number." Make a similar statement about dividing by a number that is less than 1. **Discuss.**

Multiplying and dividing are inverse operations. **Discuss** how this fact could be used to justify the statements you made earlier in this discussion exercise.

Worked Example   Without using a calculator, find   (a) 80×0.02 (b) $80 \div 0.2$.

Answer   (a) The answer will be smaller than 80.

Multiply 80 by 2 to get 160.

Since 2 is in the hundredths place, 160 must be decreased one hundred-fold.

Hence $80 \times 0.02 = 1.60$.

(b) The answer will be larger than 80.

Divide 80 by 2 to get 40.

Since 2 is in the tenths place, 40 must be increased ten-fold.

Hence $80 \div 0.2 = 400$.

Alternative solutions to   (a) 80×0.02 (b) $80 \div 0.2$ are as follows.

$$\textbf{(a)} \ 80 \times 0.02 = 80 \times \frac{2}{100}$$
$$= (80 \times 2) \div 100$$
$$= 160 \div 100$$
$$= 1.6$$

$$\textbf{(b)} \ 80 \div 0.2 = 80 \div \frac{2}{10}$$
$$= 80 \times \frac{10}{2} \ \text{(since} \times \text{and} \div \text{are inverse operations)}$$
$$= \frac{80}{2} \times 10$$
$$= 40 \times 10$$
$$= 400$$

EXERCISE 2:2

Do not use the calculator in this exercise.

1. Which of the following calculations will have an answer less than 200 and which will have an answer greater than 200?

   (a) 200×0.4 (b) $200 \div 0.2$ (c) 200×0.01 (d) 200×0.5
   (e) $200 \div 0.004$ (f) $200 \div 0.05$ (g) 200×0.004 (h) 200×4.5
   (i) $200 \div 4.5$ (j) $200 \div 54$ (k) 200×54

2. Which of the following calculations will have an answer less than 0.4 and which will have an answer greater than 0.4?

   (a) $0.4 \div 0.1$ (b) 0.4×0.1 (c) $0.4 \div 0.02$ (d) $0.4 \div 0.004$
   (e) 0.4×0.002 (f) 0.4×0.04 (g) 0.4×2.4 (h) $0.4 \div 24$
   (i) $0.4 \div 2.4$ (j) 0.4×24

3. Find the answer to these.
    (a) 40×0.4 (b) 40×0.004 (c) $40 \div 0.4$ (d) $40 \div 0.04$
    (e) $600 \div 0.003$ (f) 600×0.03 (g) 100×0.005 (h) $100 \div 0.05$
    (i) 8×0.1 (j) $6 \div 0.1$ (k) $4 \div 0.02$ (l) 2×0.02
    (m) $0.8 \div 0.2$ (n) 0.8×0.2 (o) 0.5×0.01 (p) $0.5 \div 0.01$
    (q) 0.9×0.03 (r) $0.9 \div 0.003$

4. A manufacturer of sweat shirts ordered sufficient ribbing to make 400 shirts. Each needed 0·6m of ribbing. How much ribbing did the manufacturer order?

5. Oil costs £0·80 per litre. What is the cost of 20 litres of this oil?

6. Find the cost of 0·3kg of a vegetable which costs £0·90 per kg.

7. *The answer is 20.* Write down many calculations, similar to those in **question 3,** which have an answer of 20.

Review 1   Find the answers to these.
    (a) $60 \div 0.3$ (b) 600×0.003 (c) 60×0.3 (d) $6 \div 0.03$

Review 2   A Swiss tourist exchanged 500 Swiss Francs for pounds.
           For each franc, this tourist received £0·40. How many pounds did this tourist receive?

USING the CALCULATOR to MULTIPLY and DIVIDE DECIMALS

Numbers, such as those in the previous section, which have just one significant figure can usually be multiplied or divided mentally.
Numbers which have more than one significant figure are best multiplied or divided using the calculator.

When using the calculator, always estimate the answer. It is very easy to press a wrong digit key or operation key. By estimating the answer, an incorrect keying can often be detected.

EXERCISE 2:3

1. The answer to the calculation 2.47×1.9 is 4·693.
   The calculation 2.47×1.9 was keyed into the calculator incorrectly to give an answer of 0·4693. Which of the following mistakes was made?
       A. Keyed + instead of ×.   B. Keyed 2·74 instead of 2·47.
       C. Keyed ÷ instead of ×.   D. Keyed 0·19 instead of 1·9.

2. A deposit of £25 was made on a leather jacket which cost £178·60. The balance was paid in 24 equal monthly amounts. How much was paid each month?

3. Seadown Youth Club hired a bus for a day outing. The total cost of this hire was £124·20, which consisted of a fixed charge of £45 and 45p per kilometre travelled. How many kilometres did the Seadown Youth Club travel on this outing?

4. Amanda fills up her petrol tank with petrol that costs 48p per litre. Amanda's car took 56·5 litres. How much did this amount of petrol cost?

5. The petrol consumption rate for Amanda's car was 13·4km per litre.
   (a) Amanda travelled from Aberdeen to Birmingham, a distance of 711 kilometres. How many litres of petrol would her car use on this journey?
   (b) What distance could Amanda travel on 28 litres of petrol?
   (c) Amanda used the conversion rate "1 mile is about 1·609km" to work out the distance she had travelled in miles. To the nearest mile, she calculated the distance to be 442 miles. Was she correct?
   (d) On a 113km section of the journey, Amanda travelled at a constant speed. This section of the journey took Amanda 1 hour 21 minutes. About how many kilometres did Amanda travel each 15 minutes?

6. In one day, a factory made 73 skirts and 22 jackets.
   The sizes made and the material used for each size is given in the table below.

	Size	Material (metres)	Number
Skirt	10	1·2	18
Skirt	12	1·3	32
Skirt	14	1·5	23
Jacket	10–12	2·5	10
Jacket	12–14	2·9	12

   (a) How much material was used on this day?
   (b) The next day, the same amount of material was used to make a quantity of size 14 skirts. How many skirts were made?
   (c) On the day that 73 skirts were made, one person did all the finishing work on them. This person was paid a daily wage of £30 with an extra 75p for every skirt in excess of 50 that were finished. How much did this person earn on this day?
   (d) One of the tailors was paid an hourly rate of £6·20 for the first $7\frac{1}{2}$ hours worked, then £9·30 per hour after that. How many hours did this tailor work on a day in which he earned £60·45?

Review   Keung measured the length of his desk as 60cm. How many desks of this length could be placed side by side along a classroom wall that is 26 feet long?
(Use 1 foot = 0·3048 metres.)

INVESTIGATION 2:4

RECURRING DECIMALS

Using the calculator, the decimal value displayed for the fraction $\frac{3}{8}$ is 0·375. This is said to be a terminating decimal.

Using the calculator, the decimal value displayed for the fraction $\frac{5}{18}$ is 0·2777777.

Hence $\frac{5}{18} = 0·2\dot{7}$. This is said to be a repeating or recurring decimal.

Using the calculator, the decimal value displayed for the fraction $\frac{2}{7}$ is

0·2857142. Could it be that the decimal value for $\frac{2}{7}$ is a recurring decimal? **Investigate**.

Investigate the recurring decimals for $\frac{1}{11}$, $\frac{2}{11}$, $\frac{3}{11}$ etc.

Investigate the recurring decimals for $\frac{1}{7}$, $\frac{2}{7}$, $\frac{3}{7}$ etc.

Are all fractions with denominator of 9 recurring decimals? **Investigate**.
What if the denominator is 13?
What if the denominator is 17?
What if . . .

Investigate to find which denominators give terminating decimals and which give repeating decimals? Can all fractions be written as either repeating or terminating decimals? What factors must the denominator of a fraction have if the fraction is a recurring decimal?
What if the recurring decimal of a fraction has some non recurring digits at the beginning?

What is the fraction for $0·\dot{4}\dot{8}$?

$$100 \times 0·\dot{4}\dot{8} = 48·484848\ldots$$
$$-\quad\ 0·\dot{4}\dot{8} = 0·484848\ldots$$
$$99 \times 0·\dot{4}\dot{8} = 48$$
$$\text{Hence } 0·\dot{4}\dot{8} = \frac{48}{99} \text{ or } \frac{16}{33}$$

Investigate the fractions for other repeating decimals. Be sure to include decimals such as $0·\dot{6}$, $0·1\dot{6}$, $0·\dot{2}\dot{7}$, $0·2\dot{1}\dot{3}$, $0·4\dot{2}1\dot{3}$.

PUZZLE 2:5

At a Bring and Buy sales table, slices of apple pie were priced at 40p per slice. When none had been sold at this price, a decision was made to reduce them to less than half price. Once this had been done, they all sold quickly for a total of £3·91.
By how much was the price of each slice reduced?

USING the CALCULATOR BRACKETS and MEMORY

Consider the calculation $\frac{8+12}{2}$. This is $\frac{20}{2}$ or 10.

If $\frac{8+12}{2}$ is keyed into the calculator as 8 $\boxed{+}$ 12 $\boxed{\div}$ 2 $\boxed{=}$ we do not get the correct answer of 10. Instead we get 14.

The keying sequence 8 $\boxed{+}$ 12 $\boxed{\div}$ 2 $\boxed{=}$ instructed the calculator to work out $8 + \frac{12}{2}$. (Remember the scientific calculator does $\div$ before $+$.)

To ensure the calculator divides the answer to $8 + 12$ by 2 we can key as
8 $\boxed{+}$ 12 $\boxed{=}$ $\boxed{\div}$ 2 $\boxed{=}$ or we can use brackets.

INVESTIGATION 2:6

USING BRACKETS on the CALCULATOR

Investigate keying sequences which involve brackets for calculations such as:

$$\frac{8+12}{2} \qquad \frac{144}{2 \times 3} \qquad \frac{8+12}{2+3} \qquad \frac{8+12\,(11-7)}{4 \times 7} \qquad \frac{8+12\,(11-7)}{16-2\,(3+4)}$$

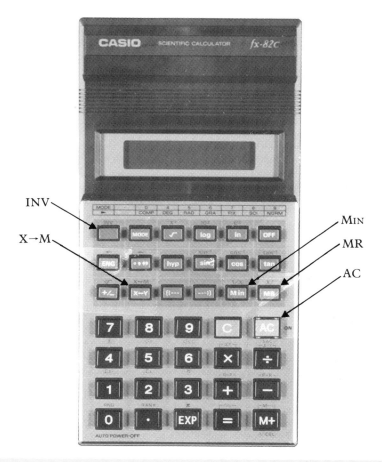

Using the **memory function,** $\dfrac{8 + 12}{2 + 3}$ can be keyed as

8 $\boxed{+}$ 12 $\boxed{=}$ $\boxed{\text{Min}}$ 2 $\boxed{+}$ 3 $\boxed{=}$ $\boxed{\text{INV}}$ $\boxed{\text{X} \to \text{M}}$ $\boxed{\div}$ $\boxed{\text{MR}}$ $\boxed{=}$ to get answer of 4.

Notes on each part of this keying sequence follow.

Notes **1.** 8 $\boxed{+}$ 12 $\boxed{=}$ The top line is calculated ; 20 is displayed.

  2. $\boxed{\text{Min}}$ The result, 20, is stored in the memory.

  3. 2 $\boxed{+}$ 3 $\boxed{=}$ The bottom line is calculated ; 5 is displayed.

  4. $\boxed{\text{INV}}$ $\boxed{\text{X} \to \text{M}}$ The value displayed and the value stored in the memory are swapped ; 20 is now displayed and 5 is stored in the memory.

  5. $\boxed{\div}$ $\boxed{\text{MR}}$ $\boxed{=}$ The value currently displayed is divided by the value recalled from memory (MR) to give answer of 4.

If more than one calculation is to be done using the memory function, the memory must be cleared after each calculation.

Keying $\boxed{\text{MR}}$ recalls the value stored in the memory ; it does not clear that value from the memory.

To clear the memory **Key** $\boxed{\text{AC}}$ $\boxed{\text{Min}}$

INVESTIGATION 2:7

USING the MEMORY FUNCTION on the CALCULATOR

Keying sequences using the memory function, other than that shown above, are possible for the calculation $\dfrac{8+12}{2+3}$. Investigate.

Investigate the use of the $\boxed{\text{M+}}$ key on the calculator.

EXERCISE 2:8

---

1. (a) The calculation $\dfrac{13+5}{10-1}$ was keyed as

$\boxed{(}\ 13\ \boxed{+}\ 5\ \boxed{=}\ \boxed{\div}\ \boxed{(}\ 10\ \boxed{-}\ 1\ \boxed{)}\ \boxed{=}$.

What is wrong with this keying sequence?

   (b) The calculation $\dfrac{3+5\times9}{5-2}$ was keyed as

$\boxed{(}\ 3\ \boxed{+}\ 5\ \boxed{\times}\ 9\ \boxed{)}\ \boxed{\div}\ \boxed{(}\ 5\ \boxed{-}\ 2\ \boxed{=}$.

What is wrong with this keying sequence?

   (c) The calculation $\dfrac{7\times3-4\,(6-1)}{5}$ was keyed as

$\boxed{(}\ 7\ \boxed{\times}\ 3\ \boxed{-}\ 4\ \boxed{\times}\ \boxed{(}\ 6\ \boxed{-}\ 1\ \boxed{)}\ \boxed{=}\ \boxed{\div}\ 5\ \boxed{=}$.

What is wrong with this keying sequence?

   (d) The calculation $\dfrac{15\times10+12}{4\times2}$ was keyed as

$\boxed{(}\ 15\ \boxed{\times}\ 10\ \boxed{+}\ 12\ \boxed{)}\ \boxed{\div}\ 4\ \boxed{\times}\ 2\ \boxed{=}$.

What is wrong with this keying sequence?

   (e) The calculation $\dfrac{15+64-2\times4}{3\,(2+5)-1}$ was keyed as

$15\ \boxed{+}\ 64\ \boxed{-}\ 2\ \boxed{\times}\ 4\ \boxed{=}\ \boxed{\div}\ \boxed{(}\ 3\ \boxed{\times}\ \boxed{(}\ 2\ \boxed{+}\ 5\ \boxed{)}\ \boxed{-}\ 1\ \boxed{=}$.

What is wrong with this keying sequence?

2. Use brackets on the calculator to find the answer to these.

(a) $\dfrac{15}{3+2}$

(b) $\dfrac{30}{7-2}$

(c) $\dfrac{3+4\times 8}{5}$

(d) $\dfrac{96}{3\times 2}$

(e) $\dfrac{37+43}{4\times 5}$

(f) $\dfrac{35+14}{9-2}$

(g) $\dfrac{6\times 2+3}{2+3}$

(h) $\dfrac{5\times 6-4\times 3}{4+2}$

(i) $\dfrac{6\times 7+2\times 14}{5\times 7}$

(j) $\dfrac{38+2(5+6)}{5\times 8}$

(k) $\dfrac{5\times 6-7(5-3)}{2\times 8}$

(l) $\dfrac{23-5\times 3}{10-3\times 2}$

(m) $\dfrac{3\times 9+2\times 3}{2+3(7-4)}$

3. Use the memory function on the calculator to find the answers to the calculations in **question 2**.

4. Use the calculator to evaluate these. Give the answers to 3 significant figures when rounding is necessary.

(a) $\dfrac{8\cdot 1}{2-0\cdot 2}$

(b) $\dfrac{3\cdot 6+18}{4\cdot 1+2\cdot 6}$

(c) $\dfrac{8\cdot 1+0\cdot 2}{2}$

(d) $\dfrac{21\cdot 6}{4\cdot 1\times 2\cdot 6}$

(e) $\dfrac{3(4+2\cdot 5)}{1\cdot 5}$

(f) $\dfrac{6\times 2\cdot 3+4\cdot 1}{2\times 9}$

(g) $\dfrac{2+4\times 1\cdot 6}{1+3\,(2-0\cdot 4)}$

(h) $\dfrac{3+4\cdot 2(11-8\cdot 4)}{16-0\cdot 8}$

(i) $\dfrac{2\cdot 7+3\cdot 6\times 4\cdot 8}{21-8\cdot 3\times 1\cdot 5}$

(j) $\dfrac{8(2\cdot 3+1\cdot 6)-5}{2\cdot 3+1\cdot 6}$

5. If a body is moving with uniform acceleration, this acceleration may be given by the formula $\mathrm{a}=\dfrac{\mathrm{v}-\mathrm{u}}{\mathrm{t}}$.

a is the uniform acceleration, **u** is the initial velocity and **v** is the velocity at time **t**.
Use this formula to find the value of **a** (in m/s^2) if:
(a) v = 20 m/s, u = 5 m/s, t = 5 sec
(b) v = 18·6 m/s, u = 6·7 m/s, t = 10 sec
(c) v = 36·5 m/s, u = 16·8 m/s, t = 4·6 sec

6. $s = \dfrac{v^2 - u^2}{2a}$ is a formula which gives the distance, **s**, travelled by a body moving with uniform acceleration, **a**. The initial velocity is **u** and the final velocity is **v**. Use this formula to find **s** (in metres) if:

(a) a = 2 m/s², v = 6 m/s, u = 2 m/s

(b) a = 5 m/s², v = 8·5 m/s, u = 1·9 m/s

(c) a = 2·5 m/s², v = 15 m/s, u = 8·8 m/s

7. Two particles are projected vertically upwards with velocity **u**. The second particle is projected **t** seconds after the first. These particles will meet at a height **h** (metres) where **h** is given by $h = \dfrac{4u^2 - g^2t^2}{8g}$ (**g** is the acceleration due to gravity.)

Find **h** to the nearest mm if (a) u = 25 m/s, t = 5 sec, g = 9·8 m/s²

(b) u = 25 m/s, t = 1 sec, g = 9·8 m/s²

8. **M** is a mass sitting on a horizontal table. **M** is connected by a string, which passes over a pulley, to a mass **m** which is hanging over the edge of the table.

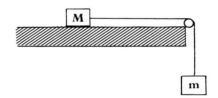

The acceleration of the masses **M** and **m** is given by the formula

$a = \dfrac{mMg}{m + M}$ where **g** is the acceleration due to gravity.

Find **a** (in m/s²) when M = 2·7 kg, m = 0·6 kg, given that g = 9·8 m/s².

Review 1 Use the memory function on the calculator to calculate the following.

(a) $\dfrac{72}{4 + 3 + 9}$ (b) $\dfrac{7 + 2 \times 4}{3 + 2}$ (c) $\dfrac{8·4 - 2·1}{1·7 + 1·3}$

Review 2 Use brackets on the calculator to find the answers to these. (Give answers to 2s.f. if rounding is necessary.)

(a) $\dfrac{82·3}{14·8 + 3·6 \times 5}$ (b) $\dfrac{6·3 \times 1·5 - 2·8}{2·1 \times 3·2 \times 0·5}$ (c) $\dfrac{43 + 8\,(7 - 4·3)}{5·2 - 2 \times 0·9}$

DISCUSSION EXERCISE 2:9

Some formulae from Physics were evaluated in the previous exercise. What formulae from other areas of the curriculum need to be worked out using brackets or the memory function of the calculator? **Discuss**.

PUZZLE 2:10

Copy the table given below.

Rewrite each number given in each row within the table using the numbers at the left of that row.

You may use +, −, ×, ÷, and brackets.

As an example, the first row has been completed.

	Use 2 of the numbers	Use 3 of the numbers	Use 4 of the numbers	Use all the numbers
2 3 16 8 5	$4 = \dfrac{8}{2}$	$9 = 8 + 3 - 2$	$1 = \dfrac{16}{8} + 2 - 3$	$18 = 2(16 - 8) - 3 + 5$
1 2 7 3 4	$10 =$	$8 =$	$42 =$	$17 =$
4 5 12 1 9	$7 =$	$8 =$	$9 =$	$10 =$
6 5 13 7 4	$28 =$	$27 =$	$22 =$	$24 =$
3 4 15 8 2	$7 =$	$0 =$	$7 =$	$12 =$
3 9 18 1 4	$36 =$	$13 =$	$1 =$	$4 =$

Were you able to complete this puzzle?

Is it possible to complete this puzzle?

PRACTICAL EXERCISE 2:11

Design a game or a puzzle using numbers.

You may like to adapt the previous puzzle.

Trial your game or puzzle with a few students, then amend it if necessary.

REWRITING a NUMBER as a PRODUCT of PRIME NUMBERS

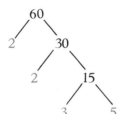

What can you say about the numbers in red?
This "factor tree" can be used to rewrite 60 as $2 \times 2 \times 3 \times 5$.
Discuss this method. **Discuss** other methods of rewriting 60 as $2 \times 2 \times 3 \times 5$.

Use your methods to rewrite other numbers as products of prime numbers. **Discuss**.

The factors of 60 are 1, 2, 3, 4, 5, 6, 10, 12, 15, 20, 30, 60. **Discuss** how to write down all the factors of 60 (other than 1) using the numbers 2, 2, 3, 5 obtained from the "factor tree".

$$72 = 2 \times 2 \times 2 \times 3 \times 3 \qquad\qquad 54 = 2 \times 3 \times 3 \times 3$$
The highest factor common to both 72 and 54 is $2 \times 3 \times 3$, that is 18. **Discuss** how this was found.

$$72 = 2 \times 2 \times 2 \times 3 \times 3 \qquad\qquad 54 = 2 \times 3 \times 3 \times 3$$
The lowest common multiple of 72 and 54 (the smallest number that both 72 and 54 divide into exactly) is $2 \times 2 \times 2 \times 3 \times 3 \times 3$, that is 216. **Discuss** how this was found.

The **highest common factor** (HCF) of two numbers is the greatest number that is a factor of both of the given numbers.

The **lowest common multiple** (LCM) of two numbers is the smallest number that is a multiple of both of the given numbers. The lowest common multiple is sometimes called the **least common multiple**.

Worked Example   Find (a) the HCF of 36 and 66
　　　　　　　　　　　(b) the LCM of 36 and 66

Answer　　(a)　　$36 = 2 \times 2 \times 3 \times 3 \qquad 66 = 2 \times 3 \times 11$
　　　　　　　　　　2×3 is common to both numbers (shown underlined).
　　　　　　　　　　Hence the HCF is 6.

　　　　　　(b)　　$36 = 2 \times 2 \times 3 \times 3 \qquad 66 = 2 \times 3 \times 11$
　　　　　　　　　　The smallest number that both 36 and 66 divide into exactly is
　　　　　　　　　　$2 \times 2 \times 3 \times 3 \times 11$ (shown underlined). Hence the LCM is 396.

EXERCISE 2:13

1. Write these numbers as products of prime numbers.
   (a) 28   (b) 63   (c) 128   (d) 210   (e) 225
   (f) 17   (g) 144   (h) 126   (i) 154   (j) 186

2. Find the HCF of the following.
   (a) 32 and 48   (b) 30 and 32   (c) 14 and 42
   (d) 100 and 340   (e) 45 and 150   (f) 72 and 252
   (g) 7 and 17   (h) 16 and 18 and 20   (i) 30 and 54 and 144

3. Repeat **question 2**, finding the LCM instead of the HCF.

4. Two nurses, Pia and Malcolm, are on shiftwork. Pia works for 3 days, then has 1 day off. Malcolm works for 4 days, then has 1 day off. Neither Pia nor Malcolm worked on New Year's Day.
   Did Pia and Malcolm have any other days off together during January? If so, which days?

Review   (a) Write each of 78, 240, 420 as a product of prime numbers.
             (b) Find the HCF of 78 and 240.
             (c) Find the LCM of 240 and 420.

PROJECT 2:14

Work in groups to produce a well researched and well presented project on some aspect of calculation.
The project could be presented in booklet form or as a wall mural or as an illustrated talk or in some other way.

Some suggestions for the project are:
   Calculating devices through the ages.
   Calculation and other cultures (e.g. Ancient Egypt).
   The Calculator.

Each group should initially discuss and make decisions on the following:
   what the project is to be about
   how information is to be gathered
   how the project is to be presented
   what tasks are to be done by each member of the group
   what date each task is to be completed by

3   Error in Measurement   3

MEASUREMENT to the NEAREST UNIT

DISCUSSION EXERCISE 3:1

A report gave the size of the crowd at a cricket match as 8000. If the size of the crowd was given to the nearest thousand, how many people might have been at the cricket match? **Discuss.**
What if the size of the crowd was given to the nearest hundred?
What if the size of the crowd was given to the nearest ten?

32cm	28cm	42cm	34cm	26cm	40cm	25cm	20cm	35cm	
31·9cm	24·8cm	29·6cm	30·4cm	29·5cm	30·5cm	29·4cm	29·8cm	30·2cm

Which of the lengths in this list would be given as 30cm, to the nearest 10cm? **Discuss.**
Discuss some other lengths which would be given as 30cm, to the nearest 10cm.
What if the length was given as 30cm, to the nearest cm?
What if the length was given as 30cm, to the nearest $\frac{1}{2}$cm?

Worked Example   The number of school children in a town is 3400, to the nearest hundred. What is the greatest possible and least possible number of school children in this town?

Answer   3450 or more children would be rounded to 3500. Hence the greatest possible number of school children is 3449.
3349 or fewer children would be rounded to 3300. Hence the least possible number of school children is 3350.

EXERCISE 3:2

1. A construction firm estimated that it had employed 1700 people during the previous five years. If this figure is correct to the nearest 10, find the greatest and least possible number of people employed by this firm during this time.

2. To the nearest 100, there are 262400 girls, under the age of 15, in Wales.
   What is the greatest and least possible number of girls, under the age of 15, in Wales?

3. Give these measurements to the nearest mm.
   (a) 6·7mm   (b) 5·2mm   (c) 1·5mm   (d) 0·8mm   (e) 15·08mm
   (f) 17·67mm   (g) 8·39mm   (h) 1·48mm   (i) 24·5mm

4. Which of the following masses would be given as 7kg, to the nearest kg?
   (a) 7·1kg   (b) 7·4kg   (c) 7·49kg   (d) 7·6kg   (e) 7·5kg
   (f) 6·9kg   (g) 6·5kg   (h) 6·48kg

5. Which of the following capacities would be given as 2·5 litres, to the nearest $\frac{1}{2}$ litre?
   (a) 2*l*   (b) 3*l*   (c) 2·4*l*   (d) 2·8*l*   (e) 1·9*l*
   (f) 1·5*l*   (g) 3·5*l*   (h) 2·1*l*   (i) 2·7*l*

6. Which of the following times would be given as 3·4 seconds, to the nearest tenth of a second?
   (a) 3·41 sec   (b) 3·47 sec   (c) 3·3 sec   (d) 3·5 sec   (e) 3·38 sec
   (f) 3·45 sec   (g) 3·35 sec   (h) 3·44 sec   (i) 3·25 sec

Review 1   The attendance at a concert was given as 840, to the nearest 10. What was the greatest and least possible number of people at this concert?

Review 2   Which of the following distances would be given as 27km, to the nearest km?
     (a) 28km   (b) 26·5km   (c) 27·8km   (d) 26·8km   (e) 27·49km

POSSIBLE ERROR in a MEASUREMENT

DISCUSSION EXERCISE 3:3

The length of a rod is given to the nearest cm.
Which of the rods shown have length given as 3cm, to the nearest cm? **Discuss**.

How much shorter than 3cm could a rod be if its length is given as 3cm to the nearest cm?
How much longer than 3cm could it be? **Discuss**.

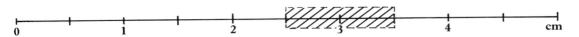

Must the end of a rod be within the shaded region for its length to be given as 3cm, to the nearest cm? **Discuss.**

Would the length of the rod illustrated be given as 2·8cm to the nearest tenth of a cm? How much shorter than 2·8cm could the rod be if its length was given as 2·8cm, to the nearest tenth of a cm? How much longer could it be? **Discuss.**

The length of a rod is given as 2·86cm, to the nearest hundredth of a cm. How much shorter than 2·86cm could it be? How much longer could it be? **Discuss.**

Discuss how to complete the following statements.

Statement 1   A measurement given as 9m, to the nearest metre, could be as short as . . . or as long as . . .

Statement 2   The error in a measurement given as 9m, to the nearest metre, could be as much as . . .

The maximum possible error in a measurement is half a unit. That is, a measurement given to the nearest mm has a possible error of 0·5mm, a measurement given to the nearest tenth of a second has a possible error of half of one tenth of a second i.e. 0·05 sec.

Worked Example   A time is given as 7·3 sec, to the nearest tenth of a second. What is the possible error in this measurement?

Answer

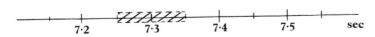

Any time, within the shaded region, would be given as 7·3 sec, to the nearest tenth of a second.

The shortest time could be 7·25 sec ; the longest time could be up to 7·35 sec. That is, the time could be as much as 0·05 sec shorter or longer than 7·3 sec. Hence the possible error is 0·05 sec.

EXERCISE 3:4

1. The length of a pencil is given as 162mm, to the nearest mm. The length of this pencil lies between:

    A. 161 and 163mm   **B.** 152 and 167mm   **C.** 161·5 and 162·5mm

2. The capacity of a freezer is 55*l*, to the nearest litre. The capacity of this freezer lies between:

    A. 50 and 60*l*   **B.** 54·5 and 55·5*l*   **C.** 54 and 56*l*

3. Janine's time to do 10 mental calculations was 58·7 seconds, to the nearest tenth of a second. Her time was between:

    A. 58·6 and 58·8 sec   **B.** 58·69 and 58·71 sec   **C.** 58·65 and 58·75 sec

4. A distance is given as 8·34km. This distance lies between:

    A. 8·335 and 8·345km   **B.** 8·24 and 8·44 km   **C.** 8·29 and 8·39km

5. What is the maximum possible error in the following measurements?
   (a) a distance given as 10km, to the nearest km
   (b) a time given as 3·6 sec
   (c) a capacity given as 1·38*l*
   (d) a mass given as 17kg
   (e) a mass given as 20kg, to the nearest kg
   (f) a time given as 28·35 sec
   (g) a length given as 124·6cm
   (h) a distance given as 28·33km
   (i) a time given as 17 sec, to the nearest sec
   (j) a capacity given as 1·25*l*

6. Give the possible error in metres, for distances given as
   (a) 82km   (b) 0·3km   (c) 3·6km   (d) 82·14km   (e) 2046km

Review 1   The mass of a precious stone is given as 143g. This mass lies between:

    A. 142 and 144g   **B.** 142·5 and 143·5g   **C.** 138 and 148g

Review 2   What is the possible error in a mass given as:

    (a) 238g   (b) 1·3kg   (c) 10·31g   (d) 50kg to the nearest kg

PRACTICAL EXERCISE 3:5

Choose a task for all the students in your class to do. Some suggestions are given below.
Measure the time each student takes to complete the task. Use each of the following timing
devices:

    a watch that does not give seconds (time to the nearest minute)
    a watch that gives seconds (time to the nearest second)
    a stopwatch (time to the nearest tenth of a second)

For each of the above timings, rank the students according to how long they took to
complete the task.

Discuss differences in the rankings and the reasons for these differences.

Suggested tasks: counting backwards from 100 to 1
                       holding one's breath
                       keying a given list of digits on the calculator

1. Without doing any calculation, state which of the following will have an answer of less than 400.

    (a) $400 \div 0\cdot2$ (b) $400 \div 2\cdot2$ (c) $400 \times 2\cdot2$ (d) $400 \times 0\cdot2$

2. Without using the calculator, find the answer to   (a) $400 \div 0\cdot2$ (b) $400 \times 0\cdot2$

3.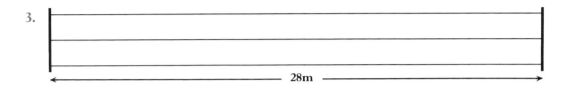

    Fence posts are to be placed 2m apart. How many fence posts are needed to build a fence of the length shown?

4. To the nearest 10, a youth group had 140 members. What is the greatest and least possible number of members of this youth group?

5. What is wrong with each of the following calculator keying sequences?

    (a) $\dfrac{18 + 24}{6}$ keyed as   18 $\boxed{+}$ 24 $\boxed{\div}$ 6 $\boxed{=}$

    (b) $\dfrac{13 + 3\,(4 + 7)}{15 + 8}$ keyed as

    $\boxed{(}$ 13 $\boxed{+}$ 3 $\boxed{\times}$ $\boxed{(}$ 4 $\boxed{+}$ 7 $\boxed{)}$ $\boxed{\div}$ $\boxed{(}$ 15 $\boxed{+}$ 8 $\boxed{)}$ $\boxed{=}$

    (c) $\dfrac{19 + 25}{15 - 4}$ keyed as   19 $\boxed{+}$ 25 $\boxed{=}$ $\boxed{\text{Min}}$ 15 $\boxed{-}$ 4 $\boxed{=}$ $\boxed{\text{INV}}$ $\boxed{\text{X} \to \text{M}}$ $\boxed{\div}$ $\boxed{\text{Min}}$ $\boxed{=}$

6. Which of the following measurements would be given, to the nearest tenth of a second, as $24\cdot2$ seconds?

    (a) $24\cdot5$ sec   (b) $23\cdot8$ sec   (c) $23\cdot5$ sec   (d) $24\cdot8$ sec   (e) $24\cdot22$ sec
    (f) $24\cdot25$ sec   (g) $24\cdot15$ sec   (h) $24\cdot18$ sec

7. A bracelet is made by threading four different coloured beads onto nylon thread.
    How many different colour combinations are possible?

Chapter 4

8. Use brackets on the calculator to find the answer to these.

   (a) $\dfrac{4 \times 5 + 3 \times 9}{19 - 3 \times 5}$ (b) $\dfrac{1\cdot2 + 4\cdot8}{1\cdot4 + 2 \times 0\cdot8}$

9. The distance between two villages is 26·5km to the nearest tenth of a kilometre.
   (a) What is the greatest possible distance between these villages?
   (b) What is the least possible distance between these villages?

10. Use the memory function on the calculator to evaluate these. (Give the answer to 3 significant figures if rounding is necessary.)

    (a) $\dfrac{24\cdot2}{3\cdot1 \times 2\cdot8}$ (b) $\dfrac{23\cdot1 + 13\cdot8}{4\cdot2 - 2\cdot7}$ (c) $\dfrac{7 + 5\,(3 + 1\cdot2)}{4\cdot1 - 0\cdot9}$

11. (a) Apex Apricot Pies are made in batches of 200. For each batch of 200 pies, 50kg of apricots are needed. These apricots cost £1·05 per kg. The other ingredients for each Apex Apricot Pie cost 27p. Preparation, baking and other costs total £34 for each batch of 200.
    If each Apex Apricot Pie is sold for £1·35, what is the profit on each batch of 200?

    (b) The manufacturer of Apex Apricot Pies buys apricots in 40lb cases. How many pies can be made from one case of apricots? (Use 1lb = 0·4536kg.)

    (c) Find the cost, to the nearest penny, of one of the 40lb cases of apricots.

    (d) The pastry for the pies is rolled out into long strips, as shown, before being cut into 9 inch diameter circles.
    How many circular pieces of pastry can be cut from each strip of pastry?
    (Use 1 inch = 2·54cm.)

    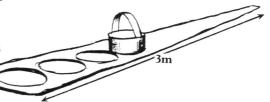

12. The capacity of a bucket is 9 litres, to the nearest litre.
    The capacity of this bucket lies between   A. 8 and 10 litres
                                                B. 8·5 and 9·5 litres
                                                C. 8·9 and 9·1 litres

13. Jimmy, John, Jason and Justin each own a dog. The dogs are called Jess, Jasper, Julip and Jip.
    John owns neither Jess nor Jip.
    Jimmy does not own Julip.
    Justin owns neither Julip nor Jess.
    If Jason owns Jasper, which dog is owned by each of the other three boys?

14. A time is given as 2·37 seconds. This time lies between   A. 2·36 and 2·38 seconds
       B. 2·27 and 2·47 seconds
       C. 2·365 and 2·375 seconds

15.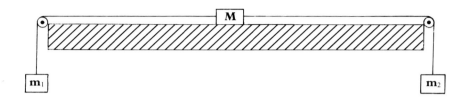

Two masses, m_1 and m_2, are attached to the ends of two strings which are connected to a mass M as shown in the diagram.

The acceleration, **a**, of the masses is given by the formula

$$a = \frac{(m_2 - m_1)\, g}{m_2 + m_1 + M}$$ where **g** is the acceleration due to gravity.

Use this formula to find **a** (in m/s²) if $m_1 = 0·6$kg, $m_2 = 1·1$kg, M = 2·8kg.
Take g = 9·8 m/s².

16. A length is given, to the nearest tenth of a metre, as 12·8m. What is the possible error in this measurement?

17. (a) Write each of 24, 45, 68 and 120 as a product of prime factors.
    (b) Find the HCF of 45 and 120.
    (c) Find the LCM of 24 and 68.

ALGEBRA

Algebra from Previous Levels

Divisibility

A number is   **divisible by 2** if it is an even number

                  divisible by 3 if the sum of its digits is divisible by 3

                  divisible by 4 if the number formed from the last two digits is divisible by 4

                  divisible by 5 if the last digit is 0 or 5

                  divisible by 6 if it is divisible by both 2 and 3

                  divisible by 8 if the number formed from the last three digits is divisible by 8

                  divisible by 9 if the sum of its digits is divisible by 9

                  divisible by 10 if the last digit is 0

Prime numbers, Factors, Multiples

A **prime number** is divisible by just two numbers, itself and 1.

The **multiples** of a number are found by multiplying the number by each of 1, 2, 3, . . . For instance, the multiples of 10 are 10, 20, 30, . . .

A **factor** of a given number is a whole number that divides exactly into the given number. For instance, the factors of 10 are 1, 2, 5, 10.

A **prime factor** is a factor that is a prime number. For instance, the prime factors of 10 are 2 and 5.

Spatial Arrangements of Numbers

The **square numbers** are $1^2, 2^2, 3^2, 4^2, . . .$ i.e. 1, 4, 9, 16, . . .

The **cube numbers** are $1^3, 2^3, 3^3, 4^3, . . .$ i.e. 1, 8, 27, 64, . . .

Finding a square and finding a square root are inverse operations as are finding a cube and a cube root. One operation "undoes" the other.

$\sqrt{64}$ is read as "the square root of 64". $\sqrt{64}$ = 8, since 8^2 = 64.

$\sqrt[3]{64}$ is read as "the cube root of 64". $\sqrt[3]{64}$ = 4, since 4^3 = 64.

The square numbers (1, 4, 9, 16, . . .), rectangular numbers (2, 6, 12, 20, . . .), triangular numbers (1, 3, 6, 10, . . .), pentagonal numbers (1, 5, 12, 22, . . .), hexagonal numbers (1, 6, 15, 28, . . .), can all be represented by a pattern of dots in the given geometric shape.

Sequences

A **sequence** is a list of numbers such as 3, 7, 11, 15, . . . By finding a pattern in a sequence, we can continue the sequence.

Sequences are sometimes based on the following special numbers – odd numbers, even numbers, squares, cubes, multiples.

The terms of a sequence are sometimes found by adding the same number to each previous term or by multiplying each previous term by the same number.

Sometimes we can continue a sequence by using the **difference method**. For instance the next term in the sequence 12, 14, 22, 36, 56, . . . can be found as follows.

$$12 \qquad 14 \qquad 22 \qquad 36 \qquad 56 \qquad 82$$
$$2 \qquad 8 \qquad 14 \qquad 20 \qquad 26$$
$$6 \qquad 6 \qquad 6 \qquad 6$$

Simplifying

ab means $a \times b$

2a means $2 \times a$

a^2 means $a \times a$

$a + a$ can be simplified to 2a

$5a + 2a$ can be simplified to 7a

$5a + 3b - a + 2b$ can be simplified to $4a + 5b$

$5(2a - 3)$ can be expanded to $10a - 15$

Formulae and Equations

$x + 3$ is an **expression**.

$p = x + 3$ is a **formula**. The value of p depends on the value of x.

$2p - 4 = 1$ is an **equation**. Here p can have only one value; $p = 2·5$.

Three methods of **solving equations** are : trial and improvement, flowchart method, balance method. The **trial and improvement** method is particularly useful for solving polynomial equations ; that is, equations which involve a square such as x^2 or a cube such as x^3.

The **flowchart method** for solving $2a - 4 = 1$ is shown below.

$$\text{Begin with} \quad a \rightarrow \boxed{\times 2} \rightarrow 2a \rightarrow \boxed{-4} \rightarrow 2a - 4$$

$$2·5 \leftarrow \boxed{\div 2} \leftarrow 5 \leftarrow \boxed{+4} \leftarrow \text{Begin with 1}$$

Hence a = 2·5.

The **balance method** for solving $2a - 4 = 1$ is shown below.

$$2a - 4 = 1$$
$$2a = 5 \quad \text{(adding 4 to both sides)}$$
$$a = 2·5 \quad \text{(dividing both sides by 2)}$$

When solving an equation always **check your solution** by substituting your solution back into the equation. For instance, to check that $a = 2.5$ is a solution for $2a - 4 = 1$ proceed as follows : If $a = 2.5$, $2a - 4 = 2 \times 2.5 - 4$
$$= 1 \text{ Correct.}$$

Graphs

The **x-axis** is the horizontal axis.
The **y-axis** is the vertical axis.

The **coordinates** of a point are a pair of numbers such as $(3, -2)$.
The first number is the x-coordinate; the second number is the y-coordinate.

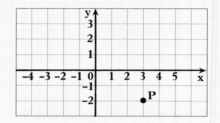

For the point $P(3, -2)$, the x-coordinate is 3 and the y-coordinate is -2.

$(3, -2)$, is also called an **ordered pair**. The ordered pair $(3, -2)$ is different from the ordered pair $(-2, 3)$.

The graph of a straight line may be drawn, from the equation of the line, as follows.
   Step 1   Find the coordinates of three points on the line.
   Step 2   Plot these points.
   Step 3   Draw the line that passes through these points.
Note: The line could be drawn by plotting just two points but for greater accuracy it is wise to plot three points.

For instance, to draw the line $y = 2x + 1$ proceed as follows.
Choose three values for x, say $-1, 0, 1$. Substitute these values for x into $y = 2x + 1$ to find the corresponding values of y – see the table below. Now plot the points $(-1, -1)$, $(0, 1)$, $(1, 3)$ and draw the line that goes through these points – see the graph below.

x	−1	0	1
y	−1	1	3

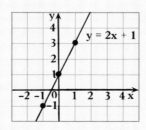

The **graph of a curve** may be drawn in a similar way to a straight line. Many points should be plotted and joined with a smooth curve.

The curve shown on this graph is called a **parabola**.

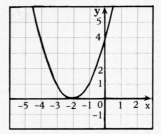

Problem Solving

Three methods of problem solving are : **finding a pattern, solving a simpler problem first, using equations**. We take the following steps to solve a problem using equations.

Step 1   Choose a variable such as n or x for the unknown quantity.
Step 2   Rewrite the statements in mathematical symbols.
Step 3   Combine these statements into an equation.
Step 4   Solve the equation.
Step 5   Check the answer with the information in the problem.

REVISION EXERCISE

1. Find the missing term in these sequences.
   (a) 1, □, 9, 16, 25, · · ·   (b) 1, 2, □, 8, 16, · · ·   (c) 1, 8, □, 64, 125, · · ·
   (d) 1, 8, □, 22, 29, · · ·   (e) 2, 5, 9, □, 20, · · ·

2.

| 65742 | 54627 | 46725 | 36472 | 47236 | 56664 | 67348 | 72654 |

Which number in this list is divisible by both 3 and 8?

3. Simplify the following.
   (a) $a \times a$ (b) $a + a$ (c) $3n - 2n$ (d) $x^2 + 3x^2$
   (e) $4n - n - n$ (f) $2a \times 5b$ (g) $5a - 3n - a + 2n$

57

4. Draw up a set of axes. Label the x-axis from –6 to 10 ; label the y-axis from –5 to 5. Plot each point in the following lists. Join the points in order, as you plot them.

   (a) (5, 2), (5, –4)   **(b)** (–5, 2), (–1, 4), (9, 4)   **(c)** (–5, –4), (–1, –2)
   (d) (–1, 4), (–1, –2), (9, –2), (9, 4), (5, 2), (–5, 2), (–5, –4), (5, –4), (9, –2)

   What do you get?

5.

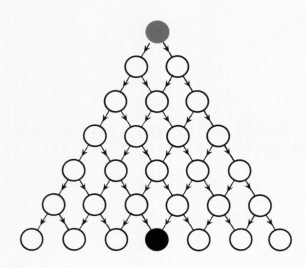

   In how many different ways could you walk from the red circle to the black circle if you must always walk in the direction given by the arrows? (Begin with a simpler problem first.)

6. Evaluate the following, giving the answer to 1d.p. when rounding is necessary.
   (a) 4^2 **(b)** $\sqrt{4}$ **(c)** 4^3 **(d)** $\sqrt{72}$ **(e)** $(3\cdot17)^3$ **(f)** $\sqrt[3]{8}$

7. **(a)** Expand $3(4n - 7)$ **(b)** Expand and simplify $3(4n - 7) + 2(3 + 2n)$

8. John's lucky number is n.
   Daniel's lucky number is twice John's.
   Beverley's lucky number is three less than Daniel's.
   Write an expression for Beverley's lucky number.

9. Use a method of your choice to solve these equations.
   (a) $2n = 15$ **(b)** $2 + n = 15$ **(c)** $4 (2n - 3) = 15$
   (d) $7n - 2n = 15$ **(e)** $7n - 3 = 5n + 4$

10. When Kate asked Nicholas what his house number was, Nicholas replied "Sixteen added to three times my house number is the same as two subtracted from five times my house number."

   (a) Write an equation for **h**, where **h** is Nicholas' house number.

   (b) Solve this equation to find Nicholas' house number.

11.

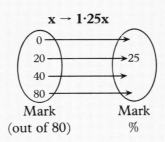

$$x \rightarrow 1{\cdot}25x$$

Mark
(out of 80)

Mark
%

The mapping x → 1·25x can be used to convert a mark out of 80 to a percentage.

   (a) Copy and complete the mapping diagram given above.

   (b) Copy and complete the following ordered pairs for this mapping.

       (0,), (20, 25), (40,), (80,)

   (c) Plot the ordered pairs on a set of axes.
      Draw the line that passes through these ordered pairs.

   (d) On a test that was marked out of 80, three students were given the following marks:
      Tamara - 76, Timothy - 28, Tewfik - 45.
      Use the graph you drew in **(c)** to find the percentage marks for these students.
      (Answers to the nearest %.)

12. Continue the sequence 8, 13, 18, . . . in at least two different ways.

13. Find the coordinates of three points on the graph of y = 2x – 1. Draw the graph of the line y = 2x – 1.

14.

          I am a factor of 36.
        I am not a multiple of 4.
      I am not a square number.
       I am not a prime number.
        I have one digit.
        What number am I?

15.

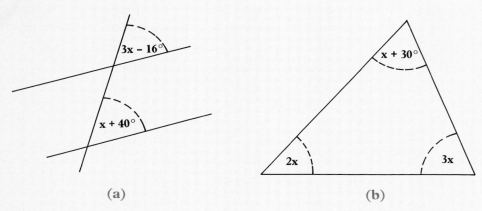

(a)   (b)

Write down an equation for x, for each of the above diagrams. Solve the equations to find the value of x in each case.

16. In words, give a rule that generates each of these sequences.
Test the rule, then write down the next three terms of each sequence.
(a) 500, 50, 5, 0·5, . . .   (b) 3, 6, 12, 24, . . .   (c) 3, 6, 9, 12, . . .
(d) 3, 12, 27, 48, . . .   (e) 1, 1, 2, 3, 5, 8, . . .

17. Use "trial and improvement" to find a solution for the equation $2x^3 + 1 = 25$. Give your solution accurate to 1 decimal place.

18.

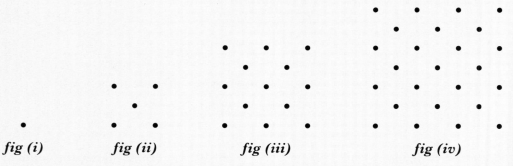

fig (i)   *fig (ii)*   *fig (iii)*   *fig (iv)*

(a) 1, 5, 13, 25 are the first four terms of the sequence of the number of dots in the diagrams shown. Draw the next diagram in this sequence to find the fifth term.
(b) Use the difference method to find the number of dots in the diagram which has 10 dots along each side.

19. Two sides of a square are $(4n + 3)$cm and $(2n + 12)$cm.
(a) Write down an equation for n. Solve this equation.
(b) Find the perimeter of the square.

20. Use "trial and improvement" to find the value of $\sqrt[3]{36}$ to 1d.p.

60

21. C = 299 + 18d + 5(d + 3). This formula gives the cost of hiring a car for 7 days or longer. **C** is the total cost in £. **d** is the number of days over 7.
Find the cost of hiring one of these cars for 11 days.

22. Write a program to print the first 100 terms of the sequence 20, 24, 28, 32, . . .

23.

x	−2	−1	0	1	2
y	7				

(a) Copy and complete this table of values for $y = x^2 + 3$.
(b) Draw the graph of $y = x^2 + 3$.

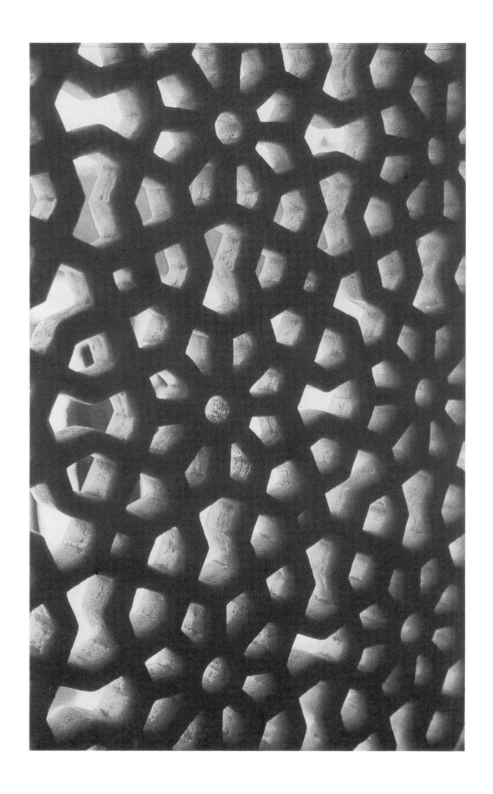

FINDING the RULE for a SEQUENCE

GARDEN PATHS

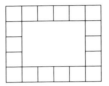

A path, made from 1m square paving stones, is to be made around a 4m × 3m garden.
How many paving stones are needed?

Investigate the number of paving stones needed for other rectangular gardens which are 1m longer than they are wide. Make and test statements as part of your investigation.
Can you predict the number of stones needed for a garden measuring 25m × 24m?
Can you predict the size of the garden if 150 stones are needed?

What if the garden is 2m longer than it is wide?
What if the garden is twice as long as it is wide?
What if the garden is square?
What if the paths are two paving stones wide?
What if . . .

t_1 means the first term of a sequence,
t_2 means the second term of a sequence,
t_3 means the third term of a sequence and so on.

In general, t_n means the nth term. For instance, t_{14} means the 14th term.

The rule for a sequence may be given as $t_n = \ldots$
For instance : $t_n = n - 1$, $t_n = 4n + 2$, $t_n = 2n$ are all rules that define sequences.

Sometimes T is used instead of t; t_3 may be called T_3 etc.

Worked Example (a) Write down the first four terms of the sequence given by the rule $t_n = 4n - 1$.

(b) Use the rule to find the 18th term of the sequence.

(c) A term of the sequence is 51. Which term is this?

Answer   (a) $t_n = 4n - 1$

Replace n by 1, 2, 3 and 4 in turn to find t_1, t_2, t_3, t_4.

$t_1 = 4 \times 1 - 1$	$t_2 = 4 \times 2 - 1$	$t_3 = 4 \times 3 - 1$	$t_4 = 4 \times 4 - 1$
$= 3$	$= 7$	$= 11$	$= 15$

The first four terms are 3, 7, 11, 15.

(b) Using $t_n = 4n - 1$, $\quad t_{18} = 4 \times 18 - 1$
$$= 71$$

(c) Using $t_n = 4n - 1$, $\quad 51 = 4n - 1$

We now solve the equation $51 = 4n - 1$ to find n. Using the balance method the solution is:

$$51 = 4n - 1$$
$$52 = 4n \quad \text{(adding 1 to each side)}$$
$$13 = n \quad \text{(dividing both sides by 4)}$$

Then $t_{13} = 51$. That is, the 13th term is 51.

INVESTIGATION 5:2

EXPLORING SEQUENCES

Consider the sequence defined by the rule $t_n = 3n + 4$.

$t_1 = 3 \times 1 + 4$	$t_2 = 3 \times 2 + 4$	$t_3 = 3 \times 3 + 4$	$t_4 = 3 \times 4 + 4$
$= 7$	$= 10$	$= 13$	$= 16$

The first four terms are 7, 10, 13, 16.

We can use the difference method to find further terms:

7		10		13		16		19		22		25
	3		3		3		3		3		3	

What is the connection between the rule for the sequence 7, 10, 13, 16, . . . and the row of 3's? **Investigate.**

As part of your investigation consider the sequences 4, 7, 10, 13, . . .
9, 12, 15, 18, . . .   2, 5, 8, 11, . . .   5, 7, 9, 11, . . .   –2, 3, 8, 13, . . .
20, 17, 14, 11, . . .   as well as others. Find and test rules for the sequences you consider.

RULES for INDICES

3^4 is called a **power** of 3; 4 is called the **index,** 3 is called the **base.**

Indices is the plural of index. For instance, if we were speaking of the numbers 4 and 7 in 3^4 and 2^7 we would call 4 and 7 the indices.

The x^y key, on the calculator, may be used to find powers.
For instance, 2^7 is found by keying   2 $\boxed{\text{INV}}$ $\boxed{x^y}$ 7 $\boxed{=}$.

INVESTIGATIONS 6:1

PATTERNS with INDICES

1.
row 1 →					1				
row 2 →				1		1			
row 3 →			1		2		1		
row 4 →		1		3		3		1	
row 5 →	1		4		6		4		1
row 6 →	1	5		10		10		5	1

The first 6 rows of Pascal's triangle are shown.
What is the sum of the numbers on each row? What is the connection between these sums and indices? **Investigate.**

2.
$$\underline{4}^5 = 102\underline{4}$$
$$\underline{6}^5 = 777\underline{6}$$
$$2\underline{4}^5 = 796262\underline{4}$$
$$3\underline{7}^5 = 6934395\underline{7}$$

What do you notice about the underlined digits? **Investigate** other numbers to the power of 5. Look for patterns. As part of your investigation, make and test statements.
What if the index was 4 rather than 5?
What if . . .

DISCUSSION EXERCISE and INVESTIGATION 6:2

$$2^3 = 2 \times 2 \times 2 \qquad 2^2 = 2 \times 2$$
$$= 8 \qquad\qquad = 4$$

$$8 \times 4 = 32$$

Write 32 as a power of 2. What do you notice about this power of 2 and the powers, 2^3 and 2^2, we began with? **Discuss.**
What if we began with different indices such as 4 and 5 instead of 3 and 2?
What if we began with the base 4 instead of 2?
What if we began with the base a?
What if we began with two different bases but the same index ; for instance, 2^3 and 5^3?
What if we began with two different bases and two different indices ; for instance, 2^3 and 4^2?

$$2^6 = 2 \times 2 \times 2 \times 2 \times 2 \times 2 \qquad 2^2 = 2 \times 2$$
$$= 64 \qquad\qquad\qquad = 4$$

$$64 \div 4 = 16$$

Write 16 as a power of 2. What do you notice about this power of 2 and the powers 2^6 and 2^2? **Discuss.**
Make and test statements about division of powers.

$$2^3 = 2 \times 2 \times 2 \qquad (2^3)^2 = 8^2$$
$$= 8 \qquad\qquad = 64$$

Write 64 as a power of 2. Compare this with $(2^3)^2$. **Discuss.**
What if the indices were 5 and 2 rather than 3 and 2?
What if the indices were 2 and 4 rather than 3 and 2?
What if the base was 4 instead of 2?
What if . . .

The answer is 2^6. Write down many expressions that could be simplified to 2^6. **Discuss.**
The answer is x^4. Write down many expressions that could be simplified to x^4. **Discuss.**

Use the results of your discussion and investigation to complete the following rules for indices.

$$a^m \times a^n = a^{\cdots}$$
$$a^m \div a^n = a^{\cdots}$$
$$(a^m)^n = a^{\cdots}$$

Worked Example   Use the rules of indices to write the following as single powers of 7.

(a) $7^4 \times 7^9$ (b) $7^8 \div 7^2$ (c) $(7^5)^3$

Answer   (a) $7^4 \times 7^9 = 7^{4+9}$ (b) $7^8 \div 7^2 = 7^{8-2}$ (c) $(7^5)^3 = 7^{5 \times 3}$

$= 7^{13}$ $= 7^6$ $= 7^{15}$

Worked Example   Simplify (a) $x^y \times x^a$ (b) $a^x \times a^y \times a^z$ (c) $\dfrac{x^a}{x^y}$

(d) $(x^{3a})^b$

Answer   (a) $x^y \times x^a = x^{y+a}$ (b) $a^x \times a^y \times a^z = a^{x+y+z}$ (c) $\dfrac{x^a}{x^y} = x^{a-y}$

(d) $(x^{3a})^b = x^{3ab}$

Worked Example   Write the following without brackets.

(a) $(b^3h^2)^4$ (b) $(2a^2b)^3$

Answer   (a) $(b^3h^2)^4 = b^3h^2 \times b^3h^2 \times b^3h^2 \times b^3h^2$

$= b^{12}h^8$

(b) $(2a^2b)^3 = 2a^2b \times 2a^2b \times 2a^2b$

$= 8\,a^6b^3$

Worked Example   Write $\dfrac{8^2 \times 2^5}{4^4}$ as a power of 2.

Answer   Since $8 = 2^3$ and $4 = 2^2$, $\dfrac{8^2 \times 2^5}{4^4}$ may be written as $\dfrac{(2^3)^2 \times 2^5}{(2^2)^4}$

$= \dfrac{2^6 \times 2^5}{2^8}$

$= 2^3$

EXERCISE 6:3

1. Write these as a single power of 5.

(a) $5^3 \times 5^6$ (b) $5^4 \times 5^3$ (c) $5^4 \times 5^4$ (d) $5^7 \times 5^{10}$

(e) $5^6 \div 5^3$ (f) $5^5 \div 5^1$ (g) $5^{16} \div 5^4$ (h) $\dfrac{5^8}{5^4}$

(i) $(5^2)^3$ (j) $(5^4)^4$ (k) $(5^3)^2$

2. Use the rules of indices to simplify these. Hence evaluate.

(a) $2^4 \times 2^3$ (b) $3^2 \times 3^3$ (c) $\dfrac{5^7}{5^5}$ (d) $2^2 \times 2^3 \times 2^2$

(e) $\dfrac{4^3 \times 4^6}{4^7}$ (f) $\dfrac{2^{13}}{2^4 \times 2^5}$ (g) $\dfrac{7^{11} \times 7^4}{7^9 \times 7^5}$ (h) $\dfrac{5^7 \times 5^3}{(5^4)^2}$

3. Which of the following statements are correct?

(a) $4^3 \times 4^2 = 4^6$ (b) $4^3 + 4^2 = 4^5$ (c) $4^3 \times 2^2 = 8^5$

(d) $(4^4)^2 = 16^6$ (e) $4^8 \div 2^3 = 2^5$ (f) $4^5 - 4^3 = 4^2$

4. Which of the following statements are correct?

(a) $a^6 \div a^2 = a^3$ (b) $a^6 \times a^2 = a^8$ (c) $a \times a^4 = a^5$

(d) $(x^2)^3 = x^6$ (e) $x^3 \times x^4 \times x = x^8$ (f) $(p^5)^3 = p^{15}$

(g) $a^6 - a^2 = a^4$ (h) $a^7 + a^2 = a^9$ (i) $(2a^3)^2 = 2a^6$

5. Simplify these.

(a) $x^4 \times x^5$ (b) $a^3 \times a^9$ (c) $p^{12} \div p^4$ (d) $x^{16} \div x^2$

(e) $b^a \times b^x$ (f) $b^a \times b^c$ (g) $a^x \div a^b$ (h) $(a^x)^y$

(i) $(x^{2a})^3$ (j) $(p^{3x})^4$ (k) $x^p \times x^p$ (l) $b^a \times b^a$

(m) $\dfrac{a^7 \times a^4}{a^3}$ (n) $\dfrac{x^4 \times x^5}{(x^3)^2}$

6. Write these without brackets.

(a) $(x^2y^3)^2$ (b) $(a^3b)^4$ (c) $(x^2yz^3)^5$ (d) $(2a^2b^3)^4$

(e) $(3p^3q^5)^3$ (f) $(4a^5x^4)^2$ (g) $(2xy^3z^3)^5$

7. (a) Write $\dfrac{9^2 \times 27}{3^5}$ as a power of 3.   (b) Write $\dfrac{125 \times 5^{10}}{25^2}$ as a power of 5.

(c) Write $\dfrac{16^3 \times 8^3}{2^9 \times 4^5}$ as a power of 2.

Review 1   Which of the following statements are correct?

(a) $4^5 + 4^7 = 4^{12}$ (b) $(3^2)^5 = 3^7$ (c) $7^7 - 7^2 = 7^5$

(d) $a^5 \times a^3 \times a^2 = a^{10}$ (e) $(2a^3)^4 = 16a^7$ (f) $x^8 \div x^2 = x^4$

Review 2   Use the rules of indices to simplify these.

(a) $\dfrac{a^{14}}{a^7}$ (b) $p^5 \times p^7$ (c) $a^2 \times a^3 \times a$ (d) $\dfrac{y^7 \times y^2}{y^5}$

(e) $(x^3)^5$ (f) $(3a^4)^2$ (g) $(2x^3y^4)^3$

Review 3   Write $\dfrac{2^8 \times 4^3}{16 \times 8^2}$ as a power of 2.

INVESTIGATION 6:4

LAST DIGITS

$3^1 = 3$
$3^2 = 9$
$3^3 = 27$
$3^4 = 81$
$3^5 = 243$
$3^6 = 729$
$3^7 = 2187$
$3^8 = 6561$
$3^9 = 19683$

The last digits form the pattern :

3, 9, 7, 1, 3, 9, 7, 1, 3, . . .

Can you predict what the last digit of 3^{24} is?

Can you predict what the last digit is of other powers of 3?

Investigate.

What if the base was a number other than 3?

Suppose we were asked to find the last two digits of 2^{250}. We could investigate to find a pattern or we could proceed as follows.

$2^5 = 32,$

$2^{10} = (2^5)^2$
$= 32 \times 32$
$= 1024$ The last two digits are 24.

$2^{20} = (2^{10})^2$
$= 1024 \times 1024$ The last two digits are found by multiplying 24 by 24.

Proceeding in this manner, we could find the last 2 digits of 2^{40}, 2^{80}, 2^{160}.

How could we use this method to find the last two digits of 2^{250}?

(**Hint** : Use $a^{m + n} = a^m \times a^n$.)

Investigate using this method and/or using a pattern to find the last two digits of any power of 2.

What if we were finding the last two digits of any power of 3?

What if . . .

RECIPROCALS

DISCUSSION EXERCISE 6:5

What is the relationship between the following pairs of numbers? Discuss.

$2, \frac{1}{2}$ $4, \frac{1}{4}$ $\frac{1}{7}, 7$ $\frac{2}{3}, \frac{3}{2}$ $\frac{5}{4}, \frac{4}{5}$ $2\frac{1}{2}, \frac{2}{5}$

Write down some other pairs of numbers with this relationship. Discuss.

The reciprocal of $\frac{3}{5}$ is $\frac{5}{3}$; the reciprocal of $\frac{a}{b}$ is $\frac{b}{a}$; the reciprocal of a is $\frac{1}{a}$.

To find the reciprocal of a number proceed as follows.

Step 1 Write down the number as a fraction, if it isn't already given as a fraction.

Step 2 Invert the fraction. That is, "tip the fraction upside down."

Worked Example Find the reciprocals of (a) $\frac{2}{5}$ (b) 5 (c) 0·8 (d) $\frac{3}{x}$ (e) 3x

Answer (a) The reciprocal of $\frac{2}{5}$ is $\frac{5}{2}$.

(b) Since $5 = \frac{5}{1}$, the reciprocal of 5 is $\frac{1}{5}$.

(c) $0·8 = \frac{8}{10}$ or $\frac{4}{5}$. The reciprocal of 0·8 is $\frac{5}{4}$ or 1·25.

(d) The reciprocal of $\frac{3}{x}$ is $\frac{x}{3}$.

(e) Since $3x = \frac{3x}{1}$, the reciprocal of 3x is $\frac{1}{3x}$.

The $\frac{1}{x}$ key on the calculator is used to find the reciprocal of a number.

For instance, the reciprocal of 2 is found by keying 2 $\boxed{\text{INV}}$ $\boxed{\frac{1}{x}}$

EXERCISE 6:6

1. Without using the calculator, find the reciprocal of these.
   (a) $\frac{2}{3}$ (b) $\frac{3}{4}$ (c) $\frac{3}{10}$ (d) $\frac{8}{7}$ (e) $\frac{5}{4}$ (f) $\frac{1}{6}$

   (g) 7   (h) 8   (i) 0·7   (j) 1·3

2. Find the reciprocal of these.
   (a) $\frac{c}{a}$ (b) $\frac{a}{c}$ (c) $\frac{z}{x}$ (d) $\frac{x}{z}$ (e) $\frac{a}{x}$ (f) $\frac{x}{a}$

   (g) x   (h) d   (i) 2z   (j) 5x   (k) $\frac{x}{4}$ (l) $\frac{2}{x}$

3. Use the calculator to find the reciprocal of these. Give the answer to 2 significant figures where rounding is necessary.
   (a) 0·14   (b) 7·2   (c) 0·3   (d) 10   (e) 25   (f) 54

Review 1 Give the reciprocal of these as a whole number or fraction.
   (a) $\frac{3}{4}$ (b) 9   (c) 0·1   (d) k   (e) 3k   (f) $\frac{a}{3k}$

Review 2 Find the reciprocal of these, giving the answer to 2d.p. where rounding is necessary.   (a) 0·6   (b) 20   (c) 1·16

DISCUSSION EXERCISE 6:7

Discuss the following statements which may be true or false. For those that are false, make a similar correct statement.

Statement 1   There is just one whole number that has no reciprocal.
Statement 2   Dividing by a number is the same as multiplying by the reciprocal of that number.
Statement 3   When a number is multiplied by its reciprocal the answer is 0.
Statement 4   Negative numbers have no reciprocals.

Adding and subtracting, multiplying and dividing, squaring and taking the square root are all inverse operations. What is the inverse operation for "taking the reciprocal"? **Discuss**.

USING RECIPROCALS to SOLVE EQUATIONS

The operation "take the reciprocal" is needed to solve some equations by the flowchart method. This operation is necessary if x is on the bottom line of the equation. Remember that the inverse operation for "taking the reciprocal" is also "taking the reciprocal".

Worked Example   Find the value of x for which $\frac{3}{x} = 5$.

Answer   Using the flowchart method:

Begin with x → | Take the reciprocal | → $\frac{1}{x}$ → | × 3 | → $\frac{3}{x}$

$\frac{3}{5}$ ← | Take the reciprocal | ← $\frac{5}{3}$ ← | ÷ 3 | ← Begin with 5

The solution is x = $\frac{3}{5}$ or 0·6.

Worked Example   Find the solution of the equation $\frac{2}{x+1} = 5$.

Answer
Begin with x → | + 1 | → x + 1 → | Take the reciprocal | → $\frac{1}{x+1}$ → | × 2 | → $\frac{2}{x+1}$

– 0·6 ← | – 1 | ← $\frac{2}{5}$ ← | Take the reciprocal | ← $\frac{5}{2}$ ← | ÷ 2 | ← Begin with 5

The solution is x = – 0·6.

EXERCISE 6:8

1. Solve these equations.
   (a) $\frac{2}{x} = 9$ (b) $\frac{4}{x} = 10$ (c) $\frac{5}{x} = 1{\cdot}8$

   (d) $\frac{2}{x-1} = 4$ (e) $\frac{5}{x+3} = 1$ (f) $\frac{1}{2x-1} = 3$

   (g) $\frac{4}{5x+2} = 5$ (h) $\frac{2}{1+3x} = 5$

2. $s = \frac{d}{t}$ is a formula which gives the average speed, **s**, if a distance, **d**, is covered in time **t**. Use this formula to find the time taken if:
   (a) s = 50km/h, d = 240km   (b) s = 120km/h, d = 500km
   (c) s = 10m/s,   d = 44m   (d) s = 20m/s,   d = 550m

3. $d = \frac{m}{v}$ gives the density, **d**, of an object of mass, **m**, and volume **v**. Find the volume of an object if: (a) d = 0·25g/cm³, m = 150g   (b) d = 1·5g/cm³, m = 60g

4. If just the hot tap is turned on, a bath can be filled in **h** minutes; if just the cold tap is turned on, a bath can be filled in **c** minutes. If both taps are turned on, a bath can be filled in **t** minutes where t is given by $\frac{1}{t} = \frac{1}{h} + \frac{1}{c}$. For Angela's bath, h = 8 minutes and c = 5 minutes. Find the time taken to fill Angela's bath if both taps are turned on. (Answer to the nearest minute.)

5.

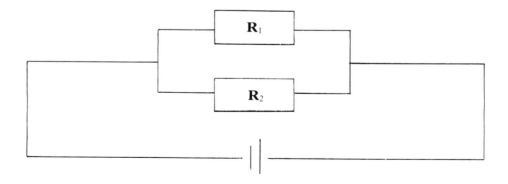

The total resistance R in this circuit, with resistors R₁ and R₂ in parallel, is given by $\frac{1}{R} = \frac{1}{R_1} + \frac{1}{R_2}$.
Find the total resistance R if R₁ = 3·5 ohms and R₂ = 4·5 ohms.

Review 1 Solve these equations. (a) $\dfrac{3}{x} = 8$ (b) $\dfrac{5}{x+2} = 2$

Review 2 Ohm's Law, $\dfrac{V}{I} = R$, gives the relationship between voltage V, current I and resistance R. V is measured in volts, I is measured in amps and R is measured in ohms.
Find the current if the voltage is 12 volts and the resistance is 2·4 ohms.

Inequalities.
Polynomial Equations

INEQUALITIES

Remember: $<$ means "is less than"
$\leq$ means "is less than or equal to"
$>$ means "is greater than"
$\geq$ means "is greater than or equal to"
$3 < n < 8$ is read as "n lies between 3 and 8"

DISCUSSION EXERCISE 7:1

For each of the following, **discuss** which inequality best describes the statement.

More than 250mm of rain fell yesterday.
$r < 250$ $r \leq 250$ $r > 250$ $r \geq 250$

The speed limit through a village is 60km/h.
$s < 60$ $s \leq 60$ $s > 60$ $s \geq 60$

T-bone steaks weigh between 100g and 200g.
$100 < w < 200$ $100 \leq w < 200$ $100 < w \leq 200$ $100 \leq w \leq 200$

18 is the smallest number, and 27 is the greatest number of students in the classes in a school.
$18 < s < 27$ $18 \leq s < 27$ $18 < s \leq 27$ $18 \leq s \leq 27$

Joanne never arrives at school later than 8·30 a.m.
$t \leq 8{\cdot}30$ $t < 8{\cdot}30$ $t \geq 8{\cdot}30$ $t > 8{\cdot}30$

Hans never arrives at school earlier than 8·30 a.m.
$t \leq 8{\cdot}30$ $t < 8{\cdot}30$ $t \geq 8{\cdot}30$ $t > 8{\cdot}30$

Shane takes between 3 and 4 minutes to iron a shirt.
$3 < t < 4$ $3 \leq t < 4$ $3 < t \leq 4$ $3 \leq t \leq 4$

The typing speeds of the students in a class were all greater than 35 words per minute.
$t < 35$ $t \leq 35$ $t > 35$ $t \geq 35$

In a test, every student gained at least 70%.
$m < 70\%$ $m \leq 70\%$ $m > 70\%$ $m \geq 70\%$

Write down some other statements that could be described by inequalities. Use inequalities to describe them. **Discuss.**

DISPLAYING INEQUALITIES on the NUMBER LINE

> ## DISCUSSION EXERCISE 7:2

If n + 4 = 6, n can have only one value. What is this one value?
Which whole number values could n have if n + 4 > 6? **Discuss.**

Is 2·5 also a solution for n + 4 > 6? Is 2·1? Is $2\frac{1}{9}$? Can you list *all* the solutions for
n + 4 > 6? **Discuss.**

Which of the following show *all* the solutions for n + 4 > 6? **Discuss.** What meaning could
be attached to the symbols ● and O? What meaning could be attached to the arrow?
Discuss.

To display an inequality on the number line proceed as follows.
Step 1   Draw a line over all the values included.
Step 2   If the end point of the line is one of values included, place the symbol ● on
this end point; if the end point is not one of the values included, place the
symbol O on this end point.

Worked Example   Display these on the number line.
   (a) x > -2   (b) a ≤ 3   (c) 1 ≤ n < 4

Answer   (a)   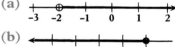   The value -2 is not included.

(b)   The value 3 is included.

(c)   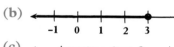   The value 1 is included; the value 4 is not
included.

Worked Example   List all the whole number solutions for
   (a) x > -2   (b) a ≤ 3   (c) 1 ≤ n < 4

Answer   We can display the inequality on the number line, then read off the whole
numbers included. The previous worked example shows these inequalities
displayed on the number line.
From the number line for (a) , the whole number solutions are -1, 0, 1, 2, . . .
From the number line for (b) , the whole number solutions are
. . ., -1, 0, 1, 2, 3.
From the number line for (c) , the whole number solutions are 1, 2, 3.

EXERCISE 7:3

1. Write down the inequalities displayed below. Use n for the variable.

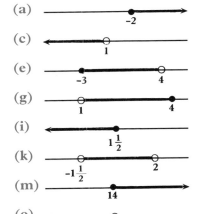
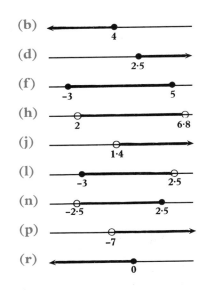

2. Display the following inequalities on the number line.
   (a) $x \geq 4$ (b) $x < 2$ (c) $a > -2$ (d) $p \leq 0$
   (e) $1 \leq n \leq 4$ (f) $-2 < n < 2$ (g) $-1 \leq a < 2$ (h) $-2 < x \leq 3$

3. Use the number line graphs you drew in **question 2** to list all the whole number solutions for the following inequalities.
   (a) $x \geq 4$ (b) $x < 2$ (c) $a > -2$ (d) $p \leq 0$
   (e) $1 \leq n \leq 4$ (f) $-2 < n < 2$ (g) $-1 \leq a < 2$ (h) $-2 < x \leq 3$

Review 1   Display each of these on the number line.
         (a) $-4 \leq x < 3$ (b) $p \leq 2$ (c) $n > -3$

Review 2   Use your answers to **Review 1** to write down all the whole number solutions for each of the following inequalities.
         (a) $-4 \leq x < 3$ (b) $p \leq 2$ (c) $n > -3$

USING the NUMBER LINE to SOLVE INEQUALITIES

The solution for inequalities such as $-3 < n - 2 \leq 2$, $2n > 4$, $n + 1 < 5$ may be displayed on the number line as shown in the following worked example.

Worked Example   Display the solution for $-3 < n - 2 \leq 2$ on a number line.

Answer   *Step 1*

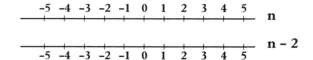

Draw two number lines, one under the other.
Label the top one as **n**, the bottom one as **n – 2**.

Step 2

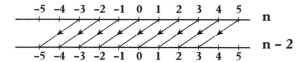

Map each whole number on the **n** number line onto a number on the **n – 2** number line. For instance, if n = 5, then n – 2 = 3 so 5 maps onto 3.

Step 3

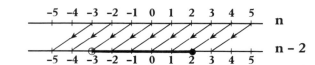

On the **n – 2** number line display the inequality $-3 < n - 2 \leq 2$.

Step 4

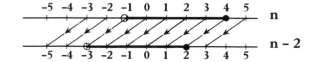

Look back to find the numbers on the **n** number line that map onto the inequality displayed on the **n – 2** number line.

Hence, the solution for the inequality $-3 < n - 2 \leq 2$ is displayed as follows.

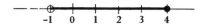

Worked Example   Write down all the whole number solutions for the inequality $-3 < n - 2 \leq 2$.

Answer   The solution for the inequality $-3 < n - 2 \leq 2$ may be displayed as

(see the previous worked example).

Hence the whole number solutions for **n** are 0, 1, 2, 3, 4.

EXERCISE 7:4

1. Which number line, A or B or C or D, shows the solution of the inequality
   $-3 < n + 1 < 3$?

   A.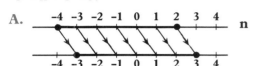

   B.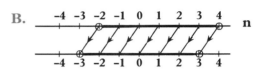

   C.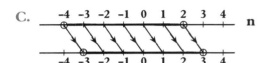

   D.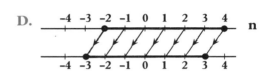

2. Which of the number lines in **question 1** show the solution for the following
   inequalities?
   (a) $-3 \le n - 1 \le 3$ (b) $-3 \le n + 1 \le 3$ (c) $-3 < n - 1 < 3$

3.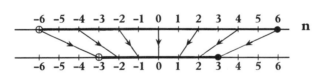

   The solution of which of the following inequalities is displayed on the top number line
   in this diagram?
   A. $-3 < 2n \le 3$ B. $-3 < \frac{n}{2} \le 3$ C. $-3 \le 2n < 3$ D. $-3 \le \frac{n}{2} < 3$

4. On the number line, display the solution for each of the following inequalities. Hence
   write down all the whole number solutions.

   (a) $-2 \le n - 3 < 1$ (b) $-4 < n + 1 < 3$ (c) $0 \le x - 2 \le 4$
   (d) $n - 2 < 1$ (e) $p + 2 > -3$ (f) $a - 1 \le -1$
   (g) $2n \ge 4$ (h) $3n > -3$ (i) $\frac{n}{2} < 1$
   (j) $-3 \le 3p < 12$ (k) $2p < 5$ (l) $4 \le 4n \le 11$

Review   Find all the whole number solutions for each of these inequalities.
             (a) $n - 1 > -3$ (b) $-5 \le 2x \le 6$

POLYNOMIAL EQUATIONS

We can solve equations such as $2x - 1 = 6\cdot5$ by using a number of methods.
We could use: the flowchart method
or trial and improvement
or the balance method

There are also a number of methods for solving equations such as $x^2 = 8$, $x^2 + 3x = 4$, $2x^3 = 16$, $2x^2 - 3x + 1 = 0$.

The "trial and improvement" method is particularly useful as it can be used to find approximate solutions for **any** equation.

Worked Example   Use "trial and improvement" to find two solutions for the equation $2x^2 + x - 7 = 0$. (Answers to 1d.p.)

Answer   Try x = 1.   If x = 1, $2x^2 + x - 7 = -4$ which is too small.
Try x = 2.   If x = 2, $2x^2 + x - 7 = 3$ which is too large.
Try x = 1·5.   If x = 1·5, $2x^2 + x - 7 = -1$ which is too small.
Try x = 1·7.   If x = 1·7, $2x^2 + x - 7 = 0\cdot48$ which is too large.
Try x = 1·6.   If x = 1·6, $2x^2 + x - 7 = -0\cdot28$ which is too small.
We now know that one solution is between 1·6 and 1·7 and is closer to 1·6 than to 1·7 since −0·28 is closer to 0 than is 0·48. We can say that, to 1d.p., one solution is 1·6.

We have found one solution for $2x^2 + x - 7 = 0$. We will now find another.

If x = 2, $2x^2 + x - 7 = 3$ which is too large.
Try x = 3.   If x = 3, $2x^2 + x - 7 = 14$ which is too large.
Try x = 4.   If x = 4, $2x^2 + x - 7 = 29$ which is even larger.
Try x = 5.   If x = 5, $2x^2 + x - 7 = 48$ which is larger still.
It seems that we are getting further and further away from 0. We will now try values of x that are less than 1.

If x = 1, $2x^2 + x - 7 = -4$ which is too small.
Try x = 0   If x = 0, $2x^2 + x - 7 = -7$ which is too small.
Try x = −1   If x = −1, $2x^2 + x - 7 = -6$ which is too small.
Try x = −2   If x = −2, $2x^2 + x - 7 = -1$ which is too small.
Try x = −3   If x = −3, $2x^2 + x - 7 = 8$ which is too large.
Try x = −2·2   If x = −2·2, $2x^2 + x - 7 = 0\cdot48$ which is too large.
Try x = −2·1   If x = −2·1, $2x^2 + x - 7 = -0\cdot28$ which is too small.
We now know that one solution is between −2·1 and −2·2 and is closer to −2·1 since −0·28 is closer to 0 than is 0·48. We can say that, to 1d.p., one solution is −2·1.
Hence, to 1d.p., the two solutions of $2x^2 + x - 7 = 0$ are 1·6 and −2·1.

DISCUSSION EXERCISE 7:5

Halima was finding solutions for the equation $6x^2 + 7x - 24 = 0$. She set out her initial working as follows.

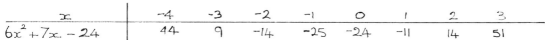

x	-4	-3	-2	-1	0	1	2	3
$6x^2 + 7x - 24$	44	9	-14	-25	-24	-11	14	51

From this working, Halima decided that one solution was between -3 and -2 and another was between 1 and 2. How did Halima come to this conclusion? Was she right? **Discuss.** As part of your discussion, use trial and improvement to find two solutions for the equation $6x^2 + 7x - 24 = 0$.

EXERCISE 7:6

1. Use "trial and improvement" to find solutions for the following equations. Where the solutions are not whole numbers give them to 1d.p.

    (a) $x^2 = 10$ (two solutions)　　　　(b) $x^2 + 2x = 10$ (two solutions)
    (c) $2x^2 - 14x + 15 = 0$ (two solutions)　(d) $x^2 - 3x - 4 = 0$ (two solutions)
    (e) $x^2 - 3x = 0$ (two solutions)　　　(f) $4x^2 + 12x = -9$ (one solution)
    (g) $x^3 = 6$ (one solution)　　　　　(h) $x^3 - 8x = 2$ (three solutions)
    (i) $x^3 + x^2 - 6x = 0$ (three solutions)

2. Three sections of a school are being extended to give each a floor area of 300m². The floor plans are shown below (the dimensions are in metres). The shaded areas are the extensions.

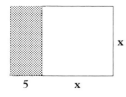
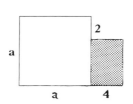
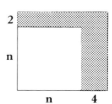

    (a) Which of these polynomial equations could be used to find **x**?
    　A. $x^2 = 5x$　　　　　　B. $x^2 + 5x = 300$　　　　C. $x^2 + 5x + 300 = 0$

    (b) Which of these polynomial equations could be used to find **a**?
    　A. $a^2 + 8 = 300$　　　　B. $a^2 + 4a - 8 = 300$　　　C. $a^2 + 8a = 300$

    (c) Which of these polynomial equations could be used to find **n**?
    　A. $n^2 + 6n + 8 = 300$　　B. $n^2 + 6n = 300$　　　　C. $n^2 + 8 = 300$

3. Solve polynomial equations to find the length of the original floor areas in **question 2**. That is, find x, a and n. (Give your answers to the nearest mm.)

Review   Find two solutions for the equation $2x^2 - 7x + 4 = 0$. Give the answers to 1d.p.

PRACTICAL EXERCISE 7:7

Once Halima had used her calculator to find that one solution of the equation $6x^2 + 7x - 24 = 0$ was between –3 and –2 she then used a computer to find this solution to 1d.p. She did this by using a spreadsheet. Calculations of $6x^2 + 7x - 24$ were made at 0·01 intervals between x = –3 and –2. Use a spreadsheet in this way to find the solutions of $6x^2 + 7x - 24 = 0$ to 1d.p.

INVESTIGATION 7:8

NUMBER of SOLUTIONS

In this investigation, you may like to use initial working similar to that in Discussion Exercise 7:5. You may like to use a spreadsheet.

Find two solutions for the equation $x^2 - 4 = 0$.
Can you find any solutions for the equation $x^2 + 4 = 0$?
Can you find more than one solution for the equation $x^2 - 9x + 3 = 0$?
Can you find more than two solutions for any equation in which the highest power of x is x^2? **Investigate.** As part of your investigation consider many equations such as $x^2 + 3x - 1 = 0$, $2x^2 - 5x + 3 = 0$, $3x^2 + 7 = 0$, $x^2 - 5x = 0$.

What is the solution to x + 3 = 0? How many solutions does this equation have?
What if the equation was 3x – 4 = 0 or 5x + 1·5 = 0?
Investigate to find the number of solutions for an equation in which the highest power of x is x.
Make and test statements about the maximum number of solutions for equations such as $x^3 + 8 = 0$, $x^3 - x^2 - 2x = 0$, $x^3 - 5x^2 + 2x + 8 = 0$; that is, equations in which the highest power of x is x^3?

You may wish to extend your investigation to equations in which the highest power of x is x^4 or x^5 or x^6 etc.

PROJECT 7:9

A spreadsheet is a useful tool to carry out calculations using "trial and improvement". It is also often used when one variable (e.g. interest rate) in a formula changes and the other variables remain the same; that is, a spreadsheet is a useful tool to answer "what if" questions.

Work as a group to produce a well researched and well presented project on the practical uses of the spreadsheet. You may like to base your project on a particular use of the spreadsheet ; for instance, budgeting. You may like to consider all the uses of the spreadsheet within one industry.

Each group should initially discuss and make decisions on the following:
  what aspect of the spreadsheet the project is to be about
  how information is to be gathered
  how the project is to be presented
  what tasks are to be done by each student in the group
  what date each task is to be completed by

Simultaneous Equations

INTRODUCTION

DISCUSSION EXERCISE 8:1

Discuss how to use "trial and improvement" to solve the following problems. Solve them.

Problem 1 A total of £8616 was received from ticket sales for the ABC concert.
How many tickets were sold?

ABC CONCERT
Tickets £12

Problem 2 800 tickets were sold, for the DEF Concert, for a total of £8540.
How many tickets were sold at each price?
Is there more than one answer to this problem?

DEF CONCERT
Adults £12
Students £8

Problem 3 800 tickets were sold, for the GHI Concert, for a total of £8092.
How many tickets were sold at each price?
Can you find more than one answer for this problem?
What if you were also told that only 50 tickets were available for door sales and all of these were sold?

GHI CONCERT
Adults £12
Students £8
Door Sales £6

For **problem 2**, the following two equations are true.

$$12a + 8s = 8540$$
$$a + s = 800$$

What does **a** stand for? What does **s** stand for?

Discuss possible equations for problem 1 and problem 3.

Discuss the following for each of the above problems.
How many unknowns are there? How many equations are needed to find these unknowns?

Simultaneous equations are equations which need to be solved together to find the values of the unknowns.
Several different methods may be used to solve simultaneous equations. Some are : trial and improvement, balance method, substitution method, graphical method.

BALANCE METHOD

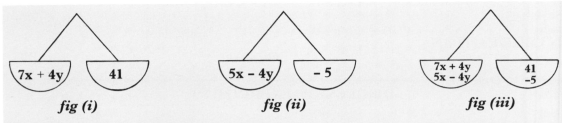

| *fig (i)* | *fig (ii)* | *fig (iii)* |

To solve the simultaneous equations $\begin{array}{l}7x + 4y = 41 \\ 5x - 4y = -5\end{array}$, consider the above diagrams.

fig (i)   shows that $7x + 4y = 41$, since the scales balance.

fig (ii)   shows that $5x - 4y = -5$, since the scales balance.

fig (iii)   shows the left-hand pans of *fig (i)* and *fig (ii)* combined and the right-hand pans combined. The scales must balance in this diagram since they did in the first two diagrams.

fig (iii)   shows that we may add each side of two equations. This is the first step of the **balance method**.

INVESTIGATION and DISCUSSION EXERCISE 8:2

Referring to *fig (iii)* of the previous diagram : What is the total on the right-hand pan? What is the total in the left-hand pan?

How can you now find the value of x? What is the value of x?

How can you now use the equation illustrated on *fig (ii)* to find the value of y? What is this value of y? **Discuss.**

Could you have used the equation illustrated on *fig (i)* to find y? **Discuss.**

Consider the equations $\begin{array}{l}4x + 3y = 13 \\ 2x + 3y = 5\end{array}$. What happens if you try to use the balance method? **Discuss.**

What if you subtracted each side of the equations instead of adding? **Discuss.**

Consider the equations $\begin{array}{l}4x + 5y = 22 \\ 3x - 2y = 5\end{array}$. What happens if you add the equations? What happens if you subtract? **Discuss.**

Make and test statements about the numbers in simultaneous equations if they are to be solved using the balance method. You could use the following simultaneous equations in your investigation or you could make up equations of your own.

$2x + y = 4$	$4a + 2b = 1$	$3p + 2q = 12$	$3x + y = 4$
$x - y = 5$	$8a - 2b = -4$	$p + 2q = 8$	$3x + 4y = -2$
$3a + 2b = 9$	$3x - 2y = 8$	$5p + 2q = 3$	
$2a - b = -1$	$4x - 5y = 6$	$2p + 3q = 1$	

The **balance method** is sometimes called the **elimination method,** since one of the unknowns is eliminated when the equations are either added or subtracted.

The working for the balance method may be written more concisely as shown in the following worked example.

Worked Example Solve $\begin{array}{l} 7x + 4y = 41 \\ 5x - 4y = -5 \end{array}$

Answer

$$\left.\begin{array}{l} 7x + 4y = 41 \\ 5x - 4y = -5 \end{array}\right\}$$

$12x \quad = 36$ (adding the left-hand sides; adding the right-hand sides)

$x = 3$ (dividing both sides by 3)

When $x = 3$, $7x + 4y = 41$ becomes $21 + 4y = 41$

$4y = 20$ (subtracting 21 from both sides)

$y = 5$ (dividing both sides by 4)

The solution is: $x = 3$, $y = 5$

Always check the solution by substituting the value of the unknowns into the original equations.

Example The check for the previous worked example is:

If $x = 3$, $y = 5$ then $7x + 4y = 7 \times 3 + 4 \times 5$

$= 41$ Correct.

and $5x - 4y = 5 \times 3 - 4 \times 5$

$= -5$ Correct.

EXERCISE 8:3

Use the balance method to solve the following simultaneous equations.

1. $3x + 2y = 14$
$5x - 2y = 18$

2. $a + b = 3$
$3a - b = 1$

3. $2x - y = 8$
$-2x + 3y = -12$

4. $5p + 4q = 8$
$3p + 4q = 4$

5. $2l + 5m = 18$
$2l + 7m = 26$

6. $5x - 2y = 17$
$3x - 2y = 9$

7. $5a - 4b = -6$
$2a - 4b = 0$

8. $3x + 2y = 4$
$4x + 2y = 7$

Review 1 $5x - 3y = 19$
$4x + 3y = -1$

Review 2 $3p + q = 5$
$2p + q = 2$

DISCUSSION EXERCISE 8:4

Consider the equation $2x + y = 5$.
Is this the same as $4x + 2y = 10$?
Is this the same as $6x + 3y = 15$?
Discuss.

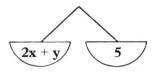

As part of your discussion, you may like to make up values for x and y that would make the equation $2x + y = 5$ true. You may also like to begin with the balance shown.

How could you use your discovery to solve the following simultaneous equations, using the balance method? **Discuss**.

$3x + y = 4$	$5x - 2y = 15$	$5x + 2y = 3$
$2x + 4y = -4$	$3x - 4y = 23$	$2x + 3y = 1$

Worked Example   Solve the simultaneous equations $3x + 4y = 6$
$2x - 3y = -13$

Answer $\left.\begin{array}{l} 3x + 4y = 6 \\ 2x - 3y = -13 \end{array}\right\}$ becomes $\left.\begin{array}{l} 9x + 12y = 18 \\ 8x - 12y = -52 \end{array}\right\}$ (multiplying both sides by 3)
(multiplying both sides by 4)

$17x = -34$ (adding the equations)
$ x = -2$ (dividing both sides by 17)

When $x = -2$, $9x + 12y = 18$ becomes $-18 + 12y = 18$
$ 12y = 36$ (adding 18 to each side)
$ y = 3$ (dividing both sides by 12)

The solution is $x = -2$, $y = 3$.

Check If $x = -2$, $y = 3$ then $3x + 4y = -6 + 12 = 6$. Correct.
 If $x = -2$, $y = 3$ then $2x - 3y = -4 - 9 = -13$. Correct.

Worked Example   Solve the simultaneous equations $\begin{array}{l} 3x = 2y - 1 \\ 3y + 4x = 10 \end{array}$

Answer   Rearrange the equations as $3x - 2y = -1$
$ 4x + 3y = 10$
Now proceed as in the previous worked example to get $x = 1$, $y = 2$.

EXERCISE 8:5

1. Solve these simultaneous equations.

(a) $2a + 3d = 7$ (b) $2x - 4y = 16$ (c) $4p - 5q = 17$
 $3a - 4d = 2$ $4x + 3y = 21$ $3p - 4q = 13$

(d) $2x + 3y = 0$
$\quad 5x + 6y = -6$

(e) $3a - 8b = 1$
$\quad 5a - 4b = -3$

(f) $3x + 2y = 9$
$\quad 2x + 3y = 1$

(g) $3a + 5b = 7$
$\quad 5a - 2b = -9$

(h) $2x + 3y = -8$
$\quad -6x + 8y = -27$

(i) $8p - 6q = 16$
$\quad 6p + 4q = -5$

(j) $2x - 3y = 5$
$\quad 3x + 4y = -18$

(k) $6x + 4y = -19$
$\quad 2x + 3y = -8$

2. *The solutions are $x = 2$, $y = -1$. Write down many pairs of simultaneous equations with these solutions.*

3. Solve the simultaneous equations. (Rearrange if necessary).

(a) $3x + 2y = 0$
$\quad 3y - x = 11$

(b) $y = x + 2$
$\quad y + x = -4$

(c) $2x + y = 0$
$\quad x = y + 3$

(d) $2x - y + 3 = 0$
$\quad 4x + 3y = 14$

(e) $4x + 3y = 11$
$\quad 3x + 2y = 9$

(f) $3a = 21 - 5b$
$\quad 2b = 4a - 2$

(g) $x - y = -2$
$\quad y = 2x - 1$

(h) $2a + 4b + 3 = 25$
$\quad b - a = 4$

Review   Solve these simultaneous equations.

(a) $5a + 3b = -6$
$\quad 4a + 5b = 3$

(b) $2x - 3y = 4$
$\quad y + x = 7$

(c) $2p = 23 + 5q$
$\quad 3q - 4p = -18$

SUBSTITUTION METHOD

INVESTIGATION and DISCUSSION EXERCISE 8:6

Consider the simultaneous equations $\begin{array}{l} 2x + y = 1 \\ 3x + 4y = 6 \end{array}$

The *first* equation may be rewritten as $y = 1 - 2x$ (subtracting $2x$ from both sides). This expression for y may now be substituted into the *second* equation to get $3x + 4(1-2x) = 6$.

Can we now find the value of x? **Discuss.**

What if the equations were $\begin{array}{l} 3a + 2b = 12 \\ a + 2b = 8 \end{array}$? **What if** the equations were $\begin{array}{l} 5x + 2y = 3 \\ 2x + 3y = 1 \end{array}$?

Could all the simultaneous equations in **Exercises 8:3, 8:4** and **8:5** be solved by this substitution method? Are some equations *best* solved by the balance method? **Discuss.**

GRAPHICAL SOLUTION

DISCUSSION EXERCISE 8:7

x + y = 1

x	–2	0	1
y	3	1	0

2x – y = –4

x	–2	0	1
y	0	4	6

The line x + y = 1 may be drawn by joining the points (–2, 3), (0, 1) and (1, 0).
The line 2x – y = – 4 may be drawn by joining the points (–2, 0), (0, 4) and (1, 6).
Both the lines x + y = 1 and 2x – y = – 4 are drawn on the following graph. What are
the coordinates of the point which lies on *both* graphs?

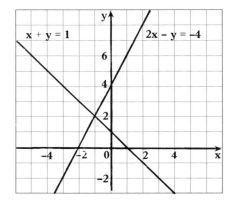

Solve the simultaneous equations $\begin{array}{c} x + y = 1 \\ 2x - y = -4 \end{array}$ using the balance method or the
substitution method. Compare the values of x and y obtained with the graphs of the lines
 x + y = 1 and 2x – y = –4. What do you notice? **Discuss.**

Could all the simultaneous equations in **Exercises 8:3, 8:4,** and **8:5** be solved by drawing
graphs? **Discuss.** As part of your discussion you may like to draw the graphs of some of
these.

Discuss how the instructions in the following steps, for solving simultaneous equations
graphically, could be completed.

    Step 1   Find the coordinates of three points on . . .
    Step 2   Draw . . .
    Step 3   From the graph, read off . . .
    Step 4   Write down . . .
    Step 5   Check the solution by . . .

EXERCISE 8:8

1.

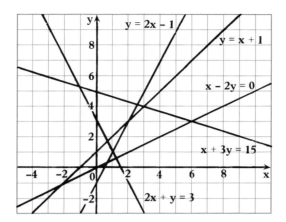

Use the above graph to write down the solutions of the following simultaneous equations.

(a) $y = 2x - 1$
    $y = x + 1$

(b) $x - 2y = 0$
    $x + 3y = 15$

(c) $2x + y = 3$
    $y = 2x - 1$

(d) $y = x + 1$
    $x - 2y = 0$

2. Draw graphs to find the solution of these simultaneous equations.

(a) $x - y = 3$
    $2x + y = 0$

(b) $2x - y = -1$
    $x - y = 1$

(c) $y - 2x = 3$
    $y - x = 5$

(d) $x + y = 2$
    $y = 2x - 1$

(e) $2x + y = 4$
    $y = 2x + 2$

Review   Solve these simultaneous equations graphically.

(a) $x + y = -1$
    $2x + y = 1$

(b) $y = 2x - 1$
    $x - y = -2$

PRACTICAL EXERCISE 8:9

Use either a computer graphics package or a graphics calculator to solve simultaneous equations. You could make up your own equations or you could use any of the simultaneous equations given in **Exercises 8:3, 8:4, 8:5 or 8:8**.

PROBLEM SOLVING

Problems which have two unknowns may be solved by using simultaneous equations if two equations can be written down. The following are the steps that need to be taken.

Step 1   Allocate a letter to each of the unknowns.

Step 2   From the given information, write down two equations that involve the unknowns.

Step 3   Solve these two simultaneous equations using a method of your choice.

Step 4   Check the solutions.

Worked Example   Tickets for a concert cost £12 for an adult and £8 for a student. 800 tickets were sold altogether for a total of £8540. How many tickets were sold to adults and how many to students?

Answer   *Step 1*   Let **a** be the number of tickets sold to adults and **s** be the number sold to students.

Step 2 $a + s = 800$
$12a + 8s = 8540$

Step 3   The balance method could be used as follows:

$$\left.\begin{array}{l} a + s = 800 \\ 12a + 8s = 8540 \end{array}\right\} \text{ becomes } \left.\begin{array}{l} 12a + 12s = 9600 \\ 12a + 8s = 8540 \end{array}\right\} \text{ (multiplying both sides by 12)}$$

$$\begin{array}{ll} 4s = 1060 & \text{(subtracting the equations)} \\ s = 265 & \text{(dividing both sides by 4)} \end{array}$$

If $s = 265$, $a + s = 800$ becomes $a + 265 = 800$

$a = 535$ (subtracting 265 from both sides)

Step 4   If $s = 265$, $a = 535$ then $a + s = 535 + 265 = 800$. Correct.

and $12a + 8s = 12 \times 535 + 8 \times 265 = 8540$. Correct.

Note   We don't need to list the steps. The steps are listed in the worked example to show the procedure clearly.

EXERCISE 8:10

1. Physics textbooks are advertised at £7 if ordered before publication date and £8 if ordered after publication date. If 5000 of these were sold for a total of £38500, how many were ordered before publication date and how many after?

2. Lance owned 500 R.J. shares and 200 F.T. shares. Altogether, Lance's shares were worth £2300. Ann owned 50 R.J. shares and 100 F.T. shares. Altogether Ann's shares were worth £550. How much was one R.J. share worth? How much was one F.T. share worth?

Chapter 8

3. Two numbers add to 95 and subtract to 21. Find these numbers.

4. The school hall, which seats 550, has some rows which seat 25 and some which seat 15. If there are 26 rows altogether, how many of these seat 15?

5. In a sale of hard-cover books, all the fiction books were the same price; all the non-fiction were the same price. In the first hour of the sale, 30 fiction and 20 non-fiction books sold for a total of £120. In the next hour, 50 fiction and 30 non-fiction books sold for a total of £190. What price were the fiction books?

6. The ages of an elderly couple add to 154. If the wife is 6 years older than her husband, how old is the wife?

7. Yesterday, Chun's bank balance was twice as large as Katie's. After Chun had deposited an extra £15 today, her bank balance was £100 more than Katie's. How much did Chun have in her bank account yesterday?

8. Find two numbers such that twice their sum is 66 and their difference is 3.

9. The Lindale Hotel has some single rooms which accommodate one person and some double rooms which accommodate two people. On Monday night, 78 people stayed at this hotel and 47 rooms were occupied. How many single rooms were occupied? (Assume that all of the double rooms did indeed have two people in each of them.)

10. The charge for each person occupying a single room in the Lindale Hotel is £70. The charge for each person occupying a double room is £60. On Tuesday night, 40 people stayed at this hotel for a total cost of £2520. How many of these people occupied single rooms?

Review   The Great Outdoors Boating Company has 20 large and 5 small canoes for hire. The New Canoe Company has 10 large and 15 small canoes for hire. The Great Outdoors Boating Company canoes can carry a maximum of 185 people while the New Canoe Company canoes can carry a maximum of 155 people. How many people can each of the large canoes carry?

INTERPRETING LINE GRAPHS

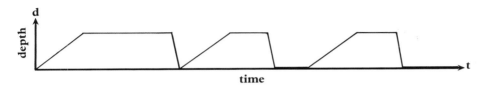

This graph shows the depth of water in a washing machine during one complete cycle. Which parts of this graph show the machine filling, rinsing, spinning and draining? **Discuss**.

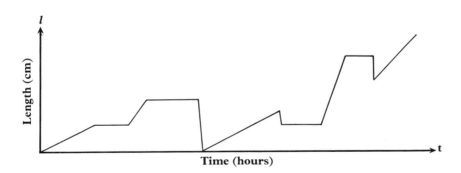

This graph shows the length of a scarf that Anna is knitting. **Discuss** each section of this graph.

What might this graph represent?
Discuss.
What if temperature was replaced with distance?

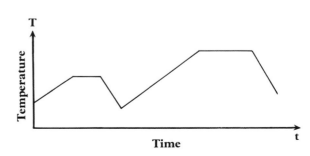

EXERCISE 9:2

1. This graph
   shows the cost
   of four
   different cuts
   of beef.

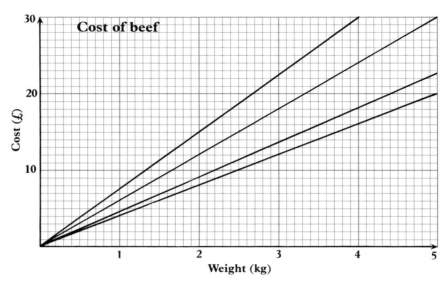

(a) What is the cost of 2kg of the most expensive cut?
(b) What is the cost of 2·5kg of the cheapest cut?
(c) Sam paid £13·50 for 3kg. Which cut did Sam buy?
(d) What is the price per kg of each of the four cuts?
(e) Aaron and Ann each bought 2kg of beef. Ann paid £1 more than Aaron. Which cuts did Aaron and Ann buy?

2. A sauce is being heated slowly. This graph shows the temperature of the sauce during the first minute.

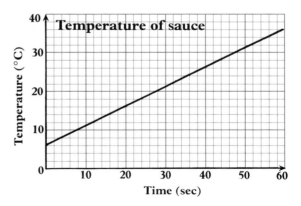

(a) What was the temperature of the sauce after 40 seconds?
(b) What was the initial temperature of the sauce?
(c) How long did it take for the sauce to reach 20°C?
(d) What was the increase in temperature for each 10 seconds of heating?
(e) How long would it take for the sauce to reach 80°C?

104

3.

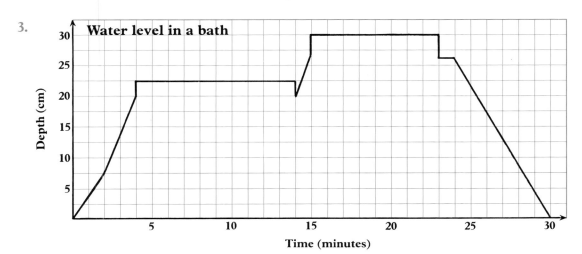

Ramon baths his two dogs, Jasper and Jess. He baths Jess first, then Jasper. This graph shows the water level in the bath.

(a) Does it appear as if Ramon filled the bath with both the hot and cold taps turned on together?

(b) Which dog is bathed for the longer time?

(c) Which dog is larger, Jess or Jasper?

(d) How long after Jasper is taken out of the bath, does Ramon begin to empty it?

(e) Is Ramon more likely to add hot or cold water after Jess is taken out of the bath?

(f) Use your answers to (a) and (e) to decide if Ramon initially put cold water or hot water into the bath.

4.

This graph shows the monthly profit (to the nearest £1000) of a car sales firm.
   (a) Which month, or months, had the greatest profit?
   (b) Which two consecutive months had the same profit?
   (c) What was the increase in profit between the end of May and the end of June?
   (d) How much profit was made during the whole year?
   (e) What reasons can you think of for the rapid decrease in profit during September and October?
   (f) Find the average monthly profit for this year. (Answer to the nearest £1000.)

5.

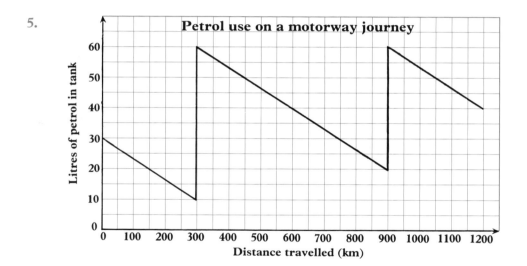

This graph shows the amount of petrol in the fuel tank of Tamara's car during a journey on a motorway in Europe.
   (a) How much petrol was in the tank at the beginning of the journey?
   (b) What total distance did Tamara travel?
   (c) How many times did she stop for petrol?
   (d) Assuming that Tamara filled the tank up each time she stopped, what was the capacity of the tank?
   (e) Did the fuel gauge read "$\frac{1}{2}$" or "$\frac{1}{4}$" or "$\frac{3}{4}$" at the beginning of the journey?
   (f) How much petrol was used altogether on this journey?
   (g) Could Tamara have completed the journey if she had only filled the tank up once?
   (h) What was the petrol consumption rate, in km/l, on this journey?
   (i) Find the petrol consumption rate in litres per 100km. (Answer to 1d.p.)

106

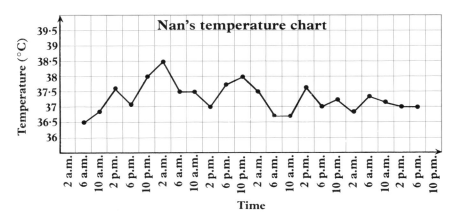

Nan's temperature was taken at four-hourly intervals, during her stay in hospital.

(a) If Nan was admitted to hospital on March 4th, on what date was she discharged?

(b) What time of day, morning or afternoon or evening, was Nan admitted?

(c) What was Nan's temperature at 10 p.m. on her first day in hospital?

(d) How many times did Nan's temperature increase?

(e) What was the highest temperature Nan had?

(f) When was the lowest temperature recorded?

(g) "During Nan's stay in hospital, her average temperature reading was about 37·3°C." Is this statement true?

INVESTIGATION 9:3

LEAKING WATER

Water is leaking from a hole in the bottom of a cylindrical container. A graph could be plotted to show the depth of water in the container every minute. Would you expect this to be a straight line graph? Investigate.

What if water is leaking from a bucket such as that shown?

Investigate.

You may like to investigate water leaking from containers of other shapes. As part of your investigation carry out some experiments.

DISCUSSION EXERCISE 9:4

1. What questions could be asked and answered from the following graph? Discuss.

Radio and television audiences [1] throughout the day, 1989 [2]

United Kingdom

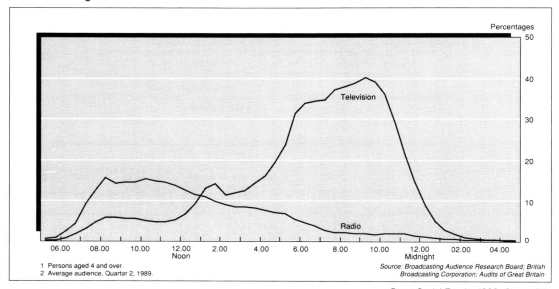

1 Persons aged 4 and over.
2 Average audience, Quartar 2, 1989.

Source: Broadcasting Audience Research Board; British Broadcasting Corporation; Audits of Great Britain

Source: Key Data 1990/91

From: Social Trends, 1990, Chart 10.5

2. Collect other line graphs from newspapers or magazines. Discuss these graphs.

DRAWING LINE GRAPHS

DISCUSSION EXERCISE 9:5

Which of the following graphs would consist of a straight line and which would consist of a series of lines? Discuss.

A graph to convert pounds (£) to U.S. dollars ($).
The graph of the daily rainfall at Inverness during one month.
A graph showing the height climbed, at 5 minute intervals, by a rock climber.
A graph showing the monthly earnings of a salesperson on commission.
A graph showing the depth of water in a pond as the water is being pumped out of the pond.

Think of other graphs which would be a straight line and others which would be a series of lines. Discuss.

EXERCISE 9:6

1. Abe's handmade chocolates are priced at £4·80 for 1kg.
   (a) Draw a graph which could be used to read off the cost of any quantity (up to 1kg) of these chocolates.
   (b) Use the graph to find the cost of 125g of these chocolates.

2.

Day	M	T	W	T	F	S	S
Temp. (°C)	19	22	23	18	24	15	17

The mid-day temperatures at Coventry, during one week in August, are shown in this table.
Display this information on a line graph.

3.

Age (months)	1	2	3	4	5	6	7	8	9	10	11	12
Length (cm)	38	40	41	43	44	45	47	50	51	53	53	54

The data on this table gives the length of a baby. Display this data on a line graph.

4. At Newport, at 0800 hours, the temperature was 14°C. During the next two hours, the temperature rose by 3°C each hour. Between 1000 hours and 1300 hours, the temperature stayed the same. It began dropping at 1300 hours and dropped 2°C each hour for the following three hours.
   Draw a line graph to show this information.

5. On purchases which cost between £20 and £70, Superstore gives a discount of £5. Bettashop gives a discount of 10p in every £.
   Arlene is buying a drill. This drill would cost her the same at Superstore as at Bettashop.
   Draw two lines graphs on the same set of axes to find what Arlene will pay for the drill.

Review

Area in hectares	2	6	10
Area in acres	5	15	25

Use the values given in the table to draw a graph to convert an area given in hectares to acres.
Use the graph to answer the following questions.
(a) The common near Josef's home has an area of 8 acres. What is the area of this common in hectares?
(b) Josef spends his holidays on an 8 hectare farm. What is the size of this farm in acres?

1. Gather some data that can be suitably displayed on a line graph. You could use reference books or the newspaper as a source for your data.
   Display the data on a line graph.

2. Conduct an experiment, the data from which could be suitably displayed on a line graph. Draw the line graph.
   You may like to use one of the following suggestions.

   Temperature, at hourly intervals, in a sheltered part of your school grounds.
   Increase in height, at regular intervals, of yeast dough.
   Length of a bean sprout, each day, for 5 days.
   Increase in the length of a vertical spring for different weights attached to the end.

TRAVEL GRAPHS

DISCUSSION EXERCISE 9:8

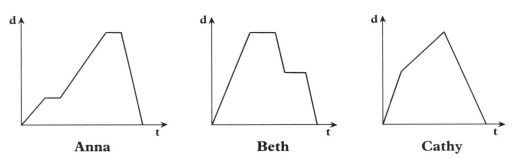

These graphs represent the journeys of three girls into town and back home again.
Discuss these graphs. Consider questions such as: Who got to town first? How many stops did each have? How do their speeds compare?

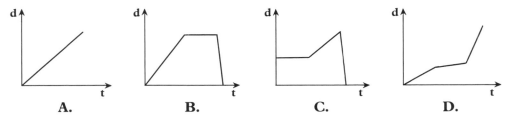

Jake cycles along a flat road, then up a hill, then down the other side. Which graph best describes Jake's cycle journey? **Discuss**.
What journeys might the other graphs represent? **Discuss**.

Chapter 9

On a distance/time graph, the slope gives the speed. The steeper the slope, the greater the speed.

Worked Example

This graph shows the distance Jill travelled on her cycle journey.
  (a) What distance did Jill travel?
  (b) How long did Jill's journey take?
  (c) For how long did Jill stop during the journey?
  (d) At what speed did Jill cycle during the last section of her journey?
  (e) What was Jill's average speed for her complete journey?

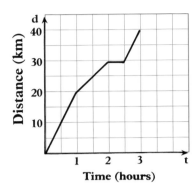

Answer   (a) 40km (reading from the vertical axis).

(b) 3 hours (reading from the horizontal axis).

(c) 30 minutes (between 2 hours and $2\frac{1}{2}$ hours the graph is horizontal i.e. no distance was covered during this time).

(d) Jill cycled 10km in $\frac{1}{2}$ hour or 20km in 1 hour. Hence her speed was 20km/h.

(e) Average speed = $\frac{\text{distance travelled}}{\text{time taken}}$

$= \frac{40}{3}$ km/h

$= 13 \cdot 3$km/h (to 1d.p.)

EXERCISE 9:9

1. The distance/time graphs for the following vehicles are shown on this graph:
     express train from Southampton
     ship from Southampton
     car from Southampton
     car from Fareham
     car in a garage at Fareham
     plane from Southampton

    Which graph belongs to which vehicle?

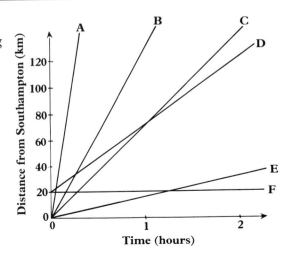

2.

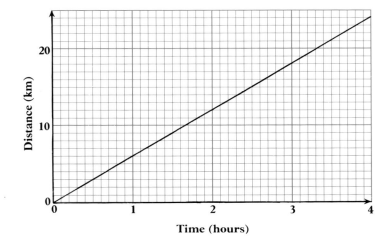

Steve walked at a steady speed for 4 hours. This distance/time graph shows his progress.

(a) How far did Steve walk in $1\frac{1}{2}$ hours?
(b) How long did Steve take to walk 18km?
(c) How far did Steve walk in 1 hour?
(d) What was Steve's speed?

3.

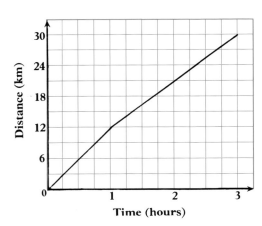

Mahmud ran for 1 hour, then jogged for 2 hours.

(a) What was Mahmud's running speed?
(b) How far did he jog in 2 hours?
(c) What was his jogging speed?
(d) What was the total distance of Mahmud's journey?
(e) What time did he take for the whole journey?
(f) What was Mahmud's average speed over the whole journey?

4.

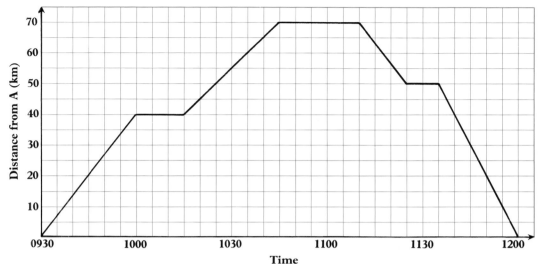

This is the distance/time graph for a coach on a journey from town A. On this journey, the coach stops at town B, then town C, then town D.
- (a) At which town did the coach stop the longest?
- (b) How far is town C from town B?
- (c) Between which two towns did the coach travel the fastest?
- (d) What was the total time for all the stops?
- (e) How long did this coach journey last for?
- (f) How many kilometres were travelled altogether?
- (g) What was the average speed for the complete journey?

5.

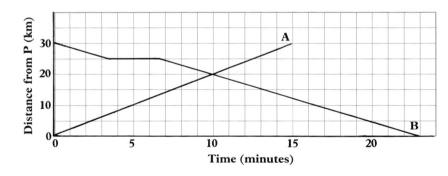

One car travels from P to Q, another travels from Q to P.
- (a) Which of the graphs, A or B, is the distance/time graph for the car travelling from Q to P?
- (b) Do both cars begin travelling at the same time?
- (c) At what time do the cars meet?
- (d) How far are the cars from P when they meet?

6.

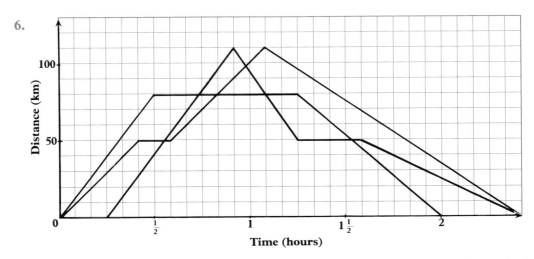

Describe the three journeys represented by the distance/time graphs on this graph. As part of your description, comment on similarities and differences between the journeys.

Review

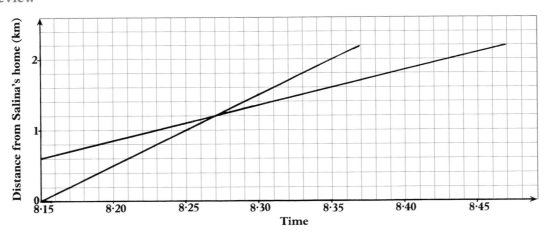

Salina and Cindy walk to Airhill School. They both leave their homes at 8·15 a.m. Salina gets to school before Cindy. Use these distance/time graphs of their journeys to school to answer the following questions.

(a) How long does it take Cindy to get to school?

(b) How far does Cindy live from school?

(c) At what time are they the same distance from school?

(d) Who walks faster, Salina or Cindy?

(e) How far does Salina live from school?

(f) What is Salina's speed? (Answer in metres per minute.)

114

DRAWING LINE GRAPHS to solve DISTANCE–TIME PROBLEMS

Worked Example Two sisters go for a day tour in their separate cars. The sister who leaves home first, travels at an average speed of 60km/h. The second sister, who leaves home 30 minutes later, travels at an average speed of 100km/h. They both pass through Cricklade at the same time. How far is it from the sisters' house to Cricklade?

Answer

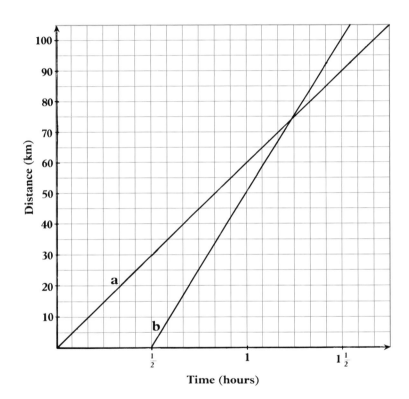

a is the distance/time graph for the sister who leaves first, **b** is the distance/time graph for the second sister. They are drawn as follows.

For the sister who leaves first: when time = 0, distance = 0; when time = 1 hour, distance = 60km. The graph is drawn by joining the points (0, 0) and (1, 60).

For the second sister : when time = $\frac{1}{2}$ hour, distance = 0; when time = $1\frac{1}{2}$ hours, distance = 100km. The graph is drawn by joining the points ($\frac{1}{2}$, 0) and ($1\frac{1}{2}$, 100).

These graphs meet where distance = 75km. That is, both sisters were 75km from home, at the same time. Hence the sisters' house is 75km from Crickdale.

EXERCISE 9:10

Draw distance/time graphs to solve the problems in this exercise.

1. Two trains are travelling in opposite directions. One is travelling East and the other West. At 1400 hours they are 80km apart. The train travelling East travels at an average speed of 200km/h; the train travelling West travels at an average speed of 160km/h. At approximately what time do these trains pass?

2. Kirstin and Tania live 100 metres apart. They both leave their homes at the same time to walk to meet each other. Kirstin walks at an average speed of 3m/s; Tania walks at an average speed of 4m/s.
   How far does Tania walk before they meet? (Answer to the nearest 5m.)

3. When the driver of the red car first sees the black car, the cars are 50 metres apart. The black car is travelling at a constant speed of 20m/s and the red car at 25m/s.
   How soon after the driver of the red car sees the black car will the red car overtake the black car?

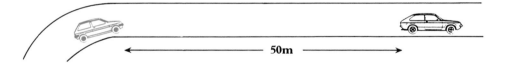

4. Antoine is jogging at a steady rate of 3m/s. When his friend Simon first sees him, Antoine is 40 metres ahead. Simon runs at a steady rate of 5m/s to catch up with Antoine.
   How far does Simon have to run? (Answer to the nearest 5m.)

Review   James and Kyle live 10km from each other. They both start out at 0810 to cycle towards the other's home. James cycles at an average speed of 26km/h; Kyle cycles at an average speed of 20km/h.
At approximately what time do they meet?

INVESTIGATION 9:11

DISTANCE/TIME GRAPHS and SIMULTANEOUS EQUATIONS

Each of the problems in the previous exercise was solved by drawing two line graphs. Could these problems have been solved by solving two equations? **Investigate**.

PROJECT 9:12

Work in groups to produce a well researched and well presented project on the actual use of line graphs.

The project could be presented in booklet form or as an illustrated talk or as a wall mural or in some other way.

Some suggestions for the project are:
    use in hospitals
    use in factories and/or businesses
    use in local Councils

Each group should initially discuss and make decisions on the following:
    what is to be included in the project
    how information is to be gathered
    how the project is to be presented
    what tasks are to be done by each student in the group
    what date each task is to be completed by

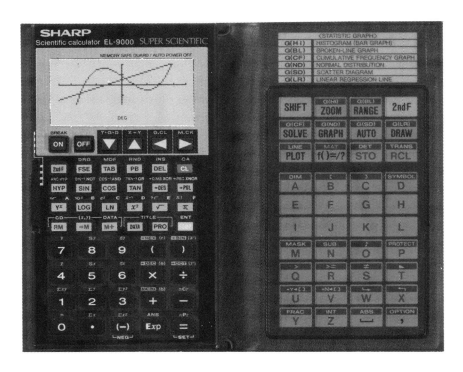

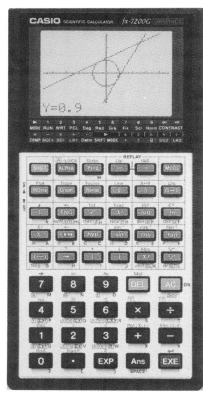

Graphs on the Calculator and Computer

EXPLORING CALCULATOR and COMPUTER GENERATED GRAPHS

INVESTIGATION and DISCUSSION EXERCISE 10:1

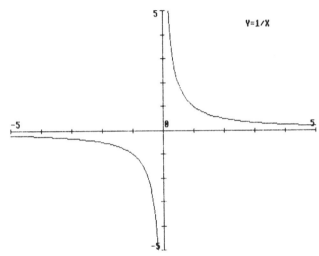

Use a graphics calculator or a computer graphics package to get this graph of $y = \frac{1}{x}$ on the screen.

Discuss the following questions in relation to this graph of $y = \frac{1}{x}$.

    Can x take all values?
    Can y take all values?
    Between which values of x does y increase as x increases?
    Between which values of x does y decrease as x increases?

On the same screen, display the following graphs. $y = \frac{1}{x}$, $y = \frac{2}{x}$, $y = \frac{3}{x}$, $y = \frac{4}{x}$
Explore relationships between these graphs.

What if 1, 2, 3 and 4 were replaced with –1, –2, –3, –4?
What if 1, 2, 3 and 4 were replaced with 0·1, 0·2, 0·3, 0·4?
What if x was replaced with x – 1?
What if x was replaced with x + 1?
What if . . .

INVESTIGATION 10:2

EXPLORING GRAPHS

Use a graphics calculator or a computer graphics package to **investigate** one or more of the groups of graphs given below.

If you wish, you may choose other graphs to investigate.

As part of your investigation, consider questions such as those in the previous exercise as well as:

Where does the graph cross the x-axis?
Where does the graph cross the y-axis?
Is there a maximum value that y can take?
Is there a minimum value that y can take?
Is there a relationship between the graphs; if so, what is this relationship?

Suggested groups of graphs to investigate.

Group 1
$y = 2^x$, $y = 3^x$, $y = 4^x$, $y = 0.5^x$ etc.

Group 2
$y = x^2$, $y = x^2 + 2$, $y = x^2 - 2$, $y = (x + 2)^2$, $y = (x - 2)^2$, $y = 2x^2$, $y = -2x^2$ etc.

Group 3
$y = x^3$, $y = x^3 + 2$, $y = x^3 - 2$, $y = (x + 2)^3$, $y = (x - 2)^3$, $y = 2x^3$, $y = -2x^3$ etc.

Group 4
$y = (x + 1)(x - 2)(x - 3)$, $y = (x + 1)^2 (x - 3)$, $y = (x + 1)^3$ etc.

Group 5
$y = 2x$, $y = 2x - 1$, $y = 2x + 1$ etc.

Group 6
$y = x + 1$, $y = 2x + 1$, $y = 3x + 1$ etc.

Group 7
$y = 2x - 1$, $y = 3x^2 + 2x - 1$, $y = 3x^3 + 5x^2 + x - 1$ etc.

INVESTIGATIONS 10:3

FURTHER EXPLORING of GRAPHS

1. **Investigate** the relationship between the graphs $y = x^2 + 4x$, $y = x^2 + 3$, $y = x^2 + 4x + 3$ and the solutions of the polynomial equations $x^2 + 4x = 0$, $x^2 + 3 = 0$, $x^2 + 4x + 3 = 0$. (Use a graphics calculator or a computer graphics package for the graphs and "trial and improvement" to solve the equations.)

2. y = · · · How might this be completed to produce graphs of the following shapes? **Investigate**.

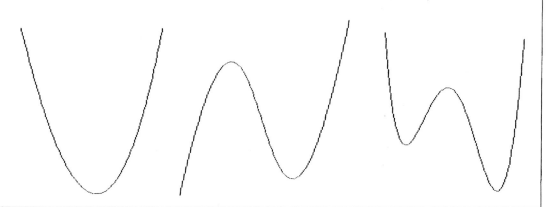

1. (a) "Last night the temperature did not fall below 6°C." Which of the following inequalities describes this statement?

    A. $T < 6°$ **B.** $T > 6°$ **C.** $T \leq 6°$ **D.** $T \geq 6°$

    (b) "No worker at A.B. Tyres earns less than £4 an hour and no worker earns more than £9 an hour." Which of the following inequalities best describes this statement?

    A. $E > £4$ **B.** $E < £9$ **C.** $£4 \leq E \leq £9$ **D.** $£4 < E < £9$

2. Write these as a single power of 3.

    (a) $3^4 \times 3^7$ (b) $\dfrac{3^9}{3^3}$ (c) $(3^2)^4$ (d) $\dfrac{9^4 \times 3^5}{27}$

3. Give the reciprocal of these as a whole number or fraction.

    (a) $\frac{1}{15}$ (b) $\frac{4}{5}$ (c) 7   (d) $\frac{b}{x}$ (e) $2z$

4.

    fig (i)   *fig (ii)*   *fig (iii)*

    Matchsticks are used to form squares, as shown in the above diagrams. 4, 7 are the first two terms of the sequence for the number of matchsticks needed.

    (a) How many matchsticks are needed to form 3 squares; how many are needed to form 4 squares?
    (b) Write down the first 5 terms of the sequence for the number of matchsticks needed.
    (c) Write the rule for the sequence as $t_n = \cdots$
    (d) Use the rule to find the number of matchsticks needed to form 87 squares.

5.

Speed in mph	0	30	60
Speed in km/h	0	48	96

    Use the values given in the table to draw a graph to convert speeds in mph to speeds in km/h.
    Use your graph to answer the following questions.

    (a) Kate is cycling at a speed of 15mph. Jason is cycling at a speed of 25km/h. Who is cycling faster?
    (b) On Nick's journey, from Peterborough to Bedford, his car averaged 50mph. On the return journey, his average speed was 85km/h. Which journey was faster and by how much? (Answer in km/h.)

6. Display the following inequalities on a number line. Hence write down all the whole number solutions.   (a) $x < 5$ (b) $-1 \le n < 5$ (c) $a \ge 0$

7. Use either the balance method or the substitution method to solve these simultaneous equations.   (a) $5x - 6y = 8$ (b) $x - 2y - 1 = 0$
    $ 4x + 3y = -17$ $ x + 4y = 4$

8. Use "trial and improvement" to find two solutions for the equation $2x^2 + x = 4$. Give the solutions to 1d.p.

9.

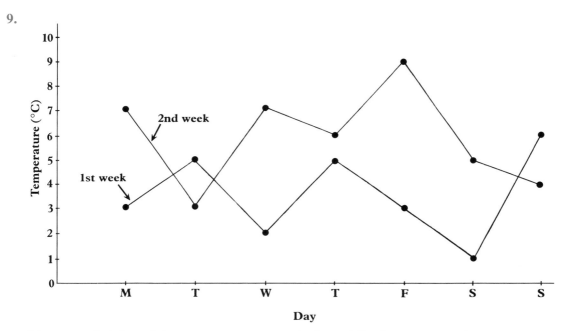

Gina recorded the minimum temperature each day, while she was on holiday on the Gower Peninsula.
   (a) On which day did Gina record the lowest temperature?
   (b) On how many days did the temperature fall below 5°C?
   (c) What was the average minimum temperature on the first week of Gina's holiday?
   (d) Write a few sentences comparing the minimum temperatures of the 1st week with those of the 2nd week.

10. A sequence is given by the rule $t_n = 2n - 1$
   (a) Write down the first five terms of this sequence.
   (b) What is the 91st term?
   (c) Which term is equal to 121?

11. On the same graph, draw the lines $x - y = 3$ and $y = 2x - 5$.
    Use your graph to write down the solution of the simultaneous equations $y = 2x - 5$ and $x - y = 3$.

123

12. Without doing any calculation, state the maximum number of solutions for the equation $x^3 + 2x^2 - x + 3 = 0$.

13. At 0630 hours, a slow train is 20km ahead of a fast train. The slow train travels at an average speed of 80km/h; the fast train at 120km/h.
    Draw distance/time graphs to find the time at which the fast train overtakes the slow train.

14.

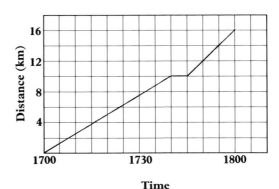

This graph is the distance/time graph showing Sue's cycle journey from her home to town. She leaves home at 1700 hours to meet a friend in town at 1800 hours. On the way, she meets and talks to her brother.

   (a) At what time did Sue meet her brother?
   (b) For how long did Sue stop to talk to her brother?
   (c) What was Sue's speed before she met her brother?
   (d) After Sue had talked to her brother, she cycled faster than before to ensure that she did meet her friend at 1800 hours. What was this faster speed?
   (e) Sue took exactly 1 hour to return home. What was her average speed on this return journey?

15. Daley decides to save £2 this week, £5 next week, £8 the week after and so on; so that in one week he will save £3 more than in the previous week. If Daley keeps to this savings plan, how much will he save in the 27th week?

16. Use the calculator to find the reciprocal of these. Give the answer to 2 significant figures if rounding is necessary.
   (a) 0·34   (b) 8·2   (c) 9   (d) 41

17. Avonlee Country Club fees are £80 per year, with a special rate of £75 if paid before the 1st of May. In 1992, the 140 members paid a total of £11100 in fees.
    Write down two simultaneous equations for **e** and **l**, where **e** is the number of members who paid before the 1st of May and **l** is the number who paid after this. How many members paid their fees before the 1st of May?

18. Use the rules of indices to simplify these.

    (a) $a^x \times a^b$ (b) $a^x \div a^b$ (c) $(a^x)^b$ (d) $\dfrac{a^x \times a^b}{a^z}$ (e) $\dfrac{a^5 \times a^7}{(a^2)^3}$ (f) $(a^3b^4)^2$

    (g) $(3a^4b)^2$

19. A square rose garden is being enlarged to an area of 40 m². The sketch shows the plan for the enlarged garden; the unshaded portion shows the original garden. (Measurements are in metres.)

    (a) Write down a polynomial equation that could be used to find x, the length of the original rose garden.

    (b) Use "trial and improvement" to solve this equation for x, giving the answer to 1d.p.

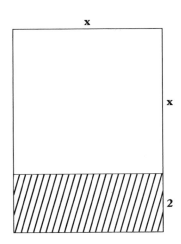

20. Find and test a rule for these sequences.

    (a) 5, 12, 19, 26, . . .   (b) 28, 25, 22, 19, . . .   (c) −2, −4, −6, −8, . . .
    (d) 3, 12, 27, 48, 75, . . .   (e) 2, 9, 28, 65, 126, . . .   (f) $\frac{2}{4}, \frac{3}{5}, \frac{4}{6}, \frac{5}{7}, \ldots$

21. On a number line, display the solution for $-2 \le n + 3 < 7$.
    Hence write down all the whole number solutions for n.

22. Use the flowchart method to solve these equations.   (a) $\frac{3}{a} = 5$ (b) $\frac{3}{a-4} = 5$

23.

Angela walks to the bus stop, waits for the bus to arrive, goes by bus then walks the remaining distance to school. Graph A is the distance/time graph which shows this.
B is the distance/time graph for Ben's journey to school. Describe a possible journey for Ben, using this graph.

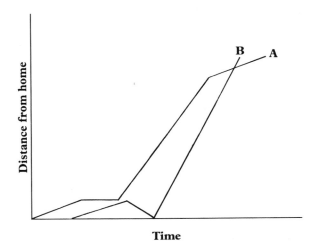

SHAPE and SPACE

Shape and Space
from Previous Levels

REVISION

Congruence. Symmetry

Congruent shapes are shapes of the same size and the same shape. Corresponding lengths are equal ; corresponding angles are equal.

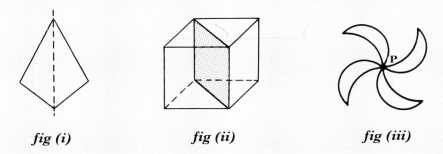

| *fig (i)* | *fig (ii)* | *fig (iii)* |

A **line of symmetry (axis of symmetry)** divides a 2–D shape into two congruent shapes – see *fig (i)*.
A **plane of symmetry** divides a 3–D shape into two congruent shapes – see *fig (ii)*.
A shape has **reflective symmetry** if it has a line or a plane of symmetry – both *fig (i)* and *fig (ii)* have reflective symmetry.
A shape has **rotational symmetry** if it coincides with itself more than once when it is rotated a complete turn about some point. The point about which it is rotated is called the **centre of rotational symmetry**. The number of times the shape coincides with itself during one complete turn is called the **order of rotational symmetry**. For instance, *fig (iii)* has rotational symmetry of order 4. P is the centre of rotational symmetry for *fig (iii)*.

Lines

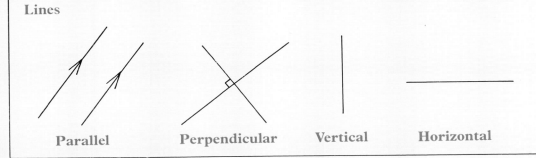

| **Parallel** | **Perpendicular** | **Vertical** | **Horizontal** |

Naming Polygons

A 3-sided polygon is a triangle.   A 4-sided polygon is a quadrilateral.
A 5-sided polygon is a pentagon.   A 6-sided polygon is a hexagon.
A 7-sided polygon is a heptagon.   An 8-sided polygon is an octagon.
A 9-sided polygon is a nonagon.   A 10-sided polygon is a decagon.
A **regular polygon** has all its sides equal and all its angles equal.

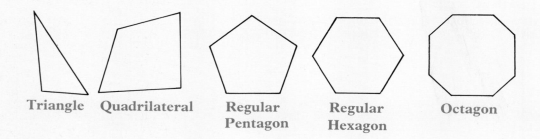

Triangle   Quadrilateral   Regular Pentagon   Regular Hexagon   Octagon

Special Quadrilaterals

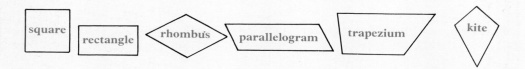

square   rectangle   rhombus   parallelogram   trapezium   kite

Some of the properties of these special quadrilaterals are shown in the following table.

	Square	Rhombus	Rectangle	Parallelogram	Kite	Trapezium
one pair of opposite sides parallel	√	√	√	√		√
two pairs of opposite sides parallel	√	√	√	√		
all sides equal	√	√				
opposite sides equal	√	√	√	√		
all angles equal	√		√			
opposite angles equal	√	√	√	√		
diagonals equal	√		√			
diagonals bisect each other	√	√	√	√		
diagonals perpendicular	√	√			√	
diagonals bisect the angles	√	√				

Angles

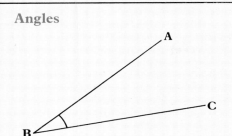

B is the **vertex** of the marked angle.
AB and CB are the **arms** of the marked angle.

The marked angle can be labelled as ∠B or ∠ABC.

The angle in a complete circle   = 360°
                half a circle   = 180°
                quarter of a circle = 90°
                three-quarters of a circle = 270°

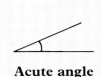

Acute angle

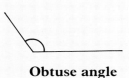

Obtuse angle

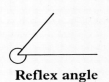

Reflex angle

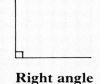

Right angle

Angles made with Intersecting Lines

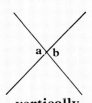

**vertically
opposite angles
a = b**

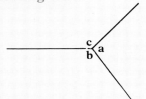

**angles at a point
a + b + c = 360°**

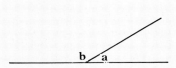

**adjacent angles on a line
a + b = 180°**

Angles made with Parallel Lines

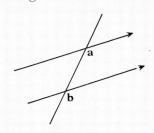

**corresponding angles
a = b**

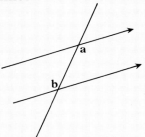

**alternate angles
a = b**

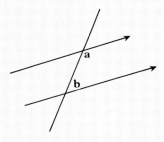

**interior angles
a + b = 180°**

Triangles

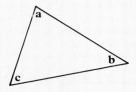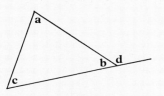

equilateral	**isosceles**	**interior angles**	**exterior angle**
a = b = c	**b = c**	**a + b + c = 180°**	**d = a + c**

Angles of a Polygon

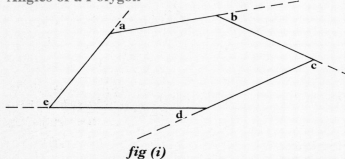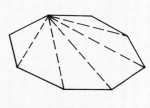

fig (i)

fig (ii)

The sum of the **exterior angles** of any polygon is equal to 360°. Hence in *fig (i)*
a + b + c + d + e = 360°.

The sum of the **interior angles** of any polygon may be found as follows.

   Step 1   From one vertex, draw all the diagonals to divide the polygon into
             triangles – see *fig (ii)*.

   Step 2   Find the sum of the angles in all of these triangles.

For instance, *fig (ii)* can be divided into 6 triangles. Hence the sum of the interior
angles of this 8-sided polygon is 6 × 180° = 1080°.

3–D shapes

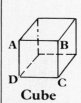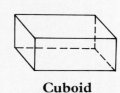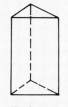

Cube	**Cuboid**	**Prism**	**Pyramid**	**Cylinder**	**Sphere**

ABCD is a **face**, AB is an **edge**, A is a **vertex**.

2-D representation of 3-D shapes

What we see when we look directly down onto a
3-D shape is called the plan.

**Look down to
find the plan.**

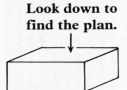

What we see when we look from the front at a 3-D
shape is called the front elevation.

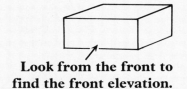

**Look from the front to
find the front elevation.**

What we see when we look from the side at a 3-D
shape is called the side elevation.

**Look from
the side to find
the side elevation.**

On an **isometric drawing** of a 3-D shape, lengths which are equal on the shape
are also equal on the drawing ; edges on the shape which are vertical are also vertical
on the drawing.

Area, Perimeter, Volume

The formulae for the area of some common shapes are given below.

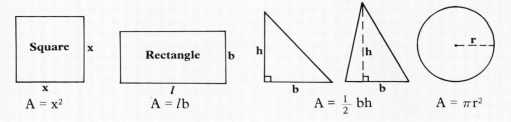

Square	Rectangle	Triangle	Triangle	Circle
$A = x^2$	$A = l b$	$A = \frac{1}{2} bh$		$A = \pi r^2$

The **perimeter** is the distance right around the outside. The perimeter of a circle is
called the **circumference**. The formula for the circumference of a circle is
$C = 2\pi r$ or $C = \pi d$; r is the radius and d is the diameter of the circle, the value
of π to 3 d.p. is 3·142.

The formulae for the **volume** of some common shapes are given below.

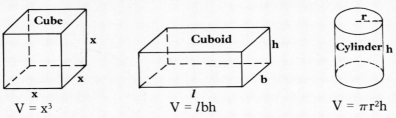

$$V = x^3 \qquad V = l\text{bh} \qquad V = \pi r^2 h$$

fig (i) below shows how one unit of area measure can be converted to another.
fig (ii) below shows how one unit of volume measure can be converted to another.

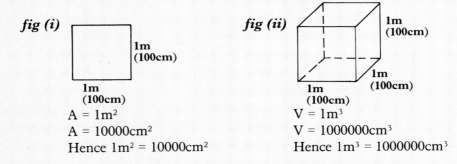

fig (i)

1m (100cm)

1m (100cm)

A = 1m²
A = 10000cm²
Hence 1m² = 10000cm²

fig (ii)

1m (100cm)

1m (100cm)

1m (100cm)

V = 1m³
V = 1000000cm³
Hence 1m³ = 1000000cm³

Movements — Reflection, Translation, Rotation. Tessellations

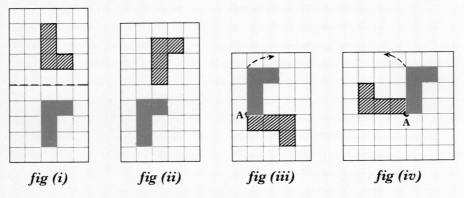

fig (i) *fig (ii)* *fig (iii)* *fig (iv)*

fig (i) illustrates a **reflection** (or **flip movement**). The red shape has been reflected in the dotted line to the shaded shape. The dotted line is called the **mirror line**. A point and its image are the same distance from the mirror line.

fig (ii) illustrates a **translation** (or **straight movement**). The red shape has been translated 1 square to the right and 4 squares up to the shaded shape.

fig (iii) and *fig (iv)* illustrate **rotation** (or **turning movement**). In *fig (iii)* the red shape has been rotated clockwise about A, through $\frac{1}{4}$ turn or 1 right angle.

In *fig (iv)* the red shape has been rotated anticlockwise about A, through $\frac{1}{4}$ turn.

The **scale factor** of an **enlargement** can be found by taking the ratio of the length of a side on the image shape to the length of the corresponding side on the original shape.

For instance, in the diagram, ABC has been enlarged to A′B′C. Scale factor = $\frac{\text{length of A′B′}}{\text{length of AB}}$ = 3.

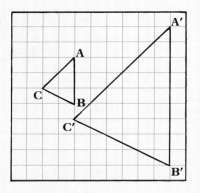

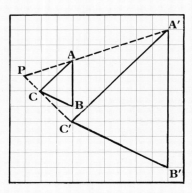

This diagram shows how the centre of enlargement can be found. The steps needed to find the centre of enlargement in this case are:

Step 1   Join A′ and A.

Step 2   Join C′ and C.

Step 3   Extend the lines A′A and C′C. The point P, where these lines meet, is the centre of enlargement.

This diagram shows how to draw an enlargement of the triangle PQR, scale factor 2, centre of enlargement C. Beginning with just the point C and the triangle PQR we proceed as follows:

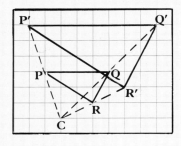

Step 1   Join C to P, C to Q and C to R.

Step 2   Extend the line CP to P′ so that the length of CP′ = twice the length of CP.

Step 3   Extend the line CQ to Q′ so that the length of CQ′ = twice the length of CQ.

Step 4   Extend the line CR to R′ so that the length of CR′ = twice the length of CR.

Step 5   Join P′, Q′ and R′ to form the image triangle P′Q′R′.

A shape is **tessellated** if, when it is translated or reflected or rotated, it completely fills a space leaving no gaps.

Compass Points

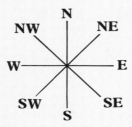

The angle between any two adjacent compass points is 45°.

Bearings from North

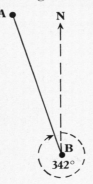

Bearings from North are always given as 3 digits.
To find the bearing of A from B proceed as follows.

Step 1   Join AB.
Step 2   Draw a North line from B.
Step 3   Measure the angle (in a *clockwise* direction) between this North line and the line AB.

In this diagram, the bearing of A from B is 342°.

Networks

The **nodes** (vertices) are marked with dots.
The **arcs** are the lines or curves that join the nodes.

Odd nodes have an odd number of arcs coming from them.
Even nodes have an even number of arcs coming from them.

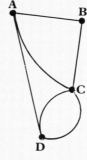

If a path can be found that goes over each arc once and only once, the network is said to be **traceable**. A network must have either 0 or 2 odd nodes to be traceable. If this path is to begin and finish at the same point, the network must have 0 odd nodes.

In the network shown there are four nodes. Nodes A and D are odd nodes ; nodes B and C are even nodes. Since this network has 2 odd nodes it is traceable. However, a path cannot be found which goes over every arc once and only once *and* begins and ends at the same point.

Compass Constructions

The following diagrams show **the construction of the bisector of the line BC.**

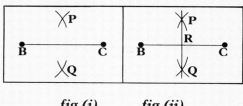

fig (i)   *fig (ii)*

Step 1   Open out the compass so the length on the compass is a little more than half the length of the line BC. Keep this length on the compass throughout.

Step 2   With compass point firstly on B and then on C, draw arcs to meet at P and Q – see *fig (i)*.

Step 3   Draw the line through P and Q – see *fig (ii)*. This line is the required bisector of the line BC.

Note   The point R, where PQ meets BC, is the **mid-point** of the line BC.

The following diagrams show **the construction of the line through A that is perpendicular to the line BC.**

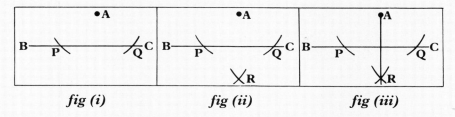

fig (i)   *fig (ii)*   *fig (iii)*

Step 1   Open out the compass to any reasonable length. This length should be such that when the compass point is placed at A two arcs can be drawn that will cross BC. Keep this length on the compass throughout.

Step 2   With compass point on A, draw two arcs to meet BC at P and Q – see *fig (i)*.

Step 3   With compass point firstly on P, then on Q, draw two arcs to meet at R – see *fig (ii)*.

Step 4   Join AR – see *fig (iii)*. AR is the required line.

The following diagrams show **the construction of the line through A that is parallel to the line BC.**

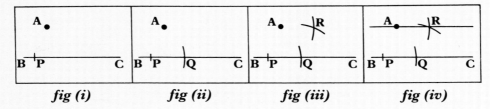

| *fig (i)* | *fig (ii)* | *fig (iii)* | *fig (iv)* |

Step 1   Mark any point P on BC – see *fig (i)*.

Step 2   Open out the compass to the length AP. Keep this length on the compass throughout.

Step 3   With compass point on P, draw an arc to meet BC at Q – see *fig (ii)*.

Step 4   With compass point firstly on Q and then on A, draw two arcs to meet at R – see *fig (iii)*.

Step 5   Draw the line through A and R – see *fig (iv)*. This is the required line.

The following diagrams show **the construction of the bisector of the angle P.**

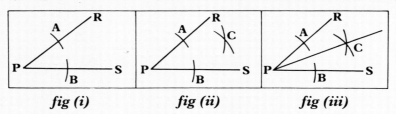

| *fig (i)* | *fig (ii)* | *fig (iii)* |

Step 1   Open out the compass to any reasonable length. This length should be less than the length of either arm (PR or PS) of the angle P. Keep this length on the compass throughout.

Step 2   With compass point on P, draw arcs to meet PR and PS at A and B – see *fig (i)*.

Step 3   With compass point firstly on A and then on B, draw two arcs to meet at C – see *fig (ii)*.

Step 4   Draw the line from P through C – see *fig (iii)*. This line is the required bisector of the angle P.

REVISION EXERCISE

1. How many planes of symmetry do each of the following shapes have?

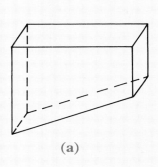   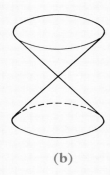   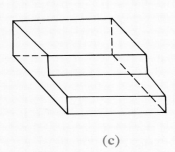

       (a)   (b)   (c)

2. In the shape drawn in **(c)** of the previous question find
    (a) the number of faces   (b) the number of vertices   (c) the number of edges

3. Name all the angles that are equal to   (a) d (b) h (c) j (d) p (e) k

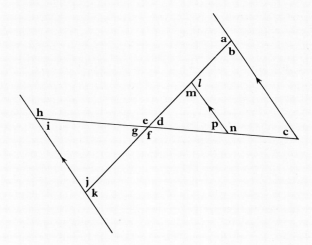

4. In the diagram in the previous question
    (a) name all the obtuse angles
    (b) name the vertically opposite angles
    (c) find the sum of e + d + f + g
    (d) find the sum of n + p

5. (a) The bearing 090° is the same as   **A.** North   **B.** South   **C.** East   **D.** West
    (b) SW is the same as a bearing of   **A.** 045°   **B.** 135°   **C.** 225°   **D.** 315°

6. Find the area and perimeter of the following shapes. (Take π = 3·14.)

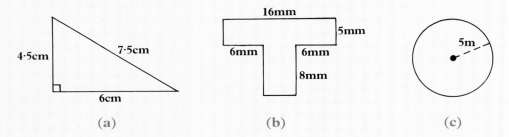

(a)   (b)   (c)

7.

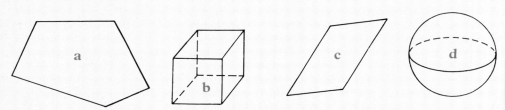

Copy this diagram.
Reflect the quadrilateral ABCD in the x-axis to A'B'C'D'.
Write down the coordinates of A', B', C', D'.

8. Name the following shapes.

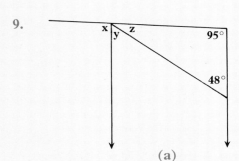

9.

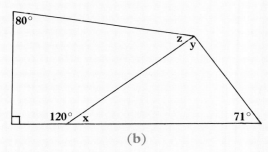

(a)   (b)

Calculate the values of x, y and z in these diagrams.

10. A quadrilateral with two axes of symmetry is a

              A. Parallelogram   **B.** Square   **C.** Rectangle   **D.** Kite

11.

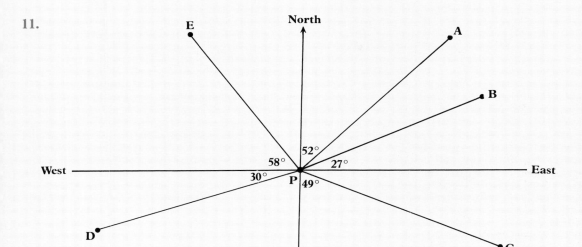

This diagram is **not** drawn to scale.

Find the bearing of each of A, B, C, D and E from P. (You will have to *calculate* some of the missing angles.)

12. (a) Name shapes which are congruent.
   (b) Name the shapes that have no axes of symmetry.
   (c) Name the shapes that have rotational symmetry.
   (d) Name the shapes that are isosceles triangles.
   (e) Together, shapes C and D form a trapezium. Which other shapes combine to form trapeziums?

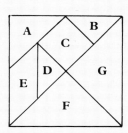

13. Find the volume of the following shapes. (Take $\pi = 3.14$.)

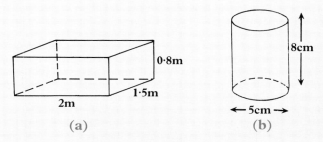

             (a)   **(b)**

14.

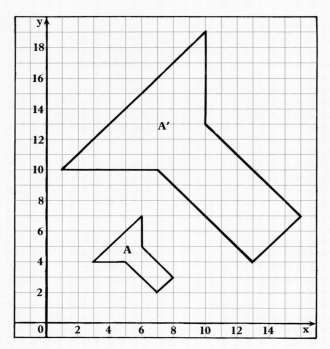

The shape A has been enlarged to the shape A'.
  (a) What is the scale factor for this enlargement?
  (b) Write down the coordinates of the centre of this enlargement.

15. What do the shapes in each of the following lists have in common?

List 1	List 2
equilateral triangle	rhombus
regular octagon	square
rhombus	kite

16. Use your protractor to find the bearing of Q from P.

17.

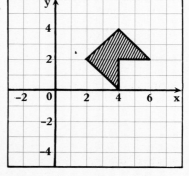

Copy this diagram.
Mark the point P(6, 4).
With centre of enlargement P, enlarge the shaded shape by a scale factor of 2.
Write down the coordinates of the vertices of the image shape.

18. Find the value of x in each of the following.

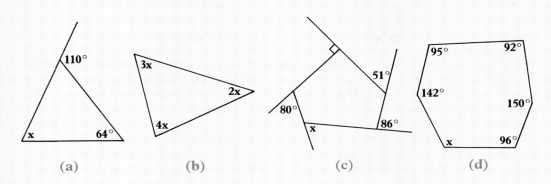

   (a)   (b)   (c)   (d)

19. Garth sails his yacht, from Harwich, on a bearing of 040° for 8km. He then sails on a bearing of 190° for 10km.
   (a) Use a scale of **1cm represents 1km** to map Garth's journey.
   (b) After Garth had sailed 18km, how far was he from Harwich?

20.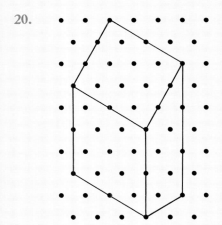

   Sketch the plan, the front elevation and the side elevation of this shape.

21. (a) On the same set of axes draw the following three triangles:
      Triangle 1: Coordinates of the vertices are (5, 7), (7, 7), (5, 10)
      Triangle 2: Coordinates of the vertices are (5, 7), (5, 1), (1, 7)
      Triangle 3: Coordinates of the vertices are (5, 7), (5, 13), (9, 7)
   (b) Triangle 1 has been enlarged to both Triangle 2 and Triangle 3. Which of these enlargements has a negative scale factor?

22. Find the size of each of the interior angles in a regular 18-sided polygon.

23.

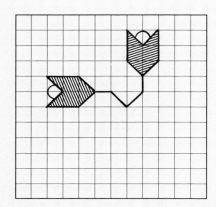

Copy and complete this diagram so it has rotational symmetry of order 4.

24. The plan, the front elevation and the side elevation of a shape are shown below. Make a 3–D sketch of the shape.

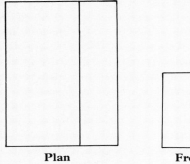

Plan   Front Elevation   Side Elevation

25.

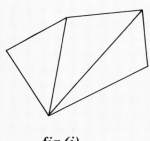 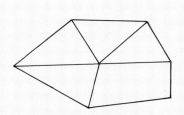 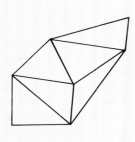

fig (i)   *fig (ii)*   *fig (iii)*

Each line in the above diagrams represents a road.
  (a) In which of the diagrams is it possible to walk over each road once and only once?
  (b) Is it possible to walk over each road once and only once *and* begin and end at the same place, in any of the above diagrams?

142

26. A "2-litre" ice-cream container is a rectangular box 17cm long, 17cm wide and 8cm high.
    (a) What is the volume of this container?
    (b) Is this container able to hold more than 2 litres of ice-cream?

27.

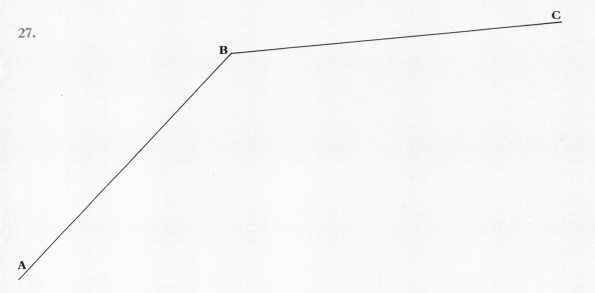

Trace this diagram into your book. Use the compass and ruler for each of the required constructions. Do **not** use the protractor.
    (a) Through A, construct the line that is parallel to BC.
    (b) Bisect the angle ABC.
    (c) Label as P, the point where the lines constructed in (a) and (b) meet.
    (d) From P, construct the line that is perpendicular to BC.
        Label as Q, the point where this line meets BC.
    (e) Measure the length of PQ. Give your answer to the nearest mm.

28. Complete the following LOGO program to draw a rhombus.

        RT   30
        FD   200
        RT   60
        FD   . . .
        RT   . . .
        FD   . . .
        RT   . . .
        FD   . . .

143

INTRODUCTION

How might the location of a car in a multi-storey carpark be described? **Discuss.**
How might the location of a car in the hold of a ship be described? **Discuss.**
How might the location of a hot-air balloon, hovering over a seaside town, be described?
Discuss.

This diagram shows a girl standing near the side of a room. In the room, there is a hanging
light and a cat asleep on the floor.
Can you describe the position of the cat using just x and y coordinates? Can you describe
the position of the lightbulb in this way? **Discuss.**
Do the x and y axes seem to be drawn in unfamiliar positions? **Discuss** how to turn the
page so they are in the familiar position.
Discuss possible coordinates for the position of the cat.
Discuss possible coordinates for the position of the lightbulb.

x, y and z COORDINATES

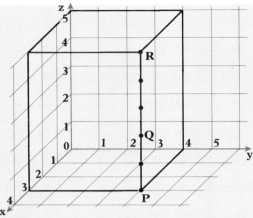

P is a point on the floor of a room. Q and R are directly above P.

All three points P, Q and R have an x-coordinate of 3 and a y-coordinate of 4. The 2–D coordinates (3, 4) do not fully describe the position of these points. We need a third coordinate to describe the height of these points. The third coordinate is called the z-coordinate.

For P, the z-coordinate is 0. (P is on the floor.)
For Q, the z-coordinate is 2. (Q is 2 units above the floor.)
For R, the z-coordinate is 5. (R is 5 units above the floor.)

P is fully described by (3, 4, 0).
Q is fully described by (3, 4, 2).
R is fully described by (3, 4, 5).

EXERCISE 12:2

1.

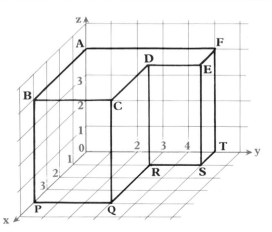

Which point is described by each of the following coordinates?
   (a) (4, 3, 4)   (b) (1, 3, 0)   (c) (1, 5, 4)   (d) (0, 5, 0)   (e) (4, 0, 4)   (f) (1, 3, 4)

2.

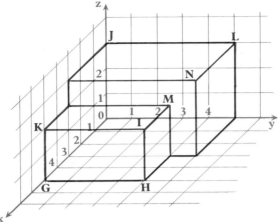

Write down the coordinates of each of the points G, H, I, J, K, L, M, N.

3.

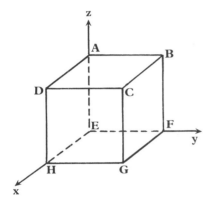

This is a cube of side 2 units.
Vertex E has coordinates (0, 0, 0).
Write down the coordinates of each of the other vertices.

4.

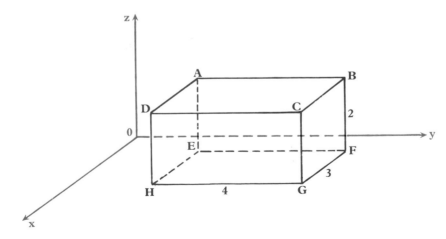

Vertex B has coordinates (1, 6, 2). Vertex H has coordinates (4, 2, 0).
Write down the coordinates of the other vertices of this cuboid.

147

5. **(a)** Pyramid ABCDT is on a
rectangular base; AB = 6,
BC = 4. The height, TM, of the
pyramid is 7.

M is the point (0, 0, 0).
Write down the coordinates of
each vertex of the pyramid.

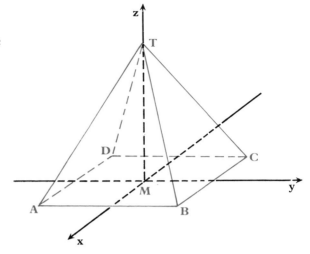

(b)

This is a cube with sides of 6 units. The
origin (0, 0, 0) is at the centre of the cube.
Vertex A is the point (3, –3, –3).

Find the coordinates of the other vertices.

Review

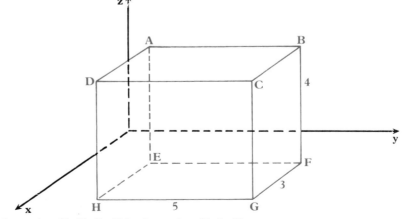

C is the point (6, 7, 4); E is the point (3, 2, 0).
Write down the coordinates of A, B, D, F, G and H.

148

INVESTIGATION 12:3

3-D ROTATIONS

Investigate possible locations of the vertices of a cube of side 2 units, given that one vertex is at the point (3, 4, 5).
What if the coordinates of the given vertex were (2, 0, 2)?
What if the coordinates of the given vertex were (0, 2, 2)?
What if the coordinates of the given vertex were (2, 2, 0)?

INVESTIGATION 12:4

JOURNEYS in 3-D

Suppose you went for a walk along the grid lines from (3, 1, 2) to (2, 3, 0).
Investigate to find the shortest route(s).

Investigate to find the least distance covered if you had to walk along every grid line on the faces of a cube which has one vertex at (3, 1, 2) and another at (2, 3, 0). Is it possible to walk along each of the grid lines once and only once?
What if every grid line contained *within* the cube was to be walked along at least once?

INVESTIGATION 12:5

3-D GAME

Invent a game that is played on a 3–D grid. You may like to base your game on a 2–D game such as "noughts and crosses" or "snakes and ladders" or "monopoly".
Trial your game thoroughly, modifying it if necessary.
Write clear, concise instructions for your game when you have perfected it.

LOCUS – Lines and Curves

DISCUSSION and PRACTICAL EXERCISE 13:1

1. Sketch the possible paths, or routes, followed by each of the following objects.
   Discuss.

     a bouncing table tennis ball
     a soccer ball kicked from one player to another
     a hockey ball hit into the goal
     a balloon on a string
     a dolphin playing in the sea
     a landing aeroplane
     a leaf falling to the ground
     a stone skimming across a pond
     a dog chained to its kennel
     the pedal of a moving cycle
     the end of a spoke of a moving cycle
     the centre of a spoke of a moving cycle
     the hand of a swimmer

2.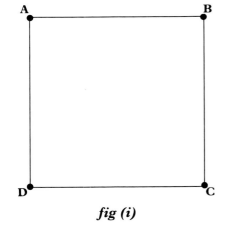

   fig (i)   *fig (ii)*

Four students stand at the corners of a square. These are represented by A, B, C and D as shown in *fig (i)*. At the same instant, each student begins walking clockwise, at the same speed, towards the next student; the first part of each path is shown in *fig (ii)*.
Find the paths followed by each of the students. Discuss. (You may like to try this yourselves.)

3. Mark, with small "stick-on" dots, three points on a coin (or a round flat object such as a saucer or a disc made from cardboard). Have one of these points (A) at the centre, another (B) on the circumference and the other (C) between the centre and the circumference.

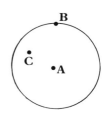

Can you predict the path of each of the points A, B and C as the coin is rolled, in a straight line, along the desk? **Discuss**. Check your predictions by rolling the coin along the desk.

Replace the coin with other objects that can be rolled ; for instance, a plastic bottle or a bucket. Make and test statements about the paths followed by various points on these objects as they are rolled along the desk.

INVESTIGATION 13:2

LADDERS and LOCUS

fig (i)   *fig (ii)*   *fig (iii)*

These drawings show three of the positions of a ladder which slides from a nearly vertical position in *fig (i)* to a nearly horizontal position in *fig (iii)*. As the top of the ladder (T) slides down the wall, the foot of the ladder (F) slides along the ground. **Investigate** the path of the point M, the mid-point of the ladder. To help in your investigation you could use a ruler to represent the ladder, and a desk pushed against a wall of your classroom.

    What if M was closer to F than to T?
    What if M was closer to T than to F?
    What if the wall was sloping?
    What if the ground was sloping?

The **locus of an object** is the set of all the possible positions that this object can occupy. In particular, the path of an object, moving according to some rule, is the locus of the object. (The plural of locus is **loci**.)

Sometimes the locus can be well described in words; sometimes it can be better described by a sketch.

To find the locus of a moving point, always sketch a few possible positions of the point.

Worked Example   The minute hand of a clock is 14mm long.
                         Describe the locus of the mid-point of this minute hand.

Answer   Some possible positions (P1, P2, . . .) of the mid-point of the minute hand are shown.
The locus is a circle, radius 7mm, the centre of which is the centre of the clockface.

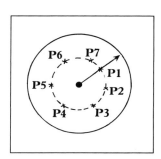

DISCUSSION EXERCISE 13:3

Jenny skis downhill between two rows of trees (represented by AB and CD). She skis in such a way that she is always the same distance from the trees on either side of her.
Sketch Jenny's locus.
Discuss how this locus could be described in words.

On the downhill run there are two marker posts (represented by R and Q). Jenny skis so that she is never closer to one than the other.
Sketch Jenny's locus. **Discuss** how to describe this locus in words.

As Jenny skis past the tow-rope (represented by ST) she stays exactly 5m from it. **Discuss** Jenny's locus. Sketch and describe this locus.

F

D **H**

As Jenny skis to the finishing post (represented by F) she stays the same distance from the spectators on the left (represented by DE) as she does from the spectators on the right (represented by GH). Sketch Jenny's locus. **Discuss** how to describe this locus in words.

G

E

Some well known loci are:

1. The locus of a point which is a constant distance from a fixed point is a circle.

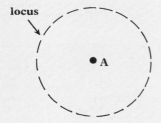

2. The locus of a point which is a constant distance from a fixed line is a pair of parallel lines.

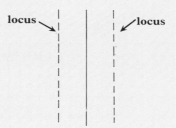

3. The locus of a point which is equidistant from two fixed points is the mediator (perpendicular bisector) of the line joining the fixed points.

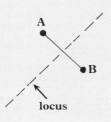

4. The locus of a point which is equidistant from two intersecting lines is the pair of lines which bisect the angles between the fixed lines.

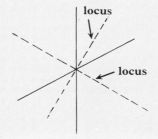

EXERCISE 13:4

Sketch the following loci. Describe each locus in words.

1. The locus of a point P which moves so that it is always 3cm from a fixed point A.

2.  The locus of a point R which moves so that it is always 25mm from the line AB.

3. The locus of a point P which is equidistant from the points C and D.

4. 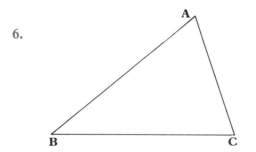 The locus of a point S which is equidistant from the arms PQ and RQ of the acute angle PQR.

5. The locus of a point P which is the same distance from the lines AB and CD.

6.
   (a) The locus of a point P which is always 2cm from the point B.
   (b) The locus of a point R which is equidistant from the lines AB and AC and which is within the triangle ABC.
   (c) The locus of a point Q which is the same distance from A and C.

Review AB, BC, CD and DA represent hedgerows that surround a field. S is a stake in the ground. Sketch and describe the following loci.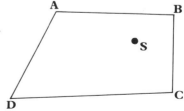
   (a) The locus of a football that is kicked so that it is always the same distance from B and D.
   (b) The locus of a cow which moves from the hedgerow DC to the corner A in such a way that it is always equidistant from the hedgerows AB and AD.
   (c) The locus of a dog which is chained to a stake at S. (The dog moves so that its chain is always taut.)

INVESTIGATION 13:5

SPECIAL CURVES

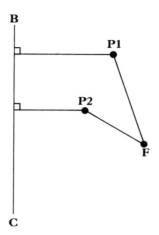

Investigate the locus of a point P which is the same distance from the point F as it is from the line BC. (Two possible positions of P are shown.)
What if BC was a sloping line?

Investigate the locus of a point R which moves so that the sum of the distances RD and RE is 5cm.
What if the sum of these distances was 6cm?
What if the sum of these distances was 8cm?
What if . . .

Investigate the locus of a point Q which moves so that the difference of the distances from two fixed points is constant.

Investigate the locus of a point R which moves so that the angle FRG is a right angle.
(Two possible positions of R are shown.)

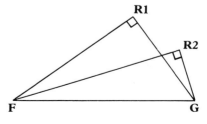

INVESTIGATION 13:6

PULLEY MOVEMENT

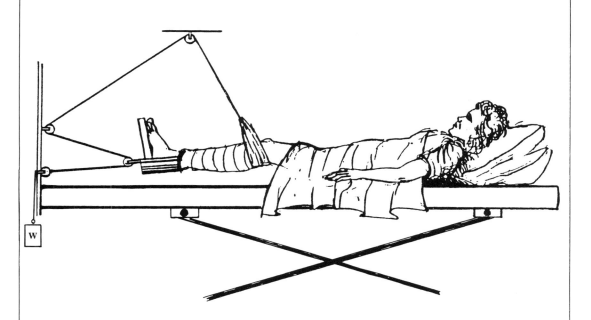

Investigate the paths of the kneecap and the pulley attached to the foot as the patient moves.

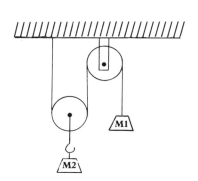

As the mass M1 moves down a distance x, the mass M2 will move up a distance $\frac{x}{2}$.

continued . . .

. . . *from previous page*

As the pulley P1 moves up a distance x,
the pulley P2 will move up a distance $\frac{x}{2}$.

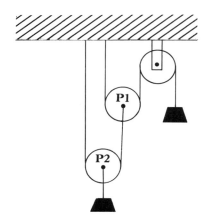

Investigate the relative movement of the masses and/or the pulleys in the following pulley systems.

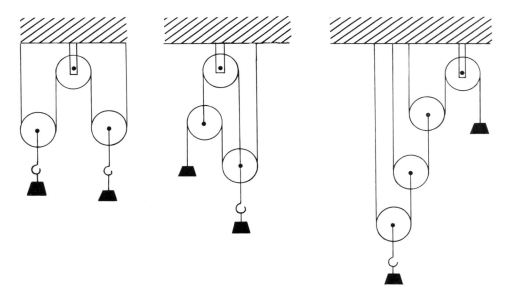

Investigate the design of different pulley systems which will raise a mass M1 four times the distance another mass M2 is raised (or lowered).

Investigate the design of different pulley systems in which each pulley moves twice the distance of an adjacent pulley.

LOCI – Regions

Worked Example

Sketch the region in which a point P would be if it is
  (a) always less than 15mm from the point A
  (b) always closer to the line BD than the line BC, and contained within the acute angle DBC.

Answer

(a)

Locus is shown shaded.
It is the interior of the
circle, centre A, radius 15mm.

(b)

Locus is shown shaded.
It is the area between the line BD
and the bisector of the angle DBC.

Note A boundary which is not included in the region is dotted.

EXERCISE 13:7

1. Draw two points A and B in positions similar
   to that shown.
   Sketch the region in which a point P would be
   if it is always closer to A than to B.

   • A

   • B

2. Sketch the region in which a point Q would be if it is always less than 2cm from a
   fixed point C.

3. Sketch the region in which a
   point R would be if it is always
   further from the line AB than
   from the line CD.

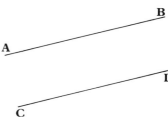

4. A point S is less than 15mm from a fixed line EF. Sketch the region in which S would be.

5. A point T is within the obtuse angle GHI and is closer to the line GH than to the line IH. Sketch the region in which T would be.

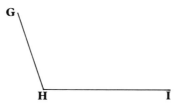

6. Two roads, represented by AB and CB, between villages A, B and C are shown. Trace this diagram.

   Samantha walks her dog each day. The region in which she walks her dog is further from BC than from AB and closer to A than B.
   Sketch the region in which Samantha walks her dog.

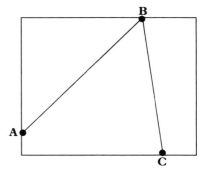

7. Two villages A and B are 20km apart; B being due south of A. The fire brigade from A services an area of radius 10km around A while the brigade from B services an area of radius 12km around B.
   Using the scale 1cm represents 4km, shade the area that is serviced by both brigades.

8.

Scale : 1cm represents 5m

AB represents a brick wall; X and Y represent two rotating sprinklers. Trace this diagram.
The sprinklers are able to water a radius of 25m. The wall is so high that no water, from the sprinklers, reaches the ground for a distance of 2m on the other side of the wall.
On your diagram, shade the region that is watered by both sprinklers.

160

9.

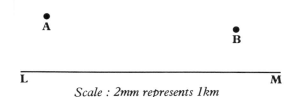

Scale : 2mm represents 1km

A and B are radio stations which can be received for a 20km radius. LM is a hill which creates a reception "shadow" so that for 5km on the far side no reception is received and for a further 5km the reception is poor.
Trace the diagram. On your diagram, shade the area that receives poor reception from both radio stations.

Review 1 *Use the scale 1cm represents 2m for this question.*

Two rotating sprinklers are placed 10m apart on a lawn. One can water an area of radius 5m, the other can water an area up to 7m away. Draw a diagram to show the area that is watered by both sprinklers.

Review 2

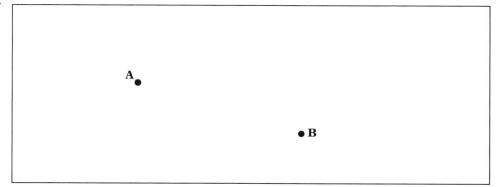

Scale : 1cm represents 5km

This diagram represents two towns at A and B. Trace this diagram.
The hospital at A will admit patients who live closer to A than to B. The fire brigades from A and B will travel a maximum of 15km.
On your diagram, shade the area in which the ambulance from the hospital at A and the fire brigade from either A or B would attend an accident.

INVESTIGATION 13:8

TETHERED ANIMALS and LOCUS

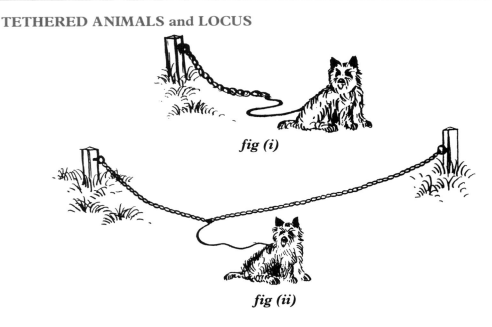

fig (i)

fig (ii)

fig (i) shows a dog tethered to a chain that is attached to a stake.
fig (ii) shows a dog tethered to a chain that is attached to two stakes. The end of the
dog's lead is attached to a ring that can slide along the chain.
Investigate the possible loci of the dog's head.

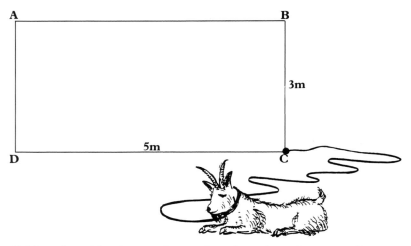

ABCD represents a field enclosed by fences. A goat is tethered, as shown, at C.
The goat cannot enter the field.
Investigate the region that the goat can graze.

Take a walk through your school grounds.

As you walk, describe your route using loci. For instance, part of your description could be "walk from the main entrance for 50 paces so that you are always equidistant from the gymnasium door and the oak tree."

Give your description to someone else to walk this route.

PYTHAGORAS' THEOREM

INVESTIGATION 14:1

RIGHT-ANGLED TRIANGLES from ROPE

We can draw right angles by measuring with a protractor or by
using a compass construction.
We can also make a right angle without using any
mathematical instruments. All we need is a piece of rope or
thick string.

Make 13 equally spaced knots in a length of rope or
thick string. Shape this rope, as shown, to make a
right-angled triangle.
The length of rope used to make this right-angled
triangle was 12 units, taking one unit to be the distance
between the centres of adjacent knots.

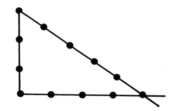

Investigate other lengths of rope that could be shaped to make right-angled triangles.
Consider rope lengths of 15, 20, 24, 30, 36, 40, 42 as well as other lengths. As part of
your investigation, make and test statements about the relationship between the
lengths of the sides in a right-angled triangle. (Instead of using equally spaced knots
you could place paper clips or clothes pegs or something similar at equally spaced
intervals along the rope or heavy string.)

INVESTIGATION 14:2

The PYTHAGORAS RELATION

On a loose piece of paper, draw a right-angled triangle with
sides of length 8cm, 6cm, 10cm.

Draw the squares on the sides of the triangle.
Cut up the squares P and Q and fit them onto
square R. You should be able to cut them in
such a way that they fit exactly onto R. What is
the relationship between these three squares?

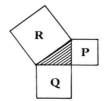

continued . . .

. . . from previous page

What if you began with this triangle?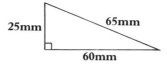

What if you began with any other right-angled triangle? **Investigate.**
What if you began with a scalene triangle? **Investigate.**

The **hypotenuse** is the longest side in a right-angled triangle. It is the side opposite the right angle. In this triangle, c is the hypotenuse.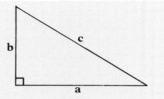

Pythagoras' Theorem gives the relationship between the lengths of the sides in a right-angled triangle. In words, this theorem is **"the square on the hypotenuse equals the sum of the squares on the other two sides."**

$$c^2 = a^2 + b^2$$

is Pythagoras' Theorem in symbols, for the triangle shown.

EXERCISE 14:3

1. Name the hypotenuse in each of these triangles.

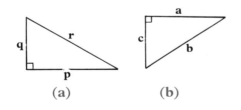 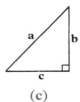 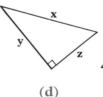 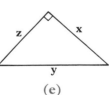

    (a)   (b)   (c)   (d)   (e)

2. For each of the triangles in **question 1**, write down the relationship between the lengths of the sides.

Review Using Pythagoras' Theorem, write down the relationship between the lengths of the sides of these triangles.

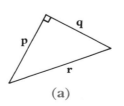 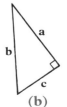

    (a)   (b)

USING PYTHAGORAS' THEOREM

We can use Pythagoras' Theorem to find the length of the third side of a right-angled triangle, if we know the lengths of the other two sides.

Worked Example   Find the value of **x** in each of these triangles.

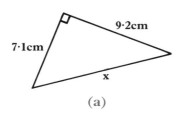

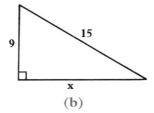

(a)   (b)

Answer (a) $x^2 = 7 \cdot 1^2 + 9 \cdot 2^2$ (Pythagoras' Theorem)
$\qquad = 50 \cdot 41 + 84 \cdot 64$
$\qquad = 135 \cdot 05$
$x = \sqrt{135 \cdot 05}$
$\qquad = 11 \cdot 6$cm (to 1d.p.)

This answer for x may be calculated from the first line, $x^2 = 7 \cdot 1^2 + 9 \cdot 2^2$, by the following calculator keying sequence:

Key 7·1 $\boxed{\text{INV}}$ $\boxed{x^2}$ $\boxed{+}$ 9·2 $\boxed{\text{INV}}$ $\boxed{x^2}$ $\boxed{=}$ $\boxed{\sqrt{}}$

(b) $15^2 = x^2 + 9^2$ (Pythagoras' Theorem)
Rewrite with x^2 first : $x^2 + 9^2 = 15^2$
$\qquad\qquad\qquad\qquad x^2 = 15^2 - 9^2$ (subtracting 9^2 from both sides)
$\qquad\qquad\qquad\qquad\quad = 225 - 81$
$\qquad\qquad\qquad\qquad\quad = 144$
$\qquad\qquad\qquad\quad x = \sqrt{144}$
$\qquad\qquad\qquad\qquad\quad = 12$

This answer for x may be obtained from the second line, $x^2 = 15^2 - 9^2$, by the following calculator keying sequence:

Key 15 $\boxed{\text{INV}}$ $\boxed{x^2}$ $\boxed{-}$ 9 $\boxed{\text{INV}}$ $\boxed{x^2}$ $\boxed{=}$ $\boxed{\sqrt{}}$

EXERCISE 14:4

Round your answers to 1d.p. when rounding is necessary.

1. Find the value of **a**.

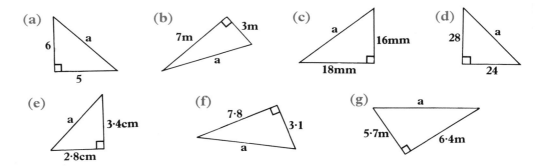

2. Find the length of the unknown side.

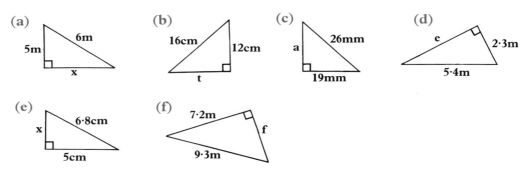

3. Find the value of **p**.

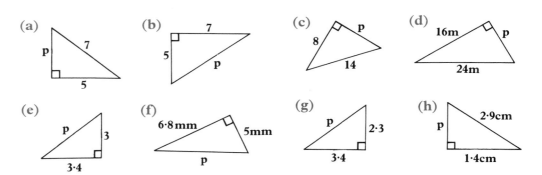

4. The two shorter sides of a right-angled triangle are 5cm and 4cm long. How long is the hypotenuse?

5. The two equal sides of a right-angled isosceles triangle are 25mm long. What is the length of the third side?

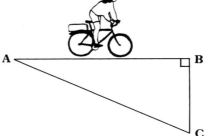

6. Anne cycles 8km from A to B, then 5km from B to C. She returns directly from C to A. How far is her return journey?

7.

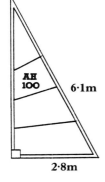

A sail, the shape shown, is made for a boat. A binding is sewn right around the edge of this sail. What total length of binding is needed?

8. What is the length of the longest straight line that can be drawn on a piece of A4 paper which measures 298mm by 210mm?

9. A helicopter flew 24km to the West, then 15km to the North. How far is the helicopter then from its starting point?

10. Find the length of the diagonals of the square, rectangle, kite and rhombus shown below.

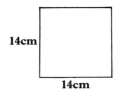
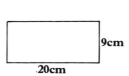

11. Find the height of the equilateral and isosceles triangles shown below.

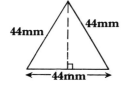
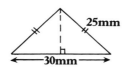

169

Review 1 Find the length of the sides marked as **x**.

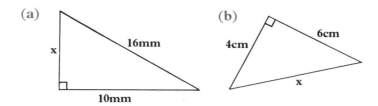

(a)

(b)

Review 2 How long are the diagonals of a square which has sides of length 140mm?

Review 3 A new section of road cuts off one of the dangerous right-angled bends on a country lane. To the nearest 10m, how much shorter is the new section of road?

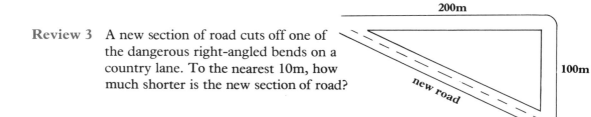

INVESTIGATION 14:5

CIRCUMCIRCLES

A circle, drawn around a triangle so that the vertices are on the circumference, is called a circumcircle.

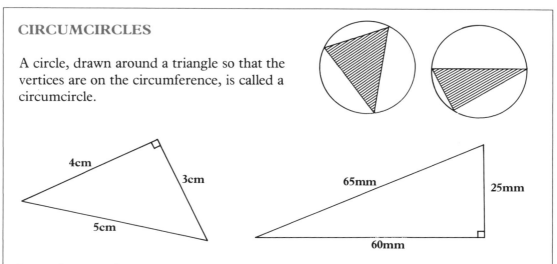

Investigate to find the circumcircles for these triangles. Where is the centre of these circumcircles? Make and test statements as part of your investigation.

What if you began with a scalene triangle? Does every triangle have a circumcircle? **Investigate**.

CALCULATIONS involving MORE COMPLEX EQUATIONS

Worked Example

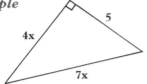

Find the value of x.

Answer

$(7x)^2 = 5^2 + (4x)^2$ (Pythagoras' Theorem)
$49x^2 = 25 + 16x^2$
$49x^2 - 16x^2 = 25$ (subtracting $16x^2$ from both sides)
$33x^2 = 25$
$x^2 = \frac{25}{33}$ (dividing both sides by 33)
$x = \sqrt{\frac{25}{33}}$
$= 0{\cdot}87$ (2 d.p.)

EXERCISE 14:6

Round answers sensibly when rounding is required.

1. Find the value of **a**.

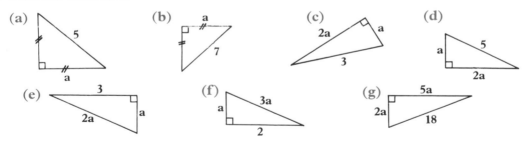

2. The diagonals of a square are 8cm long. What is the length of a side of this square?

3. An altitude of an equilateral triangle measures 48mm. Find the length of the sides of this triangle. (Remember: an altitude is the perpendicular distance from a vertex to the opposite side.)

Review   Find **a**.

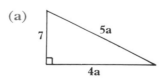

INVESTIGATION 14:7

SQUARE ROOTS and SPIRALS

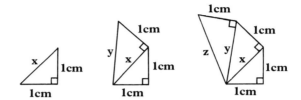

Which lengths in these diagrams are equal to $\sqrt{2}$? Which are equal to $\sqrt{3}$?

How could lengths of $\sqrt{5}$, $\sqrt{6}$, $\sqrt{7}$, ... be drawn?

Investigate to find the spiral formed by continuing the sequence of diagrams.

PYTHAGOREAN TRIPLES

INVESTIGATION 14:8

TRIPLES

Using Pythagoras' Theorem, we find the value of x is 5. The lengths of the sides of this right-angled triangle are all whole numbers. The three whole numbers 3, 4, 5 are called a Pythagorean triple.

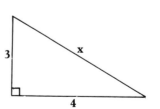

There are many other sets of three whole numbers which can be the lengths of right-angled triangles.

Investigate to find more of these Pythagorean triples.

Hint: 5, 7 or 8 are the *shortest* sides in some of the other Pythagorean triples.

Two Pythagorean triples are 3, 4, 5 and 5, 12, 13. These triples, or multiples of these triples, can sometimes be used to write down the third side of a right-angled triangle.

Example

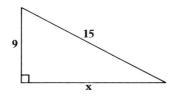

We can say that x = 12 since
3 × (3, 4, 5) is 9, 12, 15.

Worked Example

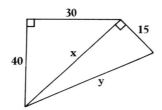

Find **x** and **y**.

Answer   x = 50   (10 × 3, 4, 5 △ by Pythagoras' Theorem)
y² = 50² + 15² (Pythagoras' Theorem)
y = √50² + 15²
   = 52·2 (to 1d.p.)

1. Copy and complete the table below for the triangle shown.
    If necessary, use c² = a² + b² but try to use the
    Pythagorean triples and their multiples.

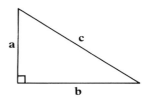

a	3		6		5	10	50	15	15		2·5
b	4	4		16	12				36	2	6
c		5	10	20		26	130	25		2·5	

2. Find the value of **e** in each of the following. Try to write this value down from your knowledge of Pythagorean triples. If you are unable to do this, calculate the value using Pythagoras' Theorem.

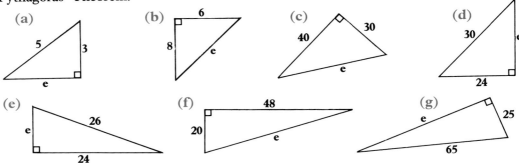

3. Find the value of **x** and **y** in each of the following. Wherever possible, use the Pythagorean triples to reduce the amount of working.

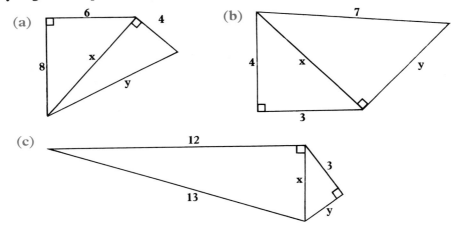

4.

(a) What is the length of AC?
(b) What is the length of BC?
(c) Use Pythagoras' Theorem to find the length of AB.

5. Find the distance between the following pairs of points.
   (a) (1, 0), (9, 6)   (b) (1, 1), (13, 6)   (c) (13, 3), (−2, −5)

6. Find **x**.

(a)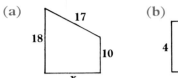

(b)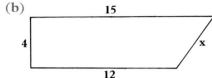

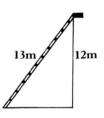

7. A windowsill in an office building is 12m above the ground. The top of a 13m ladder is resting against the windowsill. How far out, from the wall of the office building, is the foot of the ladder?

8.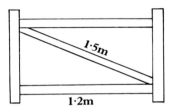

The stay on a gate is 1·5m long.
How far apart are the horizontal rails?

9. Jane put a wooden edging around this triangular garden. She used a 10m length of wood for the longest side and a 6m length for the shortest side. What total length of wood did Jane use?

10. Kyle walks 200m East, then 480m South. How far is Kyle then from his starting point?

Review 1 Find the value of **p** in each of the following.

(a)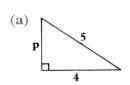

(b)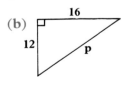

(c)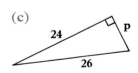

Review 2 Find the values of **a** and **b**.

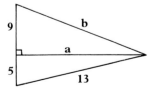

175

Review 3 The sidelight window in a vintage car is a triangular shape, as sketched. The piece of rubber around this window needs to be replaced. What length of rubber is needed?

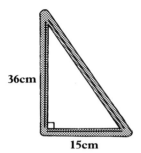

36cm

15cm

CONVERSES

Given a right-angled triangle, we can find the length of the third side if we know the lengths of the other two sides. We use Pythagoras' Theorem to find the length of the third side.

Given all three sides of a triangle, we can use the converse of Pythagoras' Theorem to find whether or not the triangle is a right-angled triangle. The converse of Pythagoras' Theorem is "if the square on one side of a triangle is equal to the sum of the squares on the other two sides, then the triangle is a right-angled triangle."

Worked Example   (a) Is the triangle with sides 25mm, 65mm, 60mm a right-angled triangle?

        (b) Is the triangle with sides 18, 25, 36 a right-angled triangle?

Answer   (a) The longest side is 65mm. $65^2 = 4225$

The sum of the squares on the other sides $= 25^2 + 60^2$
$$= 4225$$

That is, $65^2 = 25^2 + 60^2$.

Hence the triangle is right-angled. (Converse of Pythagoras' Theorem.)

    (b) The longest side is 36. $36^2 = 1296$

The sum of the squares on the other two sides $= 18^2 + 25^2$
$$= 949$$

Since $36^2 \neq 18^2 + 25^2$, the triangle is not right-angled.

EXERCISE 14:10

State whether or not the triangles, with sides of the following lengths, are right-angled triangles.

1. 2, 3, 4   2. 28, 35, 21   3. 40, 75, 85

4. 22, 32, 45   5. 7, 17, 15   6. 50, 14, 48

7. 10, 22, 27   Review 120, 35, 125

DISCUSSION EXERCISE 14:11

Jon laid the boxing for the foundation of a house.
To check that the walls of the house would be at right
angles, Jon measured the diagonals. Would Jon need
to measure anything else or do any calculations?
Discuss.

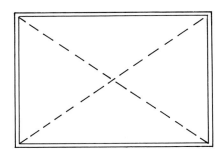

Where, on a building site, might the Theorem of Pythagoras or its converse be used?
Discuss.

Where else, in the workplace, might the Theorem of Pythagoras be applied? **Discuss.**

INVESTIGATION 14:12

RELATIONSHIPS between **PYTHAGOREAN TRIPLES**

Consider the Pythagorean triple 3, 4, 5.
Notice that $3^2 = 9$ and $4 + 5 = 9$.
Can you use this relationship to predict the other numbers in a Pythagorean triple
that has 7 as its smallest number?
  What if the smallest number was 9?
  What if the smallest number was 6?
  What if . . .
  Investigate.

PRACTICAL EXERCISE 14:13

Build an interesting model using triangles – you may like to use just right-angled triangles.
You may choose any building material you like. Some suggestions are cardboard or
polystyrene.

SQUARE, RECTANGLE, TRIANGLE, CIRCLE

ARRANGING TABLES

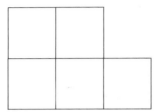

Five small square tables are used to form one large table. One arrangement is shown.
Investigate other arrangements.
As part of your investigation, consider questions such as the following.
Which arrangement has the greatest perimeter? Which has the smallest perimeter?
How many arrangements have the same perimeter? How many people could be
seated?

What if four small tables were used?
What if six small tables were used?
What if . . .

Remember: Area of rectangle ,   A = l b

                 Area of triangle ,   A = $\frac{1}{2}$ bh

                 Area of circle ,   A = πr^2

                 The perimeter of a shape is the distance around the outside. The perimeter
of a circle is called the circumference.
Circumference of circle,   C = $2\pi r$ or   C = πd

We use these formulae for area and perimeter to find the area and perimeter of a
compound shape; i.e. of a shape which consists of a combination of shapes.

Worked Example Find the area and perimeter of this shape. The curved portion is semi-circular. (Take $\pi = 3{\cdot}14$)

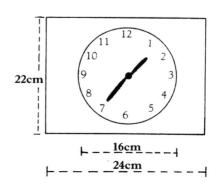

Answer Area of shape = area of rectangle + area of half a circle.

Using A = *l* b, area of rectangle = 3 × 5
$$= 15\text{m}^2$$

Using A = πr^2, area of half a circle of radius 2·5m = $\frac{1}{2} \times 3{\cdot}14 \times 2{\cdot}5^2$
$$= 9{\cdot}8\text{m}^2 \text{ (1 d.p.)}$$

Hence area of shape = 24·8m² (1 d.p.)

Perimeter of shape = circumference of semi-circle + length of 3 sides of the rectangle.

Using C = πd, circumference of semi-circle = $\frac{1}{2} \times 3{\cdot}14 \times 5$
$$= 7{\cdot}9\text{m} \text{ (1 d.p.)}$$

Hence perimeter of shape = 7·9 + 3 + 5 + 3
$$= 18{\cdot}9\text{m} \text{ (1 d.p.)}$$

Worked Example Find the area of the square which has perimeter of 36cm.

Answer Since perimeter is 36cm, each side is 9cm.
Using A = *l* b, area of square = 9 × 9
$$= 81\text{cm}^2$$

EXERCISE 15:2

Use $\pi = 3{\cdot}14$ throughout this exercise. Where rounding is needed, round the answers to 1 d.p.

1. A clockface of diameter 16cm is mounted on a rectangular board of dimensions 24cm × 22cm. Find the area of board not covered by the clockface.

180

2. Find the area of each of these shapes. (All dimensions are in cm.)

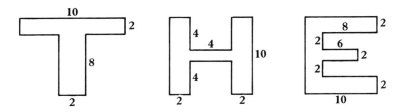

3. Find the perimeter of each of the shapes in **question 2**.

4. Find the perimeter of each of these shapes. (The curved portions are semi-circular.)

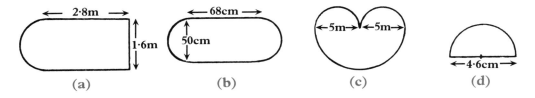

5. Find the area of each of the shapes in **question 4**.

6. A car tyre of diameter 54cm is marked at the bottom by a parking warden. The owner returns to the car and pushes the car forward so that the mark is now at the top of the tyre. How far must the owner push the car forward?

7. A 5m × 3m terrace is to be paved with tiles which measure 500mm × 500mm. How many tiles will be needed?

8.

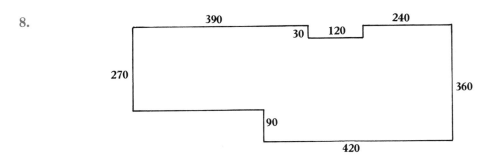

This shows the plan of an open-plan living area of a home. All measurements are in cm.

This living area is to be carpeted with 30cm square carpet tiles. How many will be needed?

181

9. 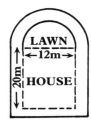 A path, 0·8m wide, goes around the sides and back of a house and around a semi-circular lawn in front of the house as shown. The house measures 12m × 20m.

   Write down the steps you will take to calculate the area of the path. Find the area of the path.

10. Pete has found a metal ring with radius 20cm. He wants to bend this ring into a square. What length will the sides of the square be?

11. This diagram shows a right-angled triangle with two rectangles drawn on the shorter sides.
    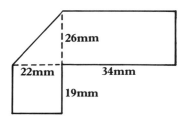
    (a) Find the total area of this shape.
    (b) Find the perimeter. (**Hint:** You will need to use Pythagoras' Theorem.)

12. 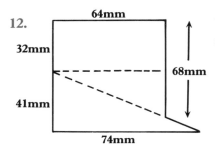 This diagram consists of a rectangle and two right-angled triangles.
    (a) Find the total area of this shape.
    (b) Find the perimeter of this shape.

13. (a) Find the area of the square which has perimeter of 28cm.
    (b) Find the perimeter of the square which has area of 100mm².

14. The perimeter of a rectangle is 18m. This rectangle is twice as long as it is wide. How long is it?

15. Use trial and improvement, or some other method, to find the length of the following mats.
    (a) A wrestling mat is 3m longer than it is wide. The mat covers an area of 108m². What is its length?
    (b) A karate mat is a square of side 8m. A judo mat is also square and has four times the area of a karate mat.
    What is the length of a judo mat?

16. A square has the same area as a circle of diameter 8cm.
    What is the length of a side of the square?

17.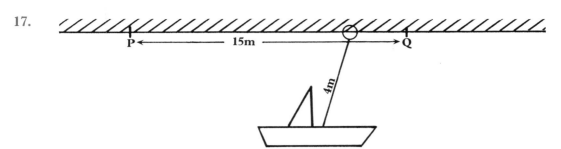

A group of children sailed a boat by attaching it to a 15m long wire along the bank of a canal. The boat was on the end of a 4m string and was attached by a ring to the wire. The ring can move along the wire from P to Q but cannot slip off the wire.

Make a sketch of the area in which the boat can be sailed.
Calculate this area.

18. Jayne's bathroom is 2·64m long, 2·20m wide and 2·42m high. Jayne is going to tile her bathroom with tiles that each take up a space of 110mm × 110mm (including an allowance for a small gap between each tile for grouting). She is going to tile all four walls.

    (a) What are the dimensions of Jayne's bathroom in mm?

    (b) A window in the back wall measures 1320mm × 990mm.
    The bathroom door measures 990mm × 2090mm.
    The window space and the door space are not to be tiled. What is the least number of tiles that Jayne will use to tile her bathroom?

19.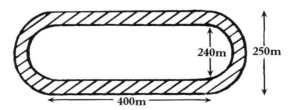

The shaded portion of this diagram represents a race track.
A horse that runs on the inside of this track will cover less distance than a horse that runs on the outside.
Find the greatest possible difference in the distance run by two horses in completing one circuit of this track.

Area, Perimeter, Volume

Review 1 Find the area of each of these shapes. (The curved portions are semi-circular.)

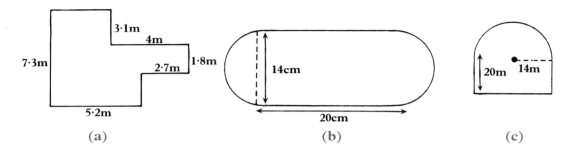

(a)   (b)   (c)

Review 2 Find the perimeter of each of the shapes in **Review 1**.

Review 3

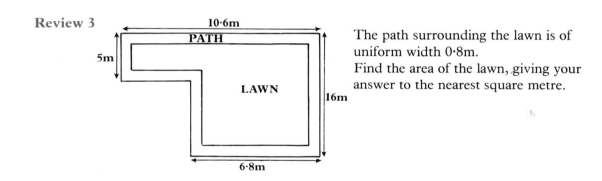

The path surrounding the lawn is of uniform width 0·8m.
Find the area of the lawn, giving your answer to the nearest square metre.

Review 4

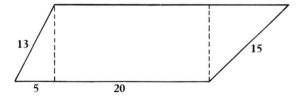

This shape consists of a rectangle and two right-angled triangles. The dimensions are in metres.
Calculate (a) the area of the shape
           (b) the perimeter of the shape

Review 5

The perimeter of the shaded shape is 314mm.
Find the length of the square.

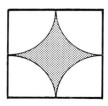

PUZZLES 15:3

1.

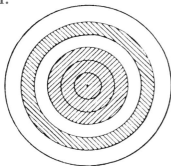

The six equally spaced circles all have the same centre.
Which of the two shaded regions has the greater area?

2. Tim and Neville walk at the same speed. They both begin at Q and finish at P. Tim walks along the large semi-circle and Neville walks along the three small semi-circles. Before they began their walk Neville claimed that he would get to P before Tim. Did he?

3.

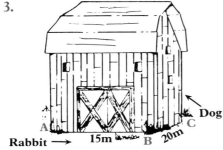

A dog, which is at C, senses a rabbit, which is at A, and begins to chase it around this shed in the direction shown. The rabbit begins to run, in the direction shown, at the same time the dog begins to run. This dog can run faster than this rabbit. The dog gains 1m on the rabbit for each complete circuit of the shed that the dog makes. How many metres does the dog have to run before it catches sight of the rabbit?

4. Lightning Lady and Stirling Monarch set off from the same point on their circular training track, with their jockeys riding them in opposite directions. The first time they meet, Lightning Lady has run 500m. The next time they meet Stirling Monarch still has 200m to go to complete his first lap. How far is it around their training track?

PRACTICAL EXERCISE 15:4

Investigate the cost of carpeting an area such as the upstairs of your house or all of the ground floor living areas of your house or a section of your school. Carpet the floors of wardrobes, cupboards etc.

You should begin by taking measurements and drawing a scale plan.

Consider questions such as the following.

Will you use wide or narrow carpet?
Will you have as few seams as possible?
Will you have all the seams in the same direction?
Which layout will use the least amount of carpet? Is this necessarily the most practical layout?

INVESTIGATION 15:5

THE DOG RUN

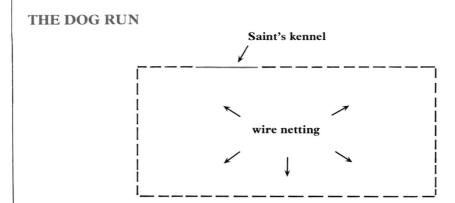

When Sue moved to London, she took her dog, Saint, with her. Saint was not used to being tied up. Since Sue's London garden had fences around it that Saint could jump, she decided to build a "run" around his kennel.
Sue bought 20 metres of wire netting and wanted to use all of this in making the "run".
She also wanted Saint's run to be the greatest possible area.
Investigate the shape of run which gives the greatest possible area.

PARALLELOGRAM, TRAPEZIUM, KITE

DISCUSSION EXERCISE 15:6

1.

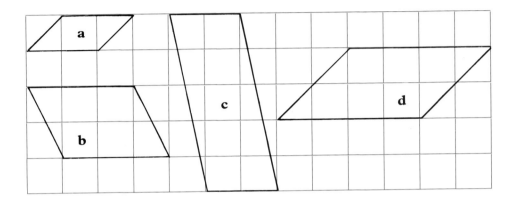

Count squares to find the area of the above parallelograms.

Discuss how the sequence of diagrams given below can be used to find the area of the parallelogram **b**. How does the area of the parallelogram relate to the area of the rectangle ABCD?

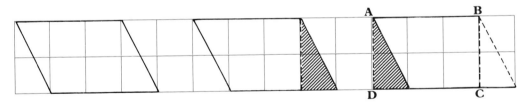

Discuss how to find the area of the parallelograms **a**, **c** and **d** without counting squares.

What if no sides of the parallelogram were horizontal?
(Consider parallelograms such as those below.)

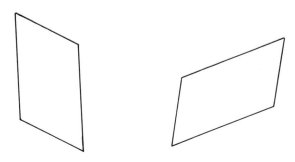

2.

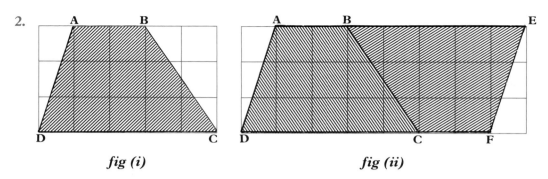

fig (i)   *fig (ii)*

Is the trapezium BEFC on *fig (ii)* congruent to the trapezium ABCD? What shape is AEFD?

Count squares to estimate the area of the trapezium ABCD.

Discuss how the diagrams shown can be used to find the area of the trapezium ABCD, without counting squares.

What if the parallel sides of the trapezium were not horizontal? (Consider diagrams such as those below.)

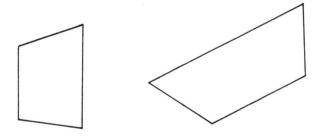

The area of the trapezium ABCD can also be found by dividing the trapezium into a parallelogram and a triangle.

Discuss how this could be done.

3. **Discuss** the relationship between the area of the kite and the area of the rectangle surrounding the kite.
   Discuss the relationship between the area of the kite and the length of the diagonals.

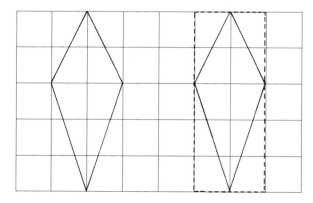

Area of parallelogram = base × height.

In these diagrams, $\boxed{\mathbf{A = bh}}$

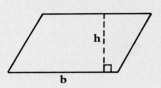
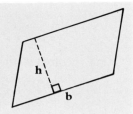

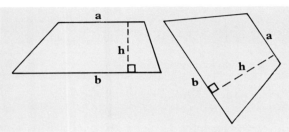

Area of trapezium = half the sum of the parallel sides × height, where the height is the perpendicular distance between the parallel sides.

In these diagrams, $\boxed{\mathbf{A = \frac{1}{2}\,(a + b) \times h}}$

Area of kite = half the product of the diagonals.

In this diagram, $\boxed{\mathbf{A = \frac{1}{2}\,ab}}$

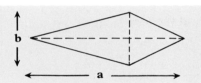

Examples

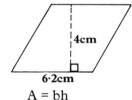

A = bh
   = 6·2 × 4
   = 24·8cm²

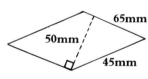

A = bh
   = 65 × 50
   = 3250mm²

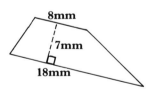

$A = \frac{1}{2}\,(a + b) \times h$
   $= \frac{1}{2}\,(8 + 18) \times 7$
   = 91mm²

Worked Example   The area of a kite is 38cm². The length of the longer diagonal is 20cm. What length is the shorter diagonal?

Answer   Using $A = \frac{1}{2}\,ab$, $38 = \frac{1}{2} \times 20 \times b$
                              38 = 10b
                              b = 3·8cm

EXERCISE 15:7

1. Find the area of these parallelograms.

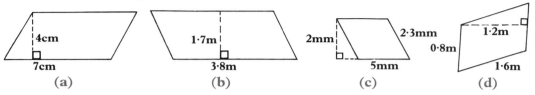

   (a)   (b)   (c)   (d)

2. The area of a parallelogram is 20cm². The base is 16cm.
   What is the height of this parallelogram?

3. Even without measurements written on this diagram, we know that the areas of the
   shaded figures are equal. How do we know?

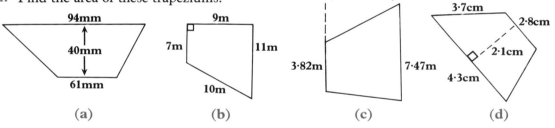

4. Find the area of these trapeziums.

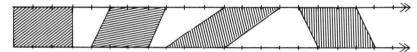

   (a)   (b)   (c)   (d)

5. Find the area of a kite with diagonals 7·3cm and 4·8cm.

6.

   30cm

   h

   20cm

   The area of this shape is 150cm².
   Find h.

7. This shows the cross-section of a swimming pool.
   What is the area of this cross section?

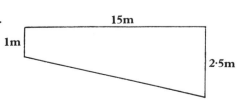

   15m

   1m

   2·5m

8. In each of the following, find the value of **x**. (**Hint:** You will need to use the Theorem of Pythagoras.) Hence find the area of each trapezium.

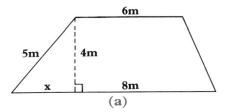

(a)

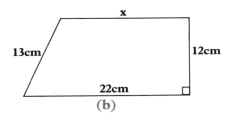

(b)

9.

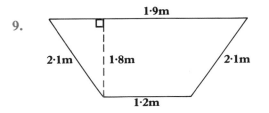

David drew this sketch of the end of a railway wagon. He measured the wagon and wrote the measurements on his sketch.
Show that the 1·8m dimension is not possible.

Review 1 Find the area of these.

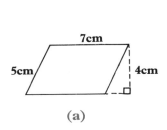

(a)

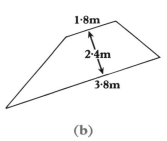

(b)

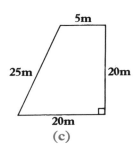

(c)

Review 2

This diagram represents an end wall of a shed. The area of this wall is 26·4m².
What is the length of the wall?

Review 3 (a) Find the value of x.
(b) Find the area of the kite.

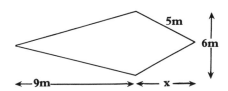

INVESTIGATION 15:8

PICK'S RULE

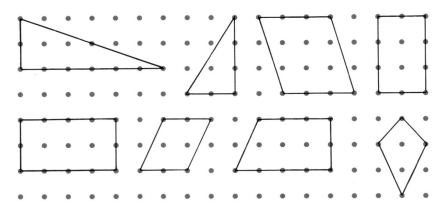

When a shape is drawn on "square dot" paper, there is a relationship between the area of the shape and the number of dots on the perimeter and in the interior of the shape. **Investigate** to find this relationship. You could begin your investigation by calculating the area of each of the shapes drawn above (take the horizontal or vertical distance between adjacent dots to be 1 unit).

You could continue your investigation by predicting the area of other shapes drawn on "square dot" paper.

What if there are no dots inside the shape?
What if there are no dots on the perimeter?
What if . . .

LAND AREAS

Common metric units for land area are the **hectare** (ha) and **square kilometre** (km²). The hectare is derived from the unit of land measure, the **are**.

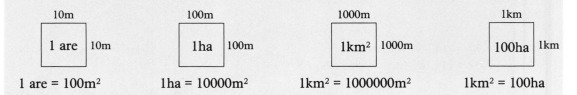

Some small land areas, such as building plots, are measured in m².

Worked Example   A park is a rectangular shape, 1560m long and 800m wide. Find the area of this park in hectares.

Answer   Using A = lb, area of park = 1560 × 800m²
$$= 1248000m²$$
$$= \frac{1248000}{10000} \text{ ha}$$
$$= 124·8ha$$

The **acre** is an imperial unit used for land areas. The approximate relationship between acres and hectares is **1 ha = 2·5 acres**.

Worked Example   Lyndale school has grounds of 8 acres.
About how many hectares is this?

Answer   8 acres = $\frac{8}{2·5}$ ha
$$= 3·2ha$$

EXERCISE 15:9

1.

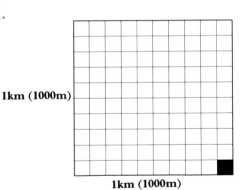

1km (1000m)

1km (1000m)

Are these statements true or false?
(a) The whole figure has an area of 1km².
(b) The whole figure has an area of 1000000m².
(c) The shaded square has an area of 10000m².
(d) The shaded square has an area of 1ha.
(e) The whole figure has an area of 100ha.

2. Write these land areas in hectares.
   (a) 4km²   (b) 8·2km²   (c) 20000m²   (d) 145600m²   (e) 0·4km²
   (f) 81·6km²   (g) 2340m²

3. Find the area of these in hectares.
   (a)
   180m
   200m

   (b)
   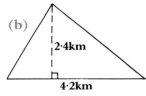
   2·4km
   4·2km

   (c)
   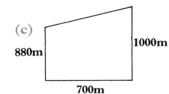
   880m
   1000m
   700m

193

4. A farm is 180ha. How many square metres is this? How many square kilometres is this? About how many acres is this?

5.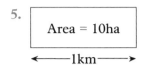

   This is a sketch of a rectangular park. How many metres wide is this park?

6.

   Each square has a length of 50m.
   (a) What is the area of each square?
   (b) How many squares make 1 hectare?
   (c) By counting squares, find the area of land sketched. (Give your answer to the nearest hectare.)

7. Which of the units of area in the box are the following most likely to be measured in?

   | m² | ha | km² |

   (a) a farm   (b) a county   (c) a sports ground
   (d) a large city   (e) a village   (f) the grounds of a church

8. Find the missing numbers.
   (a) 4ha = · · · acres   (b) 5·6 ha = · · · acres   (c) 20 acres = · · · ha
   (d) 345 acres = · · · ha

Review 1   A rectangular piece of land is 200m wide. Its area is 1ha. How long is it?

Review 2   Write these land areas in hectares.
   (a) 5km²   (b) 5000m²   (c) 50000m²   (d) 5 acres

PRACTICAL EXERCISE 15:10

Take measurements to calculate the area of either the school grounds or a local park. You could use the method outlined in **question 6** of the previous exercise if the area is an irregular shape, or you could divide the area up into a number of regular shapes.

SOLIDS of CONSTANT CROSS-SECTIONAL AREA

INVESTIGATIONS 15:11

COUNTING CUBES

1.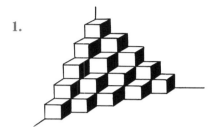

   How many cubes are in this corner?
   Investigate other symmetrical arrangements of these cubes.

2. A large cube is made from 27 small cubes. Once the large cube is assembled, all of its faces are painted.
   Investigate the number of faces of the small cubes that are painted.
   What if the large cube was made from 64 small cubes?
   What if the large cube was made from 125 small cubes?
   What if . . .

Remember :   Volume of cuboid   = $l$bh
              Volume of cylinder = $\pi r^2 h$

DISCUSSION EXERCISE 15:12

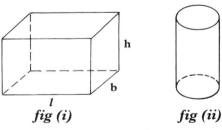

fig (i)   *fig (ii)*

What shape is a horizontal cross-section of *fig (i)*?
What is the area of a horizontal cross-section of *fig (i)*?
How could the volume of *fig (i)* be found if we were not given l and b? What would we need to be given instead? **Discuss.**

The volumes of *fig (i)* and *fig (ii)* can be found from the same formula. **Discuss** a possible formula.

Would the formula that enabled you to find the volume of *fig (i)* and *fig (ii)* also enable you to find the volume of the shapes given below? Discuss.

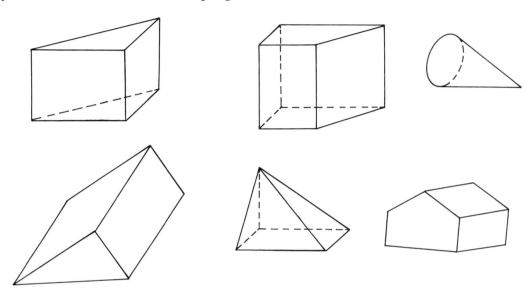

A **prism** has a pair of congruent and parallel opposite faces.
A **cuboid** is a prism with rectangular faces.
A **cylinder** has a pair of congruent and parallel circular faces.

A prism has constant cross-sectional area. Any cross-section, which is parallel to the congruent faces, is also congruent with these faces.

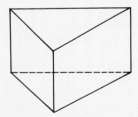
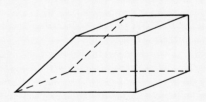
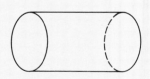

Prism – the top and bottom faces are congruent and parallel.

Prism – the front and back faces are congruent and parallel.

Cylinder – the end faces are congruent and parallel.

> **Volume of prism or cylinder = area of cross-section × length,** where the cross-section is parallel to the congruent faces.

Worked Example   Find the volume of these solid shapes.

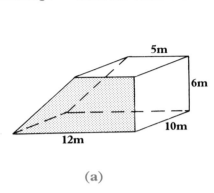

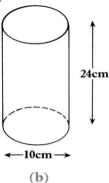

24cm

←—10cm—→

(a)   (b)

Answer   (a) The cross-section is a trapezium; the length is 10m.

Using A = $\frac{1}{2}$ (a + b) × h, Area of trapezium = $\frac{1}{2}$ (12 + 5) × 6

= 51m²

Using V = area of cross-section × length, Volume of prism = 51 × 10

= 510 m³

(b) The cross-section is a circle, the length is 24cm.

Using A = πr², Area of circle = 3·14 × 5² (taking π = 3·14)

= 78·5cm²

Using V = area of cross-section × length, Volume of cylinder = 78·5 × 24

= 1884cm³

Remember :   1ml = 1cm³ and 1l = 1000 ml

1cm³ is sometimes written as 1c.c. and sometimes as 1 cubic cm.

Worked Example   A circular spa pool has the following dimensions : diameter 2 metres, depth 1·3 metres.

How many litres of water does this pool hold if it is filled to within 20cm of the top? (Use π = 3·14.)

Answer   We will convert the dimensions to cm, then find the amount of water in ml, then convert to litres.

Diameter = 200cm, depth = 130cm

Depth of water = 130 – 20cm

= 110cm

Area of cross-section = 3·14 × 100² cm²

= 31400cm²

Volume filled with water = 31400 × 110cm³

= 3454000cm³

Amount of water = 3454000ml

= 3454l

EXERCISE 15:13

Use π = 3·14. Round your answers sensibly if rounding is necessary.

1. Find the volume of these shapes.

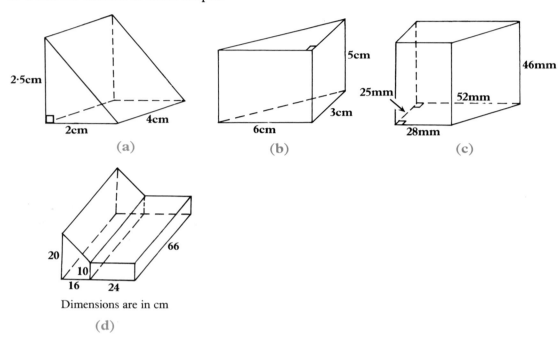

Dimensions are in cm

(d)

2.

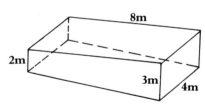

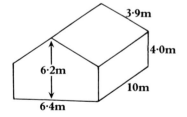

The diagram on the left represents a swimming pool. The diagram on the right represents a shed.
Find the volume of each of these.

3. These tins are filled with beans. Which tin holds more beans?

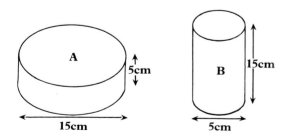

4.

24cm

16cm

←14cm→

A shape which is 10cm long has ends shaped as shown in the diagram. Find its volume.

5. Workmen are digging a ditch which is to be 30 metres long and 1·25m deep. The cross-section is a symmetrical trapezium, as shown in the diagram. The ditch must be 1·5m wide at the bottom and 2·5m wide at the top.
   (a) What are the values of a, b, and c on the cross-section?
   (b) Find the area of the cross-section.
   (c) Calculate how many cubic metres of dirt are to be excavated from the ditch.

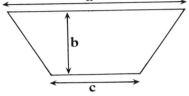

a

b

c

The workmen use an excavator and the dirt is taken away in lorries that can take 12m³ at a time.
   (d) How many full loads of dirt are taken away?
   (e) The last lorry is only partially filled up. What fraction of a full load does the last lorry take?

6. A partly filled lemonade bottle, of diameter 8cm, contains lemonade to a depth of 14cm. This lemonade is poured into ice-cube moulds each of which is a cube of side 3cm. How many of these ice-cube moulds can be completely filled?

7. A cylindrical bucket of radius 30cm and height 40cm is used to fill the trough shown with water. Find the least number of times the bucket will need to be filled and emptied into the trough.

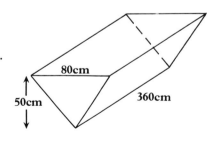

80cm

50cm

360cm

8.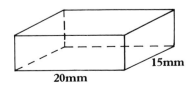

20mm

15mm

5 old coins of diameter 20mm and thickness 2mm are melted down. The metal is then poured into the illustrated box. How deep is the metal in this box? (Answer to the nearest mm.)

9. This diagram represents a swimming pool. How much water is in the pool if the water comes to within 20cm of the top?

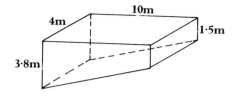

10. Jam jars of diameter 6·4cm and height 10·5cm are used as containers in which to freeze some left-over soup. 2cm "head-room" must be left to allow for expansion on freezing. How many of these jars will be needed to freeze 2*l* of soup?

11. 400m*l* of tomato sauce is in a cylindrical bottle of internal diameter 65mm. How deep is the sauce?

Review 1   Find the volume of these shapes.

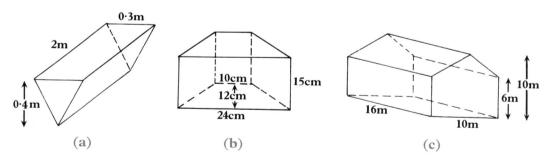

(a)   (b)   (c)

Review 2

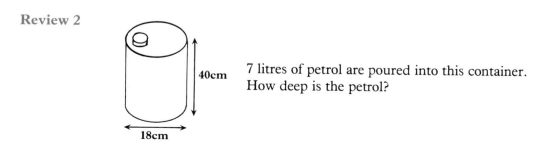

7 litres of petrol are poured into this container. How deep is the petrol?

DISCUSSION EXERCISE 15:14

List the steps you would take to solve each of the following problems. Discuss.

1. Water is poured into this horse trough at a steady rate of 10*l* per minute. How many hours does it take to fill?

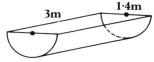

2. A shower tray is a square of side 1·4m. It is 100mm deep. Avaline turned the shower on, then went to do something else while the water was warming up. Unfortunately the shower drain was blocked. When Avaline got back to her shower, the shower tray had just begun to overflow. If the water was running into the shower at the rate of 20 litres per minute, how long was Avaline away?

3. The outlet from the kitchen sink was blocked. Kathy decided to find out how far down the pipe the blockage was by pouring in water until no more would go down the plughole. She was able to pour in 1200m*l* of water. She then put a tape measure around the pipe and found its circumference to be 13·5cm. From these two measurements, Kathy calculated how far down the blockage was.

INVESTIGATION 15:15

MAKING BOXES

fig (i)   *fig (ii)*   *fig (iii)*

Cut squares from the corners of a 240mm × 240mm piece of paper; see *fig (i)* and *fig (ii)*. Fold to make a box without a lid; see *fig (iii)*.
Investigate to find the box with the greatest volume.

What if you began with a 210mm × 210mm piece of paper?
What if you began with a 300mm × 300mm piece of paper?
What if . . .

Investigate to find relationships such as the relationship between the height of the box with the greatest volume and the length of the original piece of paper.

What if you began with a rectangular piece of paper instead of a square piece?
Investigate.

MATHEMATICAL ENLARGEMENT

In mathematics, the term **enlargement** is used for an enlargement or a reduction. In an enlargement, all lengths are enlarged (or reduced) in the same ratio. This ratio is called the **scale factor** of the enlargement.

DISCUSSION EXERCISE 16:1

a painting of a ship
a photograph of the school
a grain of sand viewed through a microscope
a 4″ × 6″ photo enlarged to 10″ × 12″
a 4″ × 6″ photo enlarged to 20″ × 30″
a model aeroplane
a map of a town centre
an ordnance survey map
the shadow of a person
a microfilm of the page of a book
a globe

Which of the above would be enlargements in the mathematical sense? **Discuss**. For those that are, **discuss** likely scale factors.

Discuss other examples of enlargement in everyday life. Estimate scale factors for each of these.

If the scale factor is greater than 1, the image is larger than the original. For instance, if the scale factor is 2, each length on the image is twice as long as the corresponding length on the original.
This diagram shows the shaded shape enlarged by a scale factor of 2.

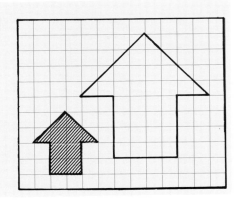

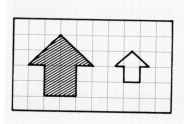 If the scale factor is less than 1, the image is smaller than the original. For instance, if the scale factor is $\frac{1}{2}$, each length on the image is half as long as the corresponding length on the original.

This diagram shows the shaded shape enlarged by a scale factor of $\frac{1}{2}$.

DRAWING ENLARGEMENTS which have a FRACTIONAL SCALE FACTOR

To **draw an enlargement**, using the ray method, we need to know both the scale factor and the centre of enlargement.

Worked Example   Enlarge the shape ABCD by a scale factor of $\frac{1}{3}$, with P as the centre of enlargement.

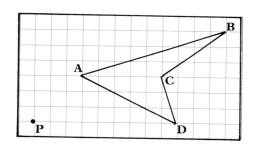

Answer   Join P to each of A, B, C and D.

Locate the positions of A′, B′, C′ and D′ by using
$PA' = \frac{1}{3} PA$, $PB' = \frac{1}{3} PB$, $PC' = \frac{1}{3} PC$, $PD' = \frac{1}{3} PD$.

The points A′, B′, C′, D′ and the completed image shape are shown below.

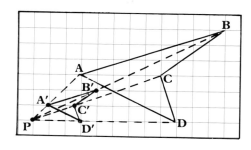

EXERCISE 16:2

1.

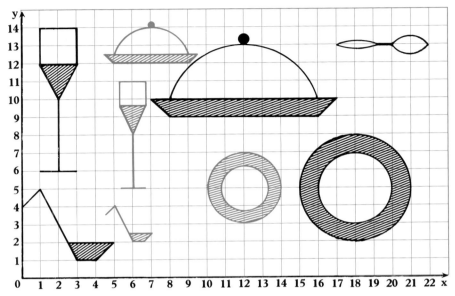

Each of the grey shapes has been enlarged to a red shape. State the scale factors for each of these enlargements.

2. Locate the centre of enlargement for each of the enlargements in **question 1**.
   Write down the coordinates of each of these centres of enlargement.

3. Copy each of the following diagrams.
   Enlarge each shape, centre P, by the given scale factor.
   Give the coordinates of the vertices of the image shapes.

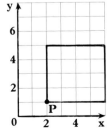

(a) Scale factor $\frac{1}{4}$

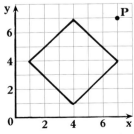

(b) Scale factor $\frac{2}{3}$

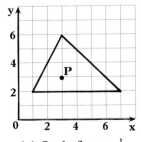

(c) Scale factor $\frac{1}{2}$

4. Draw each of the following rectangles.
   Using (2, 3) as the centre of enlargement, enlarge each by the given scale factor.
   Give the coordinates of the vertices of the image shapes.

   (a) A (2, 3),   B (5, 3),   C (5, –3),   D (2, –3)   scale factor $\frac{1}{3}$

   (b) E (–4, 5),   F (4, 5),   G (4, 1),   H (–4, 1)   scale factor $\frac{1}{2}$

   (c) I (2, 0),   J (2, –3),   K (–4, –3),   L (–4, 0)   scale factor $\frac{2}{3}$

   (d) M (7, 3),   N (7, –2),   O (–3, –2),   P (–3, 3)   scale factor $\frac{3}{5}$

   (e) Q (0, 1),   R (0, 7),   S (6, 7),   T (6, 1)   scale factor $\frac{1}{2}$

   (f) U (6, 3),   V (6, –1),   W (–2, –1),   X (–2, 3)   scale factor $\frac{1}{4}$

Copy these designs.
Enlarge by the given scale factor. Choose the centre of enlargement you will use.

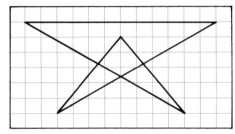

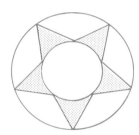

Scale factor $\frac{3}{4}$ Scale factor $\frac{4}{5}$

6. Draw each of the following triangles and the image triangles.
   Locate the centre of enlargement for each.
   State the scale factor of each enlargement.
   (a) A (2, 2),   B (12, 6),   C (12, 2).   A′ (1, 1),   B′ (6, 3),   C′ (6, 1).
   (b) P (–4, 0),   Q (2, 3),   R (2, 0).   P′ (–2, –2), Q′ (0, –1), R′ (0, –2).
   (c) X (–1, –1),   Y (3, –1),   Z (3, 1).   X′ (0, 1),   Y′ (2, 1),   Z′ (2, 2).
   (d) L (6, –1),   M (3, 2),   N (0, –1).   L′ (3, –1),   M′ (1, 1),   N′ (–1, –1).

Review 1   A (–5, 3)   B (3, 3)   C (3, –1)   D (–5, –1)
             Draw the rectangle ABCD. Draw each of the following enlargements.
             Give the coordinates of A′, B′, C′, D′.
                (a) centre of enlargement A, scale factor $\frac{1}{2}$
                (b) centre of enlargement (–1, 1), scale factor $\frac{1}{2}$
                (c) centre of enlargement (7, 7), scale factor $\frac{3}{4}$

Review 2

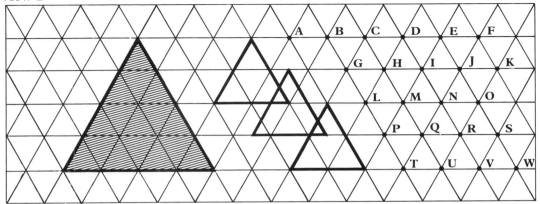

The shaded triangle has been enlarged to each of the small triangles.
What is the scale factor for these enlargements?
Name the centre of each enlargement.

CALCULATIONS involving FRACTIONAL SCALE FACTORS

If k is the scale factor of an enlargement, each length on the image is k times as long as the corresponding length on the original.

That is,

$$\frac{\text{Length on image}}{\text{Corresponding length on original}} = k$$

Worked Example P′ is an enlargement of P.
  (a) What is the scale factor?
  (b) Find the length of x.

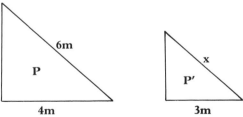

These diagrams are not drawn to scale.

Answer (a) $k = \dfrac{\text{length on image}}{\text{corresponding length on original}}$

  $= \dfrac{3}{4}$

  (b) $\dfrac{\text{length on image}}{\text{corresponding length on original}} = k$

  $\dfrac{x}{6} = \dfrac{3}{4}$

  x = 4·5m (multiplying both sides by 6)

EXERCISE 16:3

The diagrams in this exercise are not drawn to scale.

1. In each of the following, shape P is enlarged by a fractional scale factor to shape Q.
   Find the scale factor, k, for each enlargement.
   Find the value of x.

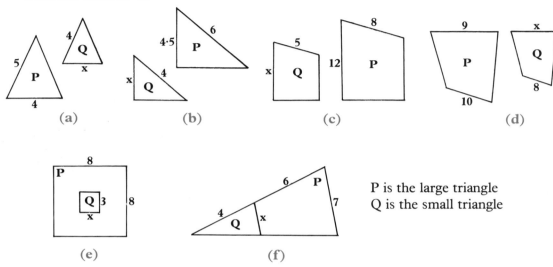

(a)   (b)   (c)   (d)

(e)   (f)   P is the large triangle
          Q is the small triangle

2. A map, which is 24cm wide, is reduced to $\frac{3}{4}$ of the original size.

   How wide is the reduced map?

3. The design on a hardcover book is to be used on the paperback version. To do this, the design is reduced to $\frac{3}{5}$ of its original size.

   How high will the design be on the paperback cover if it is 18cm high on the hardcover?

4. This diagram is reduced on a photocopier to $\frac{2}{3}$ of its original size.

   If the height of the original diagram is 156mm, how high will the reduced diagram be?

Review 1 In each of the following, shape A is enlarged to shape B.
Find the scale factor for each enlargement.
Find the value of x.

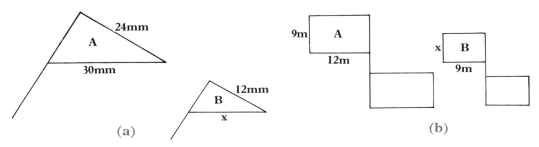

(a)

(b)

Review 2 This photo is to be reduced so that the 40cm
length becomes 16cm.
Give the dimensions of this smaller photo.

25cm

40cm

INVESTIGATIONS 16:4

SHAPES and PLACES

1.

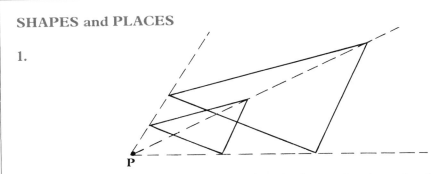

P

The small triangle has been enlarged to the large triangle under the enlargement
described by : scale factor 2, centre of enlargement P.
How would you describe the enlargement of the large triangle to the small
triangle?
This can be thought of as a "double" enlargement; the first enlargement being from
the small triangle to the large triangle and the second enlargement being from the
large triangle to the small triangle.
Investigate other "double" enlargements where the scale factor of the second
enlargement is the reciprocal of the scale factor of the first enlargement.
What if a different centre of enlargement was used for each part of the "double"
enlargement?

continued . . .

. . . *from previous page*

2. Make and test statements about the position of the image shape relative to the original shape and the centre of enlargement for enlargements with various scale factors. Be sure to include scale factors of 2, $\frac{1}{2}$, –2, $-\frac{1}{2}$, 1, –1, 1·5, –1·5, $\frac{2}{3}$, $-\frac{2}{3}$ in your investigation.

PRACTICAL EXERCISE 16:5

Draw a large shape or simple design on a piece of loose paper.
Make a number of enlargements of this shape, all with the same fractional scale factor.
Choose the centres of enlargement so that the completed design is pleasing to the eye.

You may prefer to use the same centre of enlargement and different scale factors.

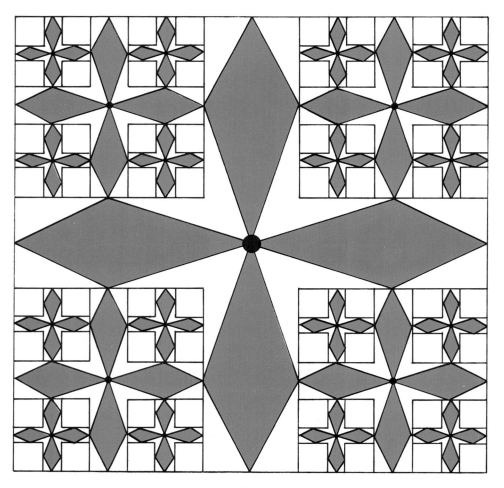

DATA HANDLING

Data Handling
from Previous Levels

Types of Data

Discrete data can take only particular values, usually whole numbers.
Continuous data can take any value within a given range.
For instance, size of shoes is discrete data ; length of shoes is continuous data.

Tables, Charts, Graphs

This **bar chart** or **bar graph** shows the number of hours of sunshine on each of the days of one week.
On Monday there were 3 hours of sunshine, on Tuesday 4 hours, on Wednesday 4 hours, on Thursday 3 hours, on Friday 8 hours, on Saturday 6 hours and on Sunday 5 hours.

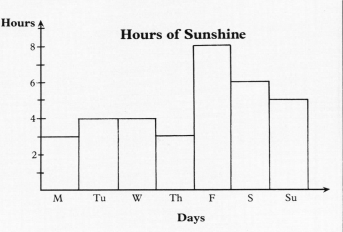

Hours of Sunshine

27 29 28 28 30 29 27 27 29 28
29 27 30 29 28 27 28 29 29 27

The figures in the above list give the number of biscuits in 20 packets. These figures are summarised on the **tally chart**.
On the tally chart, a stroke is entered as each figure is recorded (a diagonal stroke is used for every 5th entry in a category).
Once all the figures have been recorded, the strokes in each category are added to get the frequency. Because this tally chart also includes the frequency it can also be called a **frequency table**. Tally charts are often used as **observation sheets**.

Biscuits Tally Chart

Number	Tally	Frequency
27	⦀⦀	6
28	⦀⦀	5
29	⦀⦀ ‖	7
30	‖	2

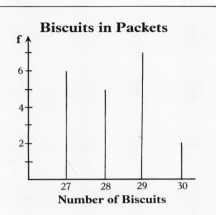

Biscuits in Packets

The data on the previous tally chart is graphed on this **bar-line graph**.

f stands for frequency.

Frequency is always graphed on the vertical axis.

The following figures give the number of times the letter e appears in each sentence on the last page of "The Clan of the Cave Bear".

1 2 2 1 6 10 2 8 3 3 5 5 3 1
6 7 3 9 3 4 5 2 4 9 11 15 0 8
This discrete data has been **grouped** into 6 categories on the combined tally chart and frequency table.

Notice that each category is of the same **width**. The first column on the table (Number of e's) could also be labelled **"class interval"**
When we group data, we should have between 6 and 15 class intervals.

e's Frequency Table

Number of e's	Tally	Frequency
0–2	𝗜𝗜𝗜𝗜 𝗜𝗜𝗜	8
3–5	𝗜𝗜𝗜𝗜 𝗜𝗜𝗜𝗜	10
6–8	𝗜𝗜𝗜𝗜	5
9–11	𝗜𝗜𝗜𝗜	4
12–14		0
15–17	𝗜	1

The information on the above tally chart is graphed on this **frequency diagram**.

This type of graph is often called a **histogram**.

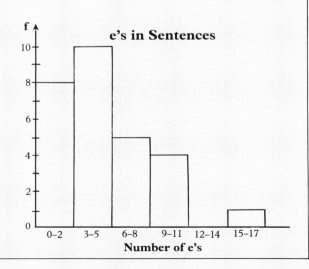

e's in Sentences

Sports Pictogram

This **pictogram** shows the number of schools competing in a sports competition.

9 are competing in Football.
6 are competing in Hockey.
5 are competing in Badminton.

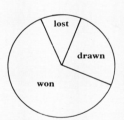

Pie Charts are circle graphs.
The circle is divided into sections.
The number of degrees in the angle at the centre of each section represents the frequency.

Hockey Matches
Won   3
Lost   15
Drawn   6

Length of throw (m)	frequency
$0 \leq l < 5$	1
$5 \leq l < 10$	2
$10 \leq l < 15$	7
$15 \leq l < 20$	5
$20 \leq l < 25$	3
$25 \leq l < 30$	2

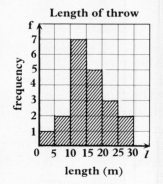

The continuous data from the table is graphed on the histogram.

During Jane's first 12 hours in hospital her temperature was taken at 4–hourly intervals.

At 8 a.m. it was 37°C, at Noon it was 38°C, at 4 p.m. it was 37·5°C and at 8 p.m. it was 37·8°C.

This **line graph** shows these temperatures. It was drawn by plotting the temperatures at 8 a.m., Noon, 4 p.m., 8 p.m. and joining the points with straight lines.

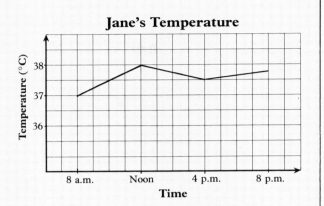

A **conversion graph** is a line graph which shows the relationship between two different units of measurement. Conversion graphs may be drawn to convert kilometres to miles, ounces to grams, °F to °C, litres to gallons, $U.S. to £ sterling etc.

A **scatter graph** displays two aspects of data. For instance, both the length and weight of dogs could be displayed on a scatter graph. A scatter graph is sometimes called a **scatter diagram** or a **scattergram**.

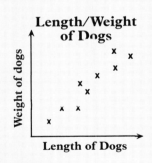
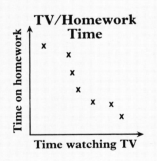
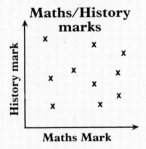

The word **correlation** is used to describe relationships between the variables on a scatter graph.
For **positive correlation** the points must be clustered around a line that slopes upwards. The scatter graph for Length/Weight of dogs shows positive correlation.
For **negative correlation** the points must be clustered around a line that slopes downwards. The scatter graph for TV/Homework time shows negative correlation.
If there is neither positive nor negative correlation, as in the scatter graph for Maths/History marks, we say there is **no correlation**.

Two-way tables are tables which display two aspects of data. On a two-way table, the total of all the columns is equal to the total of all the rows. The following table is a two-way table.

Year \ Sport	Cricket	Athletics	Tennis	Swimming	Totals
Year 7	14	35	52	18	119
Year 8	26	26	48	21	121
Year 9	34	22	25	32	113
Year 10	19	18	19	24	80
Year 11	21	15	34	17	87
Totals	114	116	178	112	520

A **Carroll diagram,** such as that shown, is a type of two-way table.

May Weather

8	2	cold
5	16	mild
raining	not raining	

Networks can be used to display data, especially data relating to routes and distances. The network shown gives the distances in kilometres.

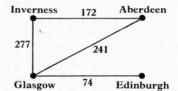

Mean and range

The mean and range are used to help describe a set of data or to make comparisons between sets of data.

The **range** of a list of data is the difference between the greatest and smallest data values. For instance, the range of 3, 2, 6, 2, 5, 3, 7 is $7 - 2 = 5$.

The **mean** is often called the **average**. Mean $= \dfrac{\text{Sum of all the data}}{\text{Number of items of data}}$

For instance, the mean of 3, 2, 6, 2, 5, 3, 7 is $\dfrac{3+2+6+2+5+3+7}{7} = 4$.

Probability

The probability of an event that is certain to happen is 1.
The probability of an event that will never happen is 0.
The probability of any other event is between 0 and 1.

0		0·5		1
No chance	Poor chance	Even chance	Good chance	Certain

Choosing at **random** means every item has the same chance of being chosen.
Equally likely outcomes are outcomes which have the same probability of
occurring. For instance, when a coin is tossed the outcomes "a head", "a tail" are
equally likely ; each of these outcomes has probability of $\frac{1}{2}$.

Exhaustive events account for all possible outcomes. If events are exhaustive, it is
certain that one of them will happen. For instance, when a die is thrown the events
"an odd number", "an even number" are exhaustive events.
The **probability of an event not happening** is equal to $1 - P(E)$, where $P(E)$ is
the probability of the event happening. For instance, when a card is chosen at
random from a pack the probability of getting the Jack of spades = $\frac{1}{52}$; the
probability of not getting the Jack of spades = $\frac{51}{52}$.

The probability of an event may be calculated if all the possible outcomes are equally
likely.
For equally likely outcomes,

$$P(\text{an event occurring}) = \frac{\text{Number of favourable outcomes}}{\text{Number of possible outcomes}}$$

For instance, the probability of getting a prime number when a die is tossed is
calculated as follows.
   Possible equally likely outcomes are 1, 2, 3, 4, 5, 6. Number of possible outcomes = 6.
   Favourable outcomes are 2, 3, 5. Number of favourable outcomes = 3.

   $P(\text{prime number}) = \frac{3}{6}$ or $\frac{1}{2}$.

Outcomes may be given as a **list,** in a **table** or in a **diagram**. For instance, the
possible equally likely outcomes when two coins are tossed could be shown in any of
the ways below.

Table:

1st coin ＼ 2nd coin	H	T
H	HH	HT
T	TH	TT

List: HH HT TH TT

Diagram:

1st coin	2nd coin	Possible outcome
H	H	HH
	T	HT
T	H	TH
	T	TT

Probability may be estimated from experiments.

$$P(\text{an event occurring}) = \frac{\text{Number of times the event occurs}}{\text{Number of trials}}$$

For instance, if a drawing pin is dropped a number of times,

$$P(\text{drawing pin landing on its side}) = \frac{\text{Number of times drawing pin landed on its side}}{\text{Number of times drawing pin was dropped}}$$

The **expected number** of times an event will occur is equal to the product of the number of trials and the probability of the event occurring in any one trial.

For instance, if a die is tossed the probability of getting a "six" is $\frac{1}{6}$; the expected number of "sixes" obtained when a die is tossed 120 times is $120 \times \frac{1}{6}$ or 20.

Surveys

The steps taken to **conduct a survey** are:
Step 1 **Decide** on the purpose of the survey.
Step 2 **Design** an observation sheet or a questionnaire.
Step 3 **Collect** the data. If necessary, collate the data.
Step 4 **Organize** the data onto tables and graphs or into a computer database.
Step 5 **Analyse** the data i.e. write some conclusions.

Some **guidelines for designing and using an observation sheet** are:
- Draw up the observation sheet after deciding which categories will be needed.
- Make some initial decisions about the way the collected data will be organized and analysed.
- Decide where and when to collect the data.
- Do not attempt to record too many details at the same time.

Some **guidelines for designing a questionnaire** are:
- Decide how the collected data is to be collated and analysed.
- Allow for *all* possible answers.
- Give clear instructions on how the questions are to be answered.
- Do not ask for information that is not needed.
- Avoid questions which people may not be willing to answer.
- Make the questions clear and concise.
- If your questions are asking for opinions, word them so that *your* opinion is not evident.
- Keep the questionnaire as short as possible.

REVISION EXERCISE

1. This table gives the quantity of apples (to the nearest tonne) produced by five neighbouring orchards.

   Draw a pictogram to illustrate this data. Use the following (or a similar) key:

   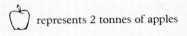 represents 2 tonnes of apples

Orchard	Tonnes
Applefields	12
Gardenways	8
J and B Apples	11
Sunvalley	10
Outram	6

2. The following scores (out of 20) were given to the 29 dogs entered in one category of an agricultural fair.

   17 15 13 16 17 14 11 13 16 17 18   8 13 16 14
   16 11 12 15   8 14 14 12 15 17 11 13 10 10

   (a) What was the average score given to these dogs? (Answer to 3s.f.)
   (b) What is the range of the scores?
   (c) Draw a bar-line graph to illustrate the data.

3.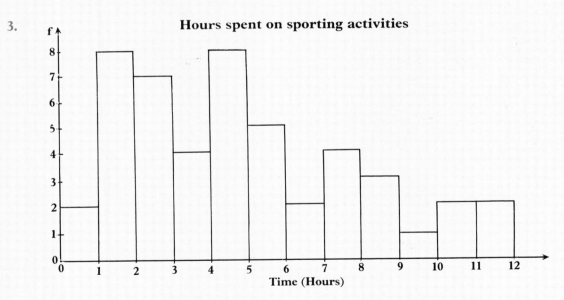

   Hours spent on sporting activities

   This histogram shows the time a number of students spent on sporting activities during one Bank Holiday weekend.
   (a) How many students spent less than one hour on sporting activities?
   (b) How many students spent less than 4 hours on these activities?
   (c) Can you tell from this graph how many students spent 8 hours on sporting activities?
   (d) How many students are represented on this graph?
   (e) What percentage of students, represented on the graph, spent less than 8 hours on sporting activities?

225

4. **Event A** : a head when a coin is tossed
   Event B : a number greater than 6 when a die is thrown
   Event C : a total of less than 13 when two dice are thrown together
   Event D : a red card when one card is drawn from a full 52-card pack
   Event E : an odd number when a die is tossed

   Which of the above events have (a) probability of 1 of occurring
   (b) probability of 0 of occurring
   (c) an even chance of occurring

5. The following data gives the number of days absent from school, during the winter term, of the Year 10 students at Bromley School.

Number of Days	Tally	f
0–4		
5–9		
10–14		
15–19		
20–24		
25–29		
30–34		
35–39		

   ```
   15   6  11   9  24   0   3   8  17  14   0
    2   3   5   7   8  12  29  17   6   0   0
   10  12   5   7   1   3  31  18   4   2   0
    1   7  11   2   3   0   5   9  29   0  36
    4   7   3   5  13   0  21   1   3   4   5
   16   0   2   5  10  20   9   1  10   3   4
    0   5  12  13   5   0   0   3   4   1   0
   21   1   0   3   9  14   1
   ```

   (a) Copy and complete the tally chart and frequency table.
   (b) Draw a histogram for the data.

6. Design a questionnaire to survey opinion on an issue of interest to you.
   You could choose a sporting issue, a schooling issue, a community issue or some other issue.

7. Which of the following data is discrete and which is continuous?
   Year of Birth   Waist Measurements   Time Spent Watching T.V.
   Length of Babies   Size of Families

8. It is estimated that the probability of a student having brown eyes is 0·21.
   (a) What is the probability of a student's eyes being a colour other than brown?
   (b) Of 500 students, how many would you expect to have brown eyes?

9.

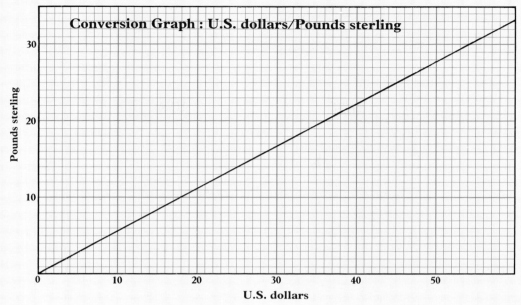

Conversion Graph : U.S. dollars/Pounds sterling

Use this conversion graph to answer the following questions.
  (a) How many U.S. dollars can be bought for £20?
  (b) What amount of U.S. currency can be bought for £100?
  (c) Erina returned from a holiday abroad with $45 U.S. She exchanged this for British currency. How much did she get?

10.

Population in Bayfield

Age Group	Female	Male	Totals
0–4	2022	2314	
5–9	2028	1999	
10–14	2136	2241	
15–19	3041	3019	
20–29	6152	6341	
30–39	5143	5025	
40–49	4149	4317	
50–59	3215	3512	
60 and over	2142	1648	
Totals			

  (a) Copy this table. Complete the totals column and row.
      What figure goes in the shaded box?
  (b) What age group has the largest number of people?
  (c) "Most people in Bayfield are in the 20–29 age group." Is this statement true?

11. A spinner is attached to a card as shown. The spinner is spun.
Find the probability that the spinner comes to rest on
    (a) a shaded region
    (b) an even number
    (c) a multiple of 4
    (d) a one-digit number
    (e) a number containing the digit 1

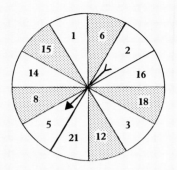

12.

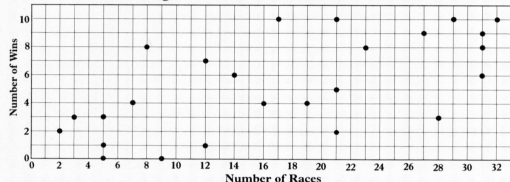

This scatter diagram shows the number of wins and the number of races run by the horses trained by W.X. Tyler.
    (a) How many horses are trained by W.X. Tyler?
    (b) How many wins have these horses had altogether?
    (c) How many races has the horse run that has had 7 wins?
    (d) One of the horses has had 16 runs. How many wins has this horse had?
    (e) How many horses have won all the races in which they have run?
    (f) Is there any evidence of correlation between the number of wins and the number of races run?

13.

Vase Number	1	2	3	4	5	6	7	8	9	10	11	12	13	14
Judge 1	7	5	4	9	6	4	5	6	7	8	7	5	4	6
Judge 2	7	6	4	8	5	5	5	5	7	9	8	5	4	6

This table gives the number of points awarded by each of two judges to the roses in the novice section of a flower show.
    (a) Would you expect there to be positive correlation between the points awarded by these two judges?
    (b) Illustrate the data on a scatter graph. (Put Judge 1 points on the horizontal axis.)
    (c) Does the graph support your answer to (a) ?

14. Two dice are tetrahedrons. Each has the numbers
1, 2, 3, 4 on the faces.
The two dice are thrown together and the numbers
obtained are added together.

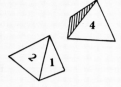

   (a) Copy and complete this table to show all the
possible outcomes.
   (b) Find the probability of getting a total of 5.
   (c) What is the probability of getting at least 5?

		Second die		
	1	**2**	**3**	**4**
1	2	3		
2			5	
3				
4				8

First die

15. Sue wrote each of the letters S, U, E, on counters and placed these in a bag. She
then drew a counter at random, noted the letter written on it and replaced the counter
in the bag. She then drew another counter and noted the letter written on it.

   (a) Copy and complete this diagram for all the possible outcomes.

1st letter	**2nd letter**	**Possible Outcome**
	S	SS
S	U	SU
	E	
	S	
U	U	
	E	
	S	
E	U	
	E	

   (b) Use your answer to (a) to find the probability that Sue drew out two counters with
vowels written on them.

16. A vet. is investigating to see if colour plays any part in cat
health. This list gives the colour of the cats seen by this vet.
during one day of her investigation.

Draw a pie chart to illustrate this data.

Ginger	38
Black	22
Black and White	21
Tortoiseshell	9

17. A coin and a die are thrown together.
    (a) List all the possible outcomes.
    (b) What is the probability of getting a prime number and a tail?

18. Which of the following groups of events are exhaustive? (Each refers to the drawing of a card from a full 52–card pack.)
    Group 1   Event A : a red card   Event B : a black card
    Group 2   Event A : a picture card   Event B : a two   Event C : a five
    Group 3   Event A : a picture card   Event B : not a picture card
    Group 4   Event A : a King   Event B : a Queen   Event C : not a picture card
    Group 5   Event A : a diamond   Event B : a black card   Event C : a red card

19.

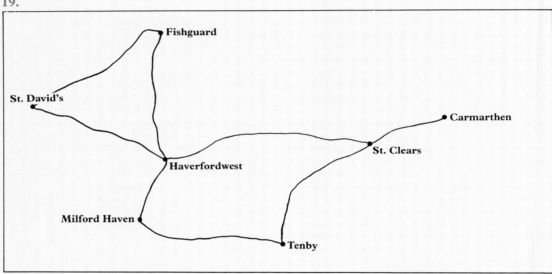

A network is to be drawn showing the roads above.
  (a) Do both the networks drawn below represent these roads?

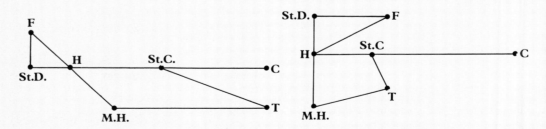

(b) Draw another network to represent these roads.

230

20. Design and conduct a probability experiment to estimate the probability of one of the following:

   the last person into the mathematics classroom tomorrow will be wearing glasses

   the next person you interview about family size will have no brothers.

18   Conducting a Survey to   18
Test an Hypothesis

SURVEYS

DISCUSSION EXERCISE 18:1

Vegetarianism increasing in UK

Almost 30,000 British adults a week are abandoning meat for a vegetarian diet, a survey has found.

Britain now has 3.6 million vegetarians and a further 4.6 million people who avoid red meat but still eat chicken or fish, according to the report commissioned by the Vegetarian Society.

But the findings were dismissed by the Meat and Livestock Commission, the voice of the red meat industry.

It insisted non-meat eaters amounted to a "tiny two per cent" of the population.

The vegetarians released their survey, carried out by Bradford University, at the launch of their first nationwide campaign to recruit adults to a "meat-free lifestyle".

"By cutting meat out of their diet vegetarians are virtually free from the dangers of food poisoning, which affects at least 10,000 people a week," the society said.

Its survey, based on interviews with 942 adults and 2651 11 to 18-year-olds, said the number of vegetarians had virtually doubled over the last year to 7 per cent of the population.

"This works out at 28,000 adults converting to vegetarianism every week over the last 12 months," the society said.

Most vegetarians were in the 16 to 24 and 55 to 64 age groups.

Discuss this article from the newspaper.

Include a discussion on each of the following:
    what the purpose of the survey might have been
    what questions might have been asked
    how the responses might have been collated
    how the responses might have been analysed
    how accurate the results of the survey are likely to be

HYPOTHESES

Surveys may be conducted for a variety of reasons. For instance, a survey on breakfast cereals may be conducted to find people's favourite cereal or a survey may be conducted to test the statement "most people eat porridge for breakfast more often than muesli."

For each of these surveys on breakfast cereals, a questionnaire could be written. The wording of the question, or questions, and the possible responses to the questions would be different in each survey.

In the survey to find people's favourite breakfast cereal, a question and some of the possible responses could be:

What is your favourite cereal?   Cornflakes ☐   Muesli ☐   Porridge ☐

In the survey to test the statement "most people eat porridge more often than muesli," a question and possible responses could be:

Do you eat porridge for breakfast more often than muesli?   Yes ☐   No ☐

The statement "most people eat porridge for breakfast more often than muesli" is an hypothesis.

The word **hypothesis**, used in this way, is a statement of one person's opinion about an issue.

The statements "I believe that the majority of students would like the school day to start later" and "I think that more people would travel by bus if the service was improved" can be rewritten as the following hypotheses (hypotheses is the plural of hypothesis):

"the majority of students would like the school day to start later"

"more people would travel by bus if the service was improved"

DISCUSSION EXERCISE 18:2

Discuss how to word the questions and possible responses on a questionnaire to test the hypothesis "the majority of students would like the school day to begin and finish later." (Your questionnaire should have more than one question.)

Discuss questions and possible responses on a questionnaire to test the hypothesis "more people would travel by bus if the service was improved."

Make other hypotheses.

Discuss questions you may ask to test each hypothesis.

DESIGNING a QUESTIONNAIRE

The design of a questionnaire is most important. Take care with the way in which you word the questions, with the possible responses you include and with the layout of the questionnaire. Some guidelines are given on the next page.

Mean, Median, Mode, Range.
Frequency Tables and Graphs

MEAN, MEDIAN, MODE, RANGE

We often need to summarize and present data in a simplified form. This can be done visually by using tables or graphs. It can also be done by trying to find a single number that represents the data.

The **range** is one such number.
Remember: range = highest data value – lowest data value.
The range gives an idea of how spread out the data values are.

An **average** is another such number. There are three types of averages often used: mean, median and mode. Each of these has advantages and disadvantages.

Remember: mean = $\frac{\text{sum of all data values}}{\text{number of data values}}$. The **mean** is what is commonly called the average.

Hence if you are asked to find the average of a set of data you would find the mean.
For instance, the mean of 1, 2, 4, 6, 10 is $\frac{1+2+4+6+10}{5} = 4 \cdot 6$.

The **mode** is the data value that occurs most frequently.
For instance, the mode of 2, 5, 3, 5, 4, 1 is 5.
A set of data may have more than one mode or no mode.
For instance 2, 5, 3, 4, 1 has no mode; 2, 5, 3, 5, 4, 3 has two modes, both 5 and 3.

The **median** is the middle value of a set of data which is written in increasing (or decreasing) order.
For instance, to find the median of 2, 5, 3, 5, 4, 1, 7 we rewrite the data in order as 1, 2, 3, 4, 5, 5, 7. The median is 4.
If there is an even number of data values, the median is the mean of the middle two values. For instance, the median of 7, 8, 8, 9, 14, 15 is $\frac{8+9}{2} = 8 \cdot 5$.

DISCUSSION EXERCISE 19:1

Which of the mean, the median, the mode would be the most useful in the following situations? **Discuss.**

a photographer arranging people for a photograph
a teacher analysing test marks
a footwear retailer doing a stocktake

Discuss other situations where one of the mean, the median or the mode would be more useful than the others. **Discuss** situations where the mean and the median would be equally useful.

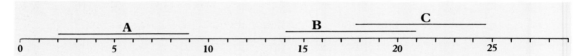

Suppose the range of a set of data is 7. The data values may be in the interval A or the interval B or the interval C or in some other interval.
Although the range gives an idea of how spread out the data is, it gives no idea of where the data is located.
Conversely, an average gives some idea of where the data is located but it gives no idea of how spread out the data is. For instance, the following sets of data all have the same median. Set 1: 2, 3, 15, 16, 16   Set 2: 1, 2, 15, 29, 45   Set 3: 13, 14, 15, 16, 18.

DISCUSSION EXERCISE 19:2

Could a set of data be well described by giving the range and the median? **Discuss.**

Could a set of data be well described by giving just the mean? **Discuss.**

If the range is large, would the median describe the location of the data better than the mean? **Discuss.**
What if the range was small? **Discuss.**

In what situations would the mode and range describe a set of data well? **Discuss.**

The calculator may be used to find the mean of a list of data.

Example   3, 5, 9, 12, 13

To find the mean of this data, key as follows.

MODE ⬚ • ⬚ 3 ⬚×⬚ 5 ⬚×⬚ 9 ⬚×⬚ 12 ⬚×⬚ 13 ⬚×⬚ INV ⬚x̄⬚ to get answer of 8·4.

Notes
- Pressing MODE followed by ⬚•⬚ gets the calculator ready to calculate statistical functions. (SD will appear on the screen.)
- Pressing ⬚×⬚ stores each value input into the memory.
- Pressing INV ⬚x̄⬚ tells the calculator to calculate the mean of the values it has stored in the memory.
- If another mean calculation is to be done before the calculator is turned off, INV followed by SAC must be pressed to clear the memory of earlier values input.
- Pressing INV ⬚n⬚ at any stage, gives the number of values entered. This can be used as a check at the end to ensure all values have been entered.

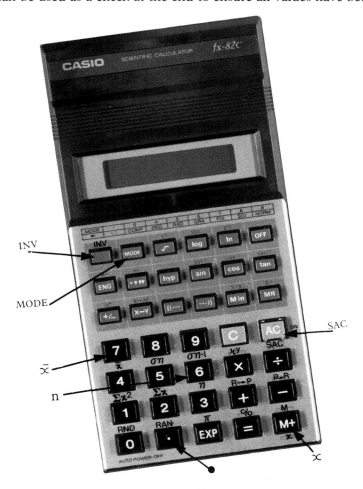

EXERCISE 19:3

Round your answers sensibly when rounding is necessary.

1. Find the mean, the median and the mode of these.
   (a) 3, 3, 4, 5, 6, 7, 7, 7, 8, 8, 9, 11, 13
   (b) 2, 5, 7, 4, 3, 2, 5, 7, 8, 11, 6, 10
   (c) 4·6, 5·1, 5·3, 7·4, 5·9, 6·7, 7·2, 6·8, 5·4, 8·3
   (d) 24, 27, 35, 41, 62, 65, 71, 74, 75, 76, 76, 83, 85, 92
   (e) 0·3, 0·5, 0·2, 0·4, 0·3, 0·1, 0·8, 0·9, 0·7, 0·6
   (f) 1·3, 1·5, 1·2, 1·4, 1·3, 1·1, 1·8, 1·9, 1·7, 1·6

2. Find the range of each of the sets of data in **question 1**.

3. The following data gives the height (in metres) of 11 boys.
   1·60 1·65 1·71 1·72 1·52 1·45 1·60 1·58 1·54 1·67 1·59
   (a) Find the median height.   (b) What is the mode?

4. The following list gives the percentage mark of each student in a class in an Aural Test.
   72   68   74   53   78   49   74   82   94   97
   63   58   75   48   58   68   71   74   57   63
   96   87   73   65   81   97   63   65   64   72
   (a) Find the range, the mean, the median and the mode.
   (b) Use your answers to (a) to make some statements about the data.

Review The rainfall (in mm) at five places, during one week, is given below.

Andover	4	0	5	24	3	0	0
Cardiff	3	0	4	0	16	0	11
Coventry	1	9	7	12	8	2	5
Richmond	0	0	5	18	6	0	8
Stirling	3	5	7	2	4	12	7

Which place had (a) the smallest mean daily rainfall for the week
(b) the greatest range in rainfall
(c) the smallest range in rainfall
(d) the greatest median daily rainfall

Which place do you think had the best climate during the week in which these readings were taken? Make some statements using your answers to the above questions.

ANALYSING DATA from FREQUENCY TABLES

x	1	4	7
f	3	2	5

x takes the values 1, 4 and 7.
1 occurs 3 times, 4 occurs twice, 7 occurs 5 times.

The data given in this frequency table could be listed as 1, 1, 1, 4, 4, 7, 7, 7, 7, 7.

The mean of this data is $\frac{1+1+1+4+4+7+7+7+7+7}{10}$ = 4·6.

Instead of adding each 1, each 4 and each 7 separately we could add together 3 × 1 and 2 × 4 and 5 × 7. That is, the top line of the calculation for the mean could be written as 3 × 1 + 2 × 4 + 5 × 7.

We can get the figure 10 for the bottom line by adding 3 + 2 + 5. (There were 3 lots of 1 added to 2 lots of 4 added to 5 lots of 7 making 10 numbers added together.)

That is, another way of calculating the mean is $\frac{3 \times 1 + 2 \times 4 + 5 \times 7}{3 + 2 + 5}$.

Compare the numbers in this calculation with the numbers in the frequency table. Can you see how to find the mean, from the frequency table, without listing each data value separately?

Σ is the Greek letter S. Σ is pronounced as "sigma". We use Σ to mean "the sum of".
Σf means "the sum of all f".
Σfx means "the sum of all fx" i.e. the sum of all the f's multiplied by the corresponding x's".

For the frequency table given above, $\Sigma f = 3 + 2 + 5$
$$\Sigma fx = 3 \times 1 + 2 \times 4 + 5 \times 7$$

That is, $\boxed{\text{mean} = \frac{\Sigma fx}{\Sigma f}}$

We sometimes talk about a frequency distribution. A **frequency distribution** shows each data value and the frequency with which each data value occurs. That is, the information in a frequency table defines a frequency distribution.

Worked Example

x	1	5	7	8	10
f	2	4	5	6	3

Find the mean of this frequency distribution.

Answer mean = $\frac{\Sigma fx}{\Sigma f}$

$= \frac{2 \times 1 + 4 \times 5 + 5 \times 7 + 6 \times 8 + 3 \times 10}{2 + 4 + 5 + 6 + 3}$

$= 6·8$ to 1 d.p.

The calculator may be used to find the mean of a frequency distribution.

Example

x	1	5	7	8	10
f	2	4	5	6	3

To find the mean of this frequency distribution, key as follows.

MODE $\boxed{\bullet}$ 1 $\boxed{\times}$ 2 $\boxed{x}$ 5 $\boxed{\times}$ 4 $\boxed{x}$ 7 $\boxed{\times}$ 5 $\boxed{x}$ 8 $\boxed{\times}$ 6 $\boxed{x}$ 10 $\boxed{\times}$ 3 $\boxed{x}$
INV $\boxed{\overline{x}}$ to get answer of 6·8 to 1 d.p.

Note For each data value, the x value is keyed, then the $\boxed{\times}$, then the frequency of the x value, then the $\boxed{x}$. A common mistake is to key the frequency before the x value. After the $\boxed{x}$ key is pressed, the display shows the x value just put in. Always check the display to make sure you have keyed in the correct order.

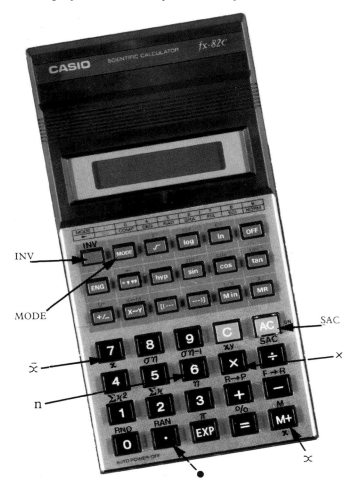

The **mode** can be read from a frequency table. It is the value of x which has the highest frequency. For instance, in the previous example, the mode is 8 since 8 occurs more frequently than any of the other values of x (8 occurs 6 times).

The **median** can also be read from a frequency table. For instance, to find the median of the frequency distribution given in the previous example proceed as follows:
Find the number of values of x : 2 + 4 + 5 + 6 + 3 = 20.
Find where the median is : It is halfway between the 10th and 11th values of x.

Now find the median:

x	1	5	7	8	10
f	2	4	5	6	3

2 values to here   6 values to here (2 + 4 = 6)   11 values to here (2 + 4 + 5 = 11)

The 10th value of x is 7, the 11th value of x is also 7. Hence the median is $\frac{7+7}{2}$ = 7.

The **range** can also be found from a frequency table. For instance, in the previous example, the highest data value is 10 and the lowest data value is 1. Hence the range is 9.

EXERCISE 19:4

Round your answers sensibly if rounding is necessary.

1. Find the mean of these frequency distributions.

(a)

x	1	2	3	4	5
f	3	3	4	1	1

(b)

x	10	20	30	40	50	60
f	2	0	3	6	2	2

(c)

x	11	15	18	20	21
f	4	1	4	2	1

(d)

x	2	4	6	8	9	10
f	1	3	2	5	6	4

2. Find the mode of the frequency distributions given in **question 1**.

3. Find the median of the frequency distributions given in **question 1**.

4. Find the range of the frequency distributions given in **question 1**.

5. Pia made this frequency table for the number of days students in her class were absent, during one week.

Days absent	1	2	3	4	5
frequency	6	0	3	1	1

(a) Find the mean, median, mode and range of this data.

(b) Pia made some statements about the data, using the answers to (a). What statements might Pia have made?

6. The following table gives the number of students in classes in a school.

Number of students in class	27	28	29	30	31	32	33
frequency	3	2	3	4	5	0	1

(a) Find the mean, median, mode and range of this data.

(b) Make some statements about the data, using your answers from (a).

Review   Winstone conducted a survey on hospital visiting. He included the following table as part of his analysis.

Visitors per patient	0	1	2	3	4	5	6	7	8
frequency	6	25	14	9	6	0	2	0	1

(a) Winstone calculated the mean number of visitors per patient and the median number. What answers should he get?

(b) Find the range.

(c) What is the mode of the above frequency distribution?

(d) Winstone wrote a few sentences about the data, using his answers to (a), (b) and (c). What might he have written?

PRACTICAL EXERCISE 19:5

Design and use an observation sheet or a questionnaire to collect some data that could be suitably displayed on a frequency table. You may wish to use one of the suggestions below. Display the data on a frequency table.

Analyse the data. As part of your analysis, calculate the mean, median, mode and range.

Suggested data   number of children in the family of students in your class
number of articles on pages of a newspaper
number of letters in surnames
mid-day temperatures at various places in the U.K. on one day

ANALYSING DATA from FREQUENCY TABLES for GROUPED DISCRETE DATA

Class interval	0–9	10–19	20–29	30–39	40–49	50–59
frequency	8	11	5	6	9	4

We cannot find the mode or median from this frequency table. However, we can read off the class interval that contains the mode, and the class interval that contains the median.

Adding the frequencies, we know there are 43 data values. The median is the 22nd data value. Since the 22nd data value occurs in the class interval 20–29, we can say the **median** lies in the class interval 20–29.

The class interval 10–19 contains more data values than any of the other intervals. We say the **modal class** is 10–19.

To find an approximate value for the **mean**, we assume that each item of data in a given class interval has the value of the mid-point of that class interval.

Example   Suppose the data in the above frequency table gives the marks obtained by a number of students in a test.
The modal class is 10–19.   The median lies in the class interval 20–29.
The calculation for the mean mark is as follows.
The class interval 50–59 contains 4 marks chosen from 50, 51, 52, 53, 54, 55, 56, 57, 58, 59. The mid-point of this class interval is 54·5. Similarly the mid-points of the other class intervals are 4·5, 14·5, 24·5, 34·5, 44·5.

Class interval	0–9	10–19	20–29	30–39	40–49	50–59
Mid-point (x)	4·5	14·5	24·5	34·5	44·5	54·5
frequency (f)	8	11	5	6	9	4

Mean $= \frac{\Sigma fx}{\Sigma f}$

$= \frac{8 \times 4\cdot5 + 11 \times 14\cdot5 + 5 \times 24\cdot5 + 6 \times 34\cdot5 + 9 \times 44\cdot5 + 4 \times 54\cdot5}{8 + 11 + 5 + 6 + 9 + 4}$

$= 26\cdot6$ (to 1 d.p.)

That is, the estimated mean mark is 26·6 to 1 d.p.

Note   The calculator could be used. The keying sequence is as follows.
$\boxed{\text{MODE}}$ $\boxed{\bullet}$ 4·5 $\boxed{\times}$ 8 $\boxed{\underline{x}}$ 14·5 $\boxed{\times}$ 11 $\boxed{\underline{x}}$ 24·5 $\boxed{\times}$ 5 $\boxed{\underline{x}}$ 34·5 $\boxed{\times}$ 6 $\boxed{\underline{x}}$ 44·5 $\boxed{\times}$
9 $\boxed{\underline{x}}$ 54·5 $\boxed{\times}$ 4 $\boxed{\underline{x}}$ $\boxed{\text{INV}}$ $\boxed{\overline{x}}$

EXERCISE 19:6

1.

Length of stay (days)	1–3	4–6	7–9	10–12	13–15	16–18	19–21	22–24
Frequency	32	27	19	10	6	14	5	18

This table gives the number of days that each of 131 guests stayed in an hotel.
Find (a) the mid-point of the 1–3 class interval   (b) the mean length of stay
       (c) the modal class   (d) the median class interval
       Make some statements about the data, based on your answers.

2. (a)

Number of correct answers	1–10	11–20	21–30	31–40	41–50
f	21	34	69	52	24

A multiple choice test was trialled on 200 students.
This table shows the number of multiple choice questions that these students answered correctly.
Find the mean number of correct answers.

   (b) Another multiple choice test was trialled on these students.
       The following table shows the results of this test.

Number of correct answers	1–10	11–20	21–30	31–40	41–50
f	11	42	54	52	41

   Find the mean number of correct answers.

   (c) What calculations could you do to help you compare the two tests in (a) and (b)?
       Write a few sentences comparing these tests.

Review   Before releasing a new disposable razor onto the market, the manufacturers
          carried out market research on its performance. One of these razors was trialled
          by each of 400 men. Each man noted the number of satisfactory shaves from the
          razor he trialled.
          The results of the market research are shown on the table.

Number of shaves	1–5	6–10	11–15	16–20	21–25	26–30	31–35
frequency	1	0	39	82	177	94	7

          Find (a) the mean number of shaves per razor   (b) the median class interval
                (c) the modal class
          Make some statements about the performance of the razor, based on the answers
          to (a), (b) and (c).

ANALYSING DATA from FREQUENCY DISTRIBUTIONS for CONTINUOUS DATA

Example

Class interval (mm)	5–	10–	15–	20–	25–	30–	35–40
frequency	8	12	14	17	5	3	1

Suppose this data was for the thickness (in mm) of books.

Any book with thickness between 4·5mm and 9·5mm will be included in the first class interval. The mid-point of this class interval is 7. Similarly, the mid-points of the other intervals are 12, 17, 22, 27, 32, 37.

An approximate value for the **mean** is found as shown below.

Class interval	5–	10–	15–	20–	25–	30–	35–40
Mid-point (x)	7	12	17	22	27	32	37
frequency (f)	8	12	14	17	5	3	1

$$\text{Mean} = \frac{\Sigma fx}{\Sigma f}$$

$$= \frac{8 \times 7 + 12 \times 12 + 14 \times 17 + 17 \times 22 + 5 \times 27 + 3 \times 32 + 1 \times 37}{8 + 12 + 14 + 17 + 5 + 3 + 1}$$

$$= 18$$

That is, mean thickness of the books is 18mm.

The mean of a frequency distribution for continuous data is found in the same way as the mean for discrete grouped data; we take the mid-point of each class interval to represent each data value in that interval.

We must take care to correctly find the mid-points of each class interval. There is no problem if the class intervals are given as in the above example. This same data could be presented in any of the following alternative ways.

1.

Class interval (mm)	f
$5 \leq w < 10$	8
$10 \leq w < 15$	12
$15 \leq w < 20$	14
$20 \leq w < 25$	17
$25 \leq w < 30$	5
$30 \leq w < 35$	3
$35 \leq w < 40$	1

2.

Class interval (mm)	f
5–10	8
10–15	12
15–20	14
20–25	17
25–30	5
30–35	3
35–40	1

3.

Class interval (mm)	f
5–9	8
10–14	12
15–19	14
20–24	17
25–29	5
30–34	3
35–39	1

Care must be taken to correctly interpret the possible values within each class interval. The possible values within each class interval of the tables 1, 2 and 3 are the same as in the table given for the previous example. The mid-points of each class interval are 7, 12, 17, 22, 27, 32, 37.

EXERCISE 19:7

1.

Weight loss (kg)	1·0–	2·0–	3·0–	4·0–	5·0–	6·0–	7·0–8·0
frequency	2	0	3	7	5	4	4

The weight loss of 25 people, during their first month on a new diet, is recorded on this table.

Find   (a) the mid-point of the first class interval
        (b) the mean weight loss
        (c) the median class interval
        (d) the modal class
Use your answers to (a), (b), (c) and (d) to make some statements about the data.

2.

Time taken (min)	30–35	35–40	40–45	45–50	50–55	55–60
Number of students	6	8	14	13	71	88

A multiple-choice maths. test was trialled on 200 students.
This table shows the time taken by these students to complete the test.
Find   (a) the mid-point of the first class interval
        (b) the mean time taken

3.

Distance (km)	0–	0·5–	1–	1·5–	2–	2·5–	3–	3·5–	4–	4·5–5
f	22	37	13	19	22	34	18	15	12	8

A questionnaire was given to the 200 students who sat the test referred to in the previous question. One of the questions asked about the distance the students travelled to get to school. The answers to this question were collated on the frequency table shown.

Find   (a) the mean distance travelled
        (b) the modal class
        (c) the median distance
Make some statements about the data, based on your answers to (a), (b), and (c).

4.

Distance (m)	120–129	130–139	140–149	150–159	160–169	170–179	180–189	190–199
frequency	4	6	13	7	7	8	5	2

52 students entered a schools' golf tournament. The table shows the distance of the longest tee shot of these students.

Find   (a) the mid-point of the first class interval

        (b) the mean distance

Make some statements about the data.

Review

Length (m)	3·0–	3·5–	4·0–	4·5–	5·0–	5·5–6·0
f	21	14	52	7	5	1

This table shows the lengths of the cars parked in one section of a hypermarket carpark.

Find   (a) the mid-point of the first class interval

        (b) the mean length of the cars

        (c) the modal class

        (d) the median class interval

Use your answers to (a), (b), (c) and (d) to make some statements about the data.

DISCUSSION EXERCISE 19:8

A QUESTION of AGES

1. Dale is 15.

Discuss the following statements to do with age and Dale's age. (Some of the statements are true and some are false.)

Age is continuous, not discrete.

Dale could be as young as $14\frac{1}{2}$ or as old as $15\frac{1}{2}$.

Dale could be just 15.

Dale could not be 16.

Dale could be as young as 15 years 1 day or as old as 15 years 364 days.

Dale could be 1 minute older than 15 or 1 minute younger than 16.

Discuss how best to describe Dale's age.

2.

Age (in years)	0–9	10–19	20–29	30–39	40–49	50–59	60–69
Mid-point (x)	5	15	25	35	45	55	65
frequency (f)	8	11	5	6	9	4	12

The data on this table gives the ages of people in a Doctor's waiting room on one day. How were the mid-points of the class intervals found? **Discuss.**

3. **Age structure of the population**
   United Kingdom   *Millions*

	Under 16	16–39	40–64	65–79	80 and over	All ages
Mid-year projections						
2001	12·8	19·2	18·0	6·7	2·5	59·2
2006	12·6	18·4	19·4	6·6	2·6	59·6
2011	12·1	18·1	20·2	7·0	2·7	60·0
2025	12·1	18·6	19·0	8·5	2·9	61·1

Source: Office of Population Censuses and Surveys: Government Actuary's Department

From Social Trends 1990

Source: Key Data 1990/91

How could the mean age of the projected population in the year 2001 be calculated? Does it matter that the class intervals are not the same width? What might the mid-point of the class interval "80 and over" be? **Discuss.**

PRACTICAL EXERCISE 19:9

Design and use an observation sheet or questionnaire to collect some grouped data; either discrete or continuous. (You may wish to use one of the suggestions below.) Decide on a sensible number of class intervals. Decide whether to have each class interval the same width.

Display the data on a frequency table.

Analyse the data. As part of your analysis find the modal class, the interval in which the median occurs and calculate an approximate value for the mean.

Suggested data

hours of sleep in one week of each of the students in a class
prices of houses advertised for sale in a newspaper
height of students in a year group
number of words on pages of this book
time taken to run a marathon by a group of runners

FREQUENCY GRAPHS

The **histogram** is a frequency graph.

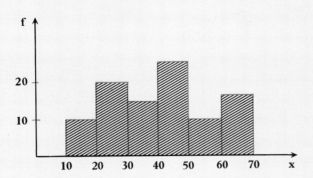

The **frequency polygon** is another frequency graph. This is a line graph. To draw a frequency polygon from a histogram, proceed as given below.

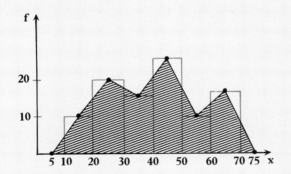

Step 1 Join the mid-points of the tops of the histogram.

Step 2 Draw the line from the mid-point of the top of the last "bar" on the histogram to the point on the x-axis that is half a class interval past the last "bar".

Step 3 Draw the line from the mid-point of the top of the first "bar" on the histogram to the point on the x-axis that is half a class interval before the first "bar".

Step 4 The closing side of the polygon is the x-axis between half a class interval before the first "bar" of the histogram and half a class interval after the last "bar".

DISCUSSION EXERCISE 19:10

Boys' Test Marks			Girls' Test Marks	
Class interval	f		Class interval	f
0–9	3		0–9	1
10–19	2		10–19	0
20–29	5		20–29	12
30–39	9		30–39	13
40–49	18		40–49	13
50–59	22		50–59	21
60–69	25		60–69	15
70–79	8		70–79	11
80–89	7		80–89	9
90–99	1		90–99	5

1. How can a frequency polygon be drawn for data without firstly drawing a histogram? **Discuss.** Use the data given above in your discussion.

2. Might it be useful to draw histograms for the above data on the same set of axes? Might it be useful to draw frequency polygons for the above data on the same set of axes? **Discuss.**

   Discuss the advantages and disadvantages of data being graphed as a histogram or a frequency polygon. As part of your discussion, draw the histograms and frequency polygons for the two sets of data given above.

3.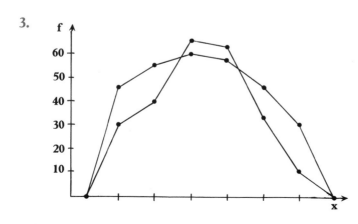

   What data might be represented on the x-axis of these frequency polygons? What title might this graph have? **Discuss.**

   Discuss how useful the frequency polygons are to compare two sets of data.

Frequency distributions can be compared by comparing the means or medians or modes or ranges. They may also be compared by comparing the shapes of their frequency polygons.

EXERCISE 19:11

1. Copy these histograms.
   Make up a title for each graph. Place suitable numbers on each axis.
   Label each axis suitably.
   Draw the frequency polygon for each.

(a) 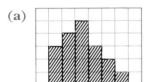   (b) 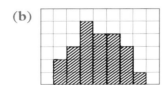   (c)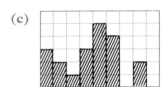

2. Draw a histogram and a frequency polygon for each of the following sets of data.

(a)
Score	10–19	20–29	30–39	40–49	50–59	60–69	70–79	80–89
f	3	4	7	5	7	4	2	1

(b)
Length (m)	0–	1–	2–	3–	4–	5–	6–7
f	5	0	3	5	2	4	6

3. The following list of data gives the scores of each of the members of a rifle club at a practice.

   24   33   21   34   35   25   24   26   28   38   45   19   24   27   37   40   17
   27   29   28   23   42   47   32   31   34   42   23   39   41   39   27   22   16
   34   47   40   37   30   19   25   35   45   43   39   38   18   29   24   31

   (a) Draw up a tally chart to group this data.
       Use the class intervals 15–19, 20–24, . . . 45–49.
   (b) Draw a frequency polygon to represent the data.

4. Fifty 20-year-old males and fifty 20-year-old females were interviewed about the way they spent their incomes. The percentage of income that each group saved is shown in the following tables.

Males

% saved	0–10	10–20	20–30	30–40	40–50	50–60
f	2	0	19	10	11	8

Females

% saved	0–10	10–20	20–30	30–40	40–50	50–60	60–70
f	3	3	14	12	9	6	3

(a) On the same set of axes, draw frequency polygons for both of these frequency distributions.
(b) Write a few sentences about the differences or similarities between these frequency polygons.

5. Both Mr Jones and Mr Smythe had their children record each phone call they made. These parents analysed these records after they had been kept for one year. As part of this analysis, each parent collated the weekly number of calls onto these frequency tables.

Jones children

No. of calls per week	0–4	5–9	10–14	15–19	20–24	25–29	30–34	35–39
Frequency	1	0	3	18	22	5	2	1

Smythe children

No. of calls per week	0–4	5–9	10–14	15–19	20–24	25–29	30–34	35–39
Frequency	0	6	5	12	4	5	7	13

Continue this analysis by drawing frequency polygons to represent this data and writing a few sentences about the shape of the polygons.

Review 1 The following list of data gives the number of mistakes made by students in a typing test.

2	3	10	5	7	1	3	11	7	9	8	22	0	3	13
0	21	8	7	18	2	0	5	12	0	1	3	5	9	2
13	10	4	5	3	7	4	28	19	2	5	8	24	11	3

(a) Use a tally chart to collate this data into the categories   0–4, 5–9, . . .
(b) Represent the grouped data on a frequency polygon.

Review 2 For one week, Mr Jones and Mr Smythe timed all the phone calls their children made. The frequency distribution for the time of these calls is shown on the following tables.

Jones children

Time (min)	0–	5–	10–	15–	20–	25–30
f	6	7	2	2	0	1

Smythe children

Time (min)	0–	5–	10–	15–	20–	25–	30–	35–40
f	2	9	3	0	0	4	3	2

(a) On the same set of axes, draw the frequency polygons for these distributions
(b) Comment on any similarities or differences between the frequency polygons.

PRACTICAL EXERCISE 19:12

Collect two sets of related data. You may wish to use one of the suggestions below.
Collate, organize and analyse your data. As part of your analysis, draw frequency polygons.

Suggested data
frequency of the digit 0 in the lines of two pages of this book
number of words read in 5 minutes by students from two different classes
time taken by boys and time taken by girls to make a given shape from tangram pieces

INVESTIGATION 19:13

AREA UNDER GRAPHS

Investigate the area of histograms and the area of the corresponding frequency polygons.

INTRODUCTION

DISCUSSION EXERCISE 20:1

We can draw a line on a scatter diagram so that there are about the same number of points above the line as below the line.

Each of the three lines on this scatter diagram has four points above it and four points below it.

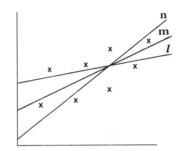

Where could other lines be drawn so that there were four points above and below? **Discuss**.

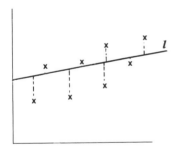
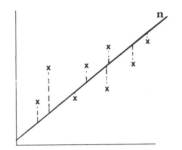
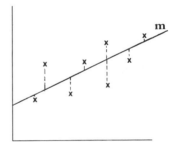

We say the line **m** "fits" the data better than the line *l* or **n**.

If we consider the vertical distance of each point from the line we see that –

    for line *l*:   the sum of the distances above the line is less than the sum of the distances below the line

    for line **n**: the sum of the distances above the line is greater than the sum of the distances below the line

    for line **m**: the sum of the distances above the line is about the same as the sum of the distances below the line

Is it possible to draw another line so that the sum of these vertical distances above the line equals the sum of the vertical distances below the line? **Discuss**.

Which of the lines **k**, *l*, **m**, or **n** do you think "fits" this data best? **Discuss.**

Can another line be drawn that "fits" the data even better? **Discuss.**

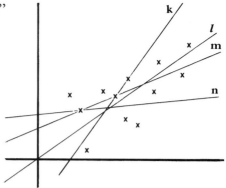

Sketch some points for which a line cannot be found to "fit" well. **Discuss.** Mention correlation in your discussion.

LINES of BEST FIT

If the data shows some correlation, we can draw a line of best fit.
The **line of best fit** has about the same number of points above and below it. Also, the sum of the vertical distances (to this line) from the points above is about the same as the sum of the vertical distances (to this line) from the points below.

Example   The following table gives the maximum monthly temperature and the monthly rainfall during April in a South American city.

Year	1980	1981	1982	1983	1984	1985	1986	1987	1988	1989	1990	1991
Rainfall (mm)	42	43	54	58	50	45	47	52	59	60	53	53
Temperature (°C)	18	17	20	24	19	17	20	19	22	23	18	22

The scatter diagram for this data is shown below. The line of best fit is drawn on.

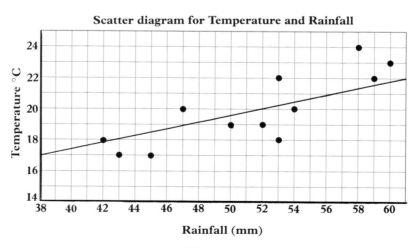

Scatter diagram for Temperature and Rainfall

260

In the previous example, the line of best fit slopes upwards.
There appears to be positive correlation between temperature and rainfall in that city.
Since the points are not clustered very closely around the line of best fit, the correlation is
not very close. That is, there is not a very close relationship between temperature and
rainfall.

We can use the line of best fit to estimate one measurement, given another. The more
closely the points are clustered around the line of best fit, the better the estimate.

Example

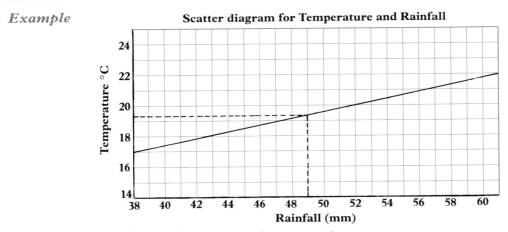

This is the scatter diagram from the previous example.

Suppose the rainfall in April 1979 was 49mm.
An estimate of the maximum temperature for April 1979 is 19·5°C, as shown by the
dotted lines on the diagram.

This estimate is not particularly reliable since the plotted points are not clustered very
closely around the line of best fit.

DISCUSSION EXERCISE 20:2

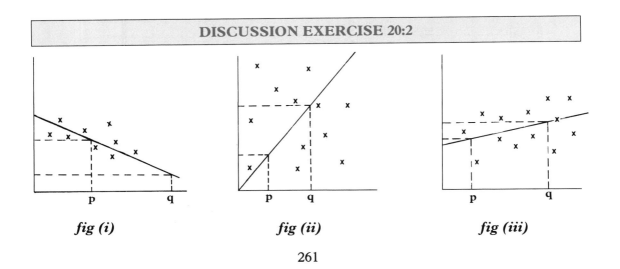

fig (i)   *fig (ii)*   *fig (iii)*

What titles might be given to each of the scatter diagrams on the previous page?
What variable might be on each of the horizontal axes?
What variable might be on each of the vertical axes?
Discuss.

For which of the previous diagrams do you think the line shown is a line of best fit?
What sort of correlation (positive, negative or no correlation) is shown on the previous diagrams?
Discuss.

Suppose the horizontal axes represented time (hours of study) and the vertical axes represented test marks.
Could any of the lines shown be used to estimate a test mark corresponding to a time **p**?
Could any of them be used to estimate a test mark corresponding to a time **q**? Would any of these be reliable estimates?
Discuss.

DISCUSSION EXERCISE 20:3

As part of an experiment, Annabel heated a liquid for 10 minutes.
She measured the temperature every minute. The graph Annabel drew is shown below.

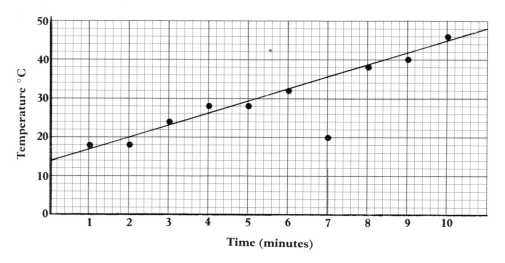

Was it reasonable for Annabel to ignore the point plotted at 7 minutes when she drew the line of best fit? **Discuss.**

EXERCISE 20:4

1. The data in the following table was collected from the first 12 pages of the book "The Plains of Passage".

Number of sentences	20	24	32	32	27	25	29	39	35	32	28	20
Number of paragraphs	11	9	11	10	7	9	10	11	10	8	9	6

  (a) Plot this data on a scatter diagram. (Have the Number of sentences on the horizontal axis.)

  (b) Comment on any correlation evident from your scatter diagram.

2. The following data gives the golf scores of 14 people on two consecutive days.

Friday	74	79	71	68	81	75	72	69	78	70	81	77	82	75
Saturday	72	76	73	69	77	75	70	71	77	72	79	75	78	74

  (a) Plot this data on a scatter diagram. (Have the Friday scores on the horizontal axis.)

  (b) Draw the line of best fit.

  (c) Estimate the Saturday score of a person who scored 68 on Friday.

  (d) Estimate the Friday score of a person who scored 79 on Saturday.

3.

Long jump (m)	4·90	4·30	5·85	5·98	5·02	5·52	4·53	6·03	5·45	4·67	5·28
High jump (m)	1·55	1·60	1·86	2·03	1·83	1·74	1·54	1·30	1·88	1·78	1·73

This table gives the long jump and high jump results of the students who entered both events.

  (a) Would you expect there to be positive correlation between these results?

  (b) Plot the data on a scatter diagram. (Have Long jump on the horizontal axis.)

  (c) Is there a line of best fit for this data? If so, draw it on the scatter diagram.

4.

Height (m) of student	1·64	1·70	1·58	1·65	1·81	1·67	1·62	1·73	1·71	1·77
Height (m) of best friend	1·72	1·69	1·82	1·70	1·74	1·64	1·58	1·68	1·60	1·70

  (a) Plot this data on a scatter diagram. (Have Height of student on the horizontal axis.)

  (b) Could you use this graph to estimate the height of the best friend of a student who was 171cm tall? Explain your answer.

5. In the Raydene School swimming sports, 15 students entered both diving events. The scores (out of 10) of these students in each event are shown in the table.

Student	A.D.	T.V.	D.P.	F.D.	P.M.	K.A.	A.Z.	E.H.	B.T.	A.A.	K.C.	L.K.	G.T.	R.B.	L.T.
High Dive	6	5	8	5·5	9	8·5	6	6·5	7	4	9	7·5	8	5	7·5
Low Dive	6·5	4	6·5	5	9	7	7·5	5	8·5	5	7	6	9	5·5	8

(a) Would you expect correlation between these results?
(b) Plot this data on a scatter diagram. (Have the high dive scores on the horizontal axis.)
(c) Is there a line of best fit for this data? If so, draw it on the scatter diagram.

Review 15 students were timed at two tasks in maths. The results are shown in this table.

The first task was to complete 50 calculations without the calculator.

The second task was to complete 50 similar calculations using the calculator.

Time (sec) for 1st task	150	128	165	126	143	133	164	148	122	156	131	145	162	136	155
Time (sec) for 2nd task	106	89	109	94	100	89	105	98	86	106	96	99	104	98	100

(a) Plot the data on a scatter diagram. (Have the 1st task on the horizontal axis.)
(b) Draw the line of best fit.
(c) Another student took 96 seconds for the 2nd task. Estimate the time this student would take for the 1st task.
(d) Estimate the time taken for the calculations using the calculator if it took 152 seconds without the calculator.

PRACTICAL EXERCISE 20:5

Gather data which is suitable for displaying on a scatter diagram. You may wish to use one of the suggestions that follow.

Before you gather the data, make an hypothesis about likely correlation between the variables.

Display your data on a scatter diagram. Draw in a line of best fit if there seems to be correlation.

Write a report. Include statements on how you gathered the data, on correlation evident and on whether your data confirmed your hypothesis about likely correlation.

Suggested data – about the students in your class.
    armspan and handspan
    circumference of head and circumference of wrist
    time spent travelling to school and time spent on homework
    number of brothers and number of sisters
    number of letters in forename and number of letters in surname
    time spent watching TV and time spent on homework
    long jump distance and high jump height
    time taken to do 50 calculations with and without the calculator

Suggested data – to be gathered from the newspaper or library.
    goals scored by home teams and goals scored by away teams
    runs scored in 2–innings of cricket
    engine size of cars and petrol consumption

CONSTRUCTING FLOW DIAGRAMS

The following shapes are used for the "boxes" in flow diagrams.

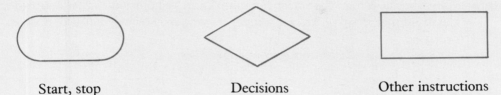

Start, stop   Decisions   Other instructions
                                                    Calculations

Each instruction is usually placed in a separate box.
Questions are placed in decision boxes. These questions must have Yes/No answers.
Arrows connect the boxes. The flow diagram is worked through in the direction given by
the arrows.

Flow diagrams are sometimes called flow charts.

Example   The following flow chart illustrates the making of a cup of coffee for someone
who takes both milk and sugar.

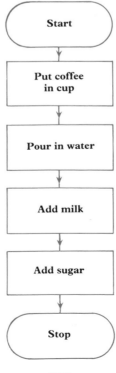

Sometimes we need to ask questions. Different parts of the flow diagram will then be followed, depending on the answers to the questions.

Example   The flow diagram in the previous example can be adjusted so that it illustrates the making of a cup of coffee for a person who may or may not take milk and/ or sugar.

We need to use decision boxes containing questions.

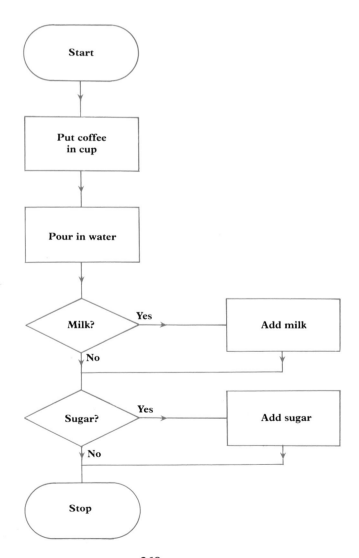

Sometimes we have to repeat a question and/or some of the instructions. We use a **loop** for this.

Examples   The flow diagram on the left illustrates the making of a cup of coffee for a person who may or may not take milk and/or any quantity of sugar.

The flow diagram on the right illustrates the making of a cup of coffee for each of 10 people.

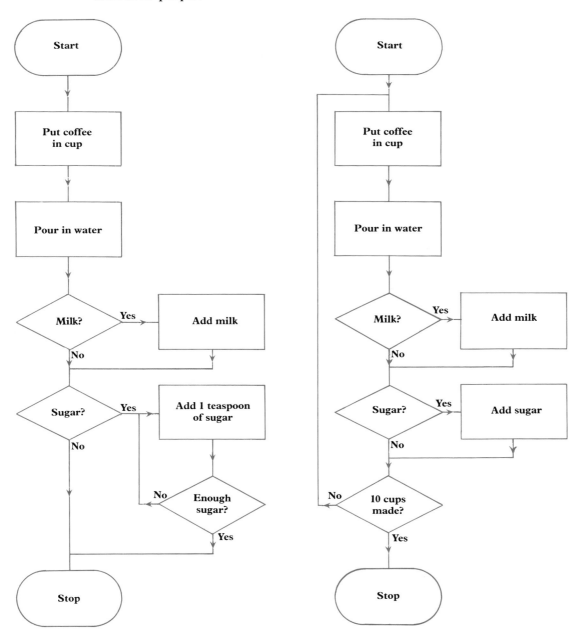

DISCUSSION EXERCISE 21:1

Could the boxes be placed in a different order in any of the flow diagrams in the previous examples? **Discuss.**

What sort of everyday tasks can be illustrated on a flow diagram? **Discuss.** As part of your discussion, attempt to draw flow diagrams for some everyday tasks.

What is the advantage of using a loop in a flow diagram? **Discuss.**

Why is each instruction usually placed in a separate box? **Discuss.**

EXERCISE 21:2

1. In each of the following, assemble the boxes into a flow diagram.

   (a) Taking the dog for a walk

   | walk | walk home | Put dog on lead | Take dog off lead | Start | Stop |

   (b) Taking a shower

   | Undress | Dress | Turn water on | Turn water off | Get dried |

   | Get into Shower | Wash | Stop | Start | Get out of shower |

   (c) Cooking mashed potatoes

   | Peel | Cook | Put in saucepan | Mash | Cooked? |

   | Start | Stop | Add water | Pour out water |

270

(d) Using the calculator to multiply two numbers

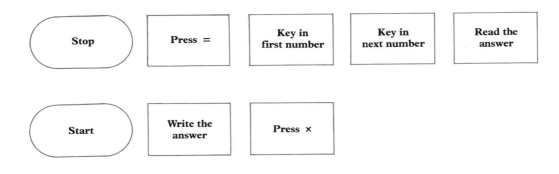

(e) Using the calculator to multiply a list of numbers

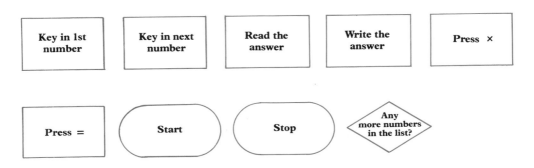

2. Write flow diagrams to do the following tasks, using the given instructions. Place the instructions in the correct type of operation or decision box.

(a) Cleaning a pair of shoes
    Brush the cleaner onto the shoes
    Put the top back on the cleaner
    Take the top off the cleaner
    Start
    Stop
    Leave cleaner to dry
    Put cleaner onto the brush
    Put cleaning box away
    Get cleaning box out
    Shine shoes

(b) Making a phone call
>   Start
>   Stop
>   Dial the number
>   Dial again
>   Is the number engaged?
>   Find the number in the phone book
>   Have conversation
>   Pick up the phone
>   Put down the phone

3. Write flow diagrams for the following tasks.
    (a) writing and posting a letter
    (b) travelling from Bournemouth to Southampton by train
    (c) inflating a car tyre to the correct pressure

Review   Write a flow diagram for "Buying lunch at the canteen."
    Use the following instructions.
>   Start
>   Stop
>   Get in a queue
>   Enter the canteen
>   Are you at the head of the queue?
>   Leave the canteen
>   Pay for your lunch
>   Order your lunch
>   Collect your lunch
>   Move up in the queue

PRACTICAL EXERCISE 21:3

Draw a flow diagram for a task you often do. This could be a game you play, a hobby, a job you do after school or something else in which you are interested.

INTERPRETING FLOW DIAGRAMS

Example

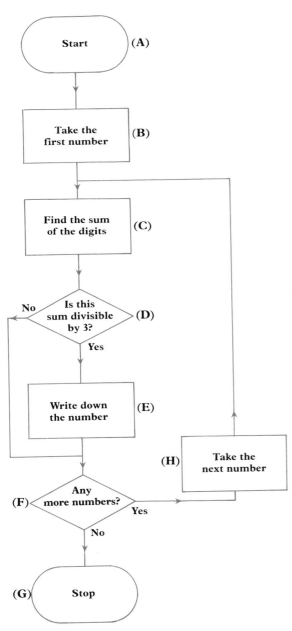

This flow chart is worked through as follows, with the data 125, 132.

Step	Box	
1	A	Start
2	B	Number = 125
3	C	Sum of digits = 8
4	D	No
5	F	Yes
6	H	Number = 132
7	C	Sum of digits = 6
8	D	Yes
9	E	Write 132
10	F	No
11	G	Stop

The input for this flow diagram is: 125, 132.
The output is: 132.
This flow diagram outputs those numbers that are multiples of 3.

Note The boxes on a flow diagram are not usually labelled as A, B, C etc. They are labelled on this example to show clearly what happens.

Data: 125, 132

EXERCISE 21:4

Work through each of these flow diagrams with the given data.
State what the output is for each.
State, in words, what each flow diagram does.

1.

2.

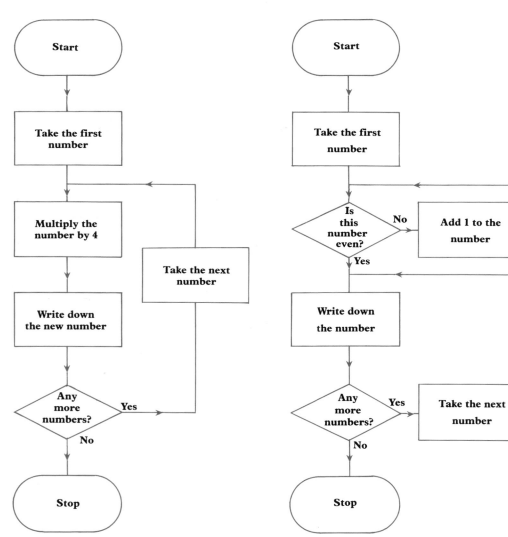

Data: 1, 2, 3, 4, 5, 6

Data: 2, 3, 5, 8, 10, 11

3.

Review

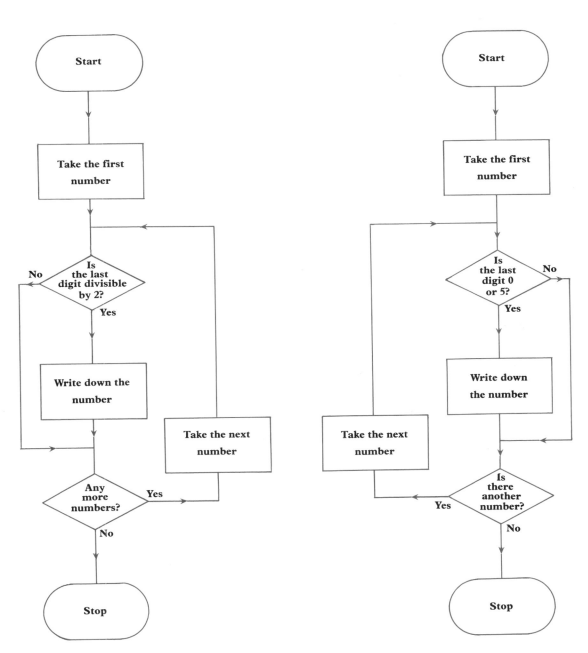

Data: 36, 25, 44, 22, 21, 19, 6, 5

Data: 20, 35, 34, 22, 95, 120

Read the next number, Input the next number, Read Number, Input Number, Read N, Input N, Read X and Input S all mean the same thing.

Write N, Output N and Print N all mean the same thing.
The symbols $>$, $<$, $\geq$, $\leq$ are frequently used on flow diagrams. For instance, we often write "$x < 4$" inside a decision box instead of "Is x less than 4?".

The value of a variable, such as N, often changes. For instance, either of the instructions "Increase N by 4", "$N = N + 4$", will change a value of $N = 5$ to a value of $N = 9$.

Example

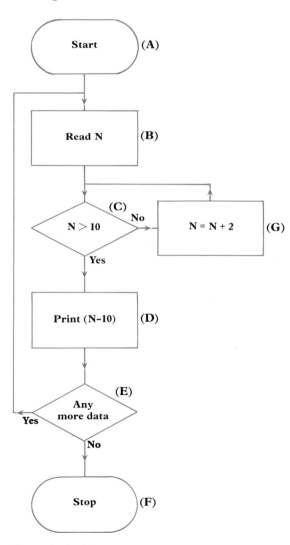

This flow diagram deals with the given data as follows.

Step	Box	
1	A	Start
2	B	N = 9
3	C	No
4	G	N = 11
5	C	Yes
6	D	Print 1
7	E	Yes
8	B	N = 8
9	C	No
10	G	N = 10
11	C	No
12	G	N = 12
13	C	Yes
14	D	Print 2
15	E	Yes
16	B	N = 11
17	C	Yes
18	D	Print 1
19	E	No
20	F	Stop

Data: 9, 8, 11

EXERCISE 21:5

Work through each of these flow diagrams with the given data.
State what the output is, in each case.

1.

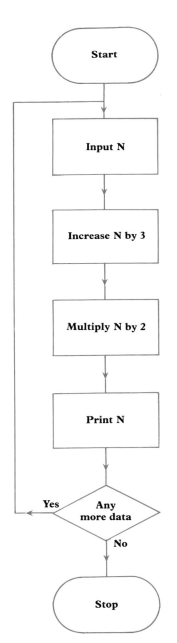

Data: 1, 2, 5

2.

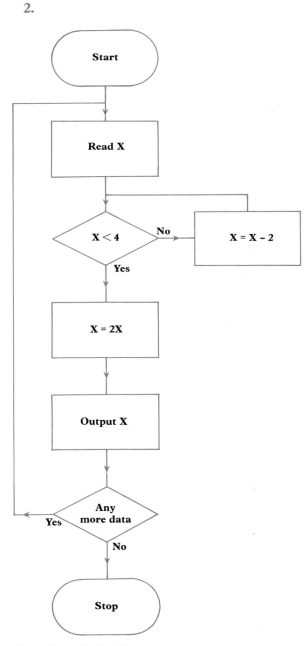

Data: 3, 8, 5, 11, 10

3.

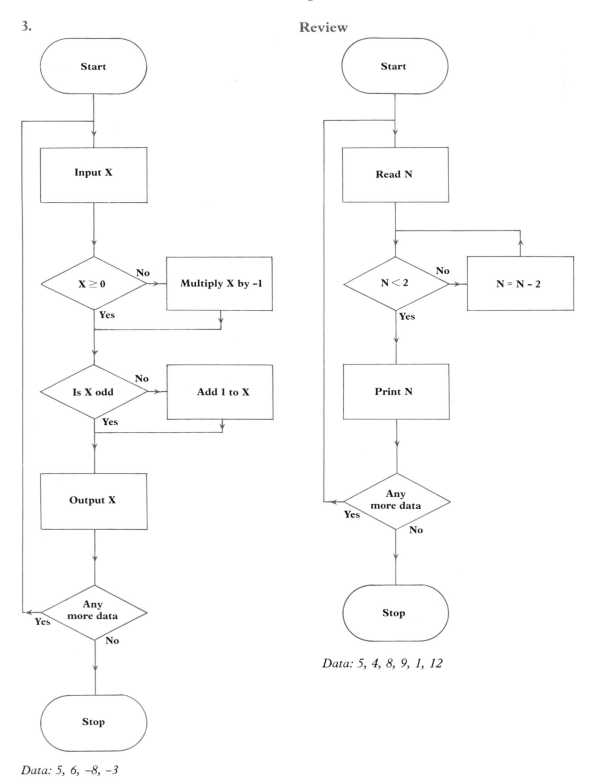

Review

Data: 5, 6, –8, –3

Data: 5, 4, 8, 9, 1, 12

DESK CHECKS

DISCUSSION EXERCISE 21:6

To keep track of what is happening throughout the flow diagram given on **page 276** we could use the following desk check.

Box	B	C	D	E
	N	**N > 10 ?**	**Output**	**More data ?**
	9	No		
	11	Yes	1	Yes
	8	No		
	10	No		
	12	Yes	2	Yes
	11	Yes	1	No

Discuss this desk check. As part of your discussion, you may like to do desk checks on the flow diagrams given in **Exercise 21:5.**

DISCUSSION EXERCISE 21:7

Rakia and Blake both adapted the previous desk check.
Discuss these.

Rakia's desk check

N	?	Output
9	NO	
11	YES	1
8	NO	
10	NO	
12	YES	2
11	YES	1

Blake's desk check

N	9	11	8	10	12	11
Output		1			2	1

The value of a variable does not need to be input as data. It may be given a value within the flow diagram by instructions such as "S = 5" or "SUM = 5" or "TOT = 5."

More than one variable may be used in a flow diagram. For instance, if three variables A, N and P are used and the value for just one of these is input as data then the values for the other two variables must be defined within the flow diagram.

Desk checks are important for flow diagrams that contain more than one variable. Each variable should have its own column on the desk check.

Example

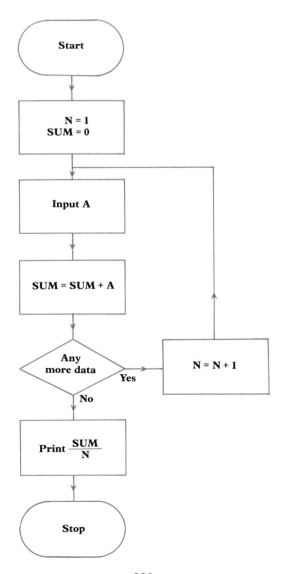

Chapter 21

There are three variables mentioned in this flow **diagram**; N, SUM, A.
The desk check should have a separate column for each of these.
The essential columns for the desk check are shown below.

N	SUM	A	More data?	Output

EXERCISE 21:8

Find the output from each of the following flow diagrams.
What does each flow diagram do?
Use a desk check to help.

1.

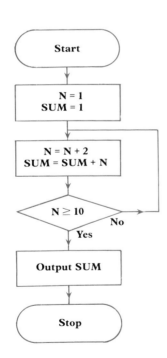

2.

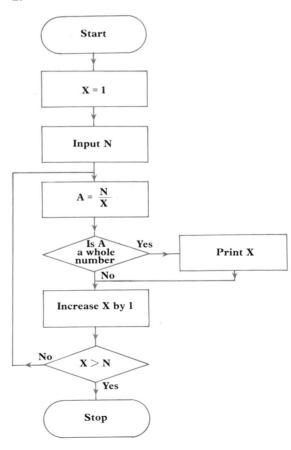

Data: 18

3. The flow diagram given in the example on **page 280,** for the data 3, 7, 10, 12.

4.   Review

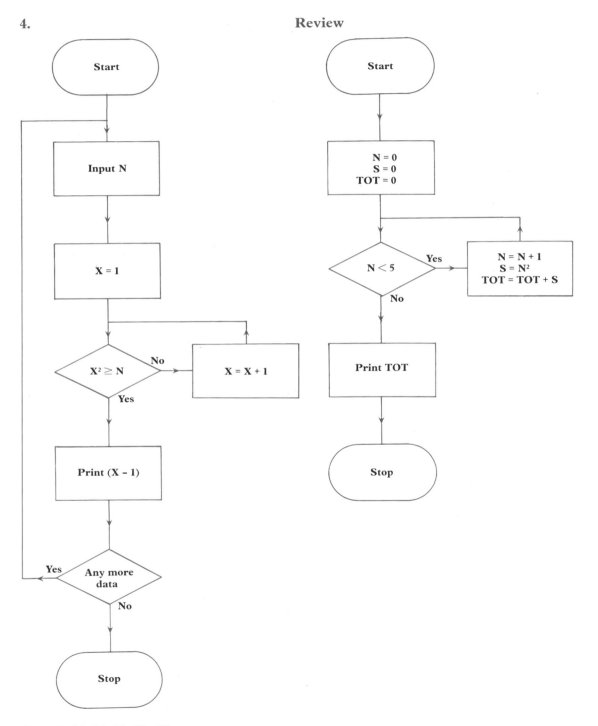

Data: 9, 10, 16, 22, 25, 35

FURTHER CONSTRUCTING FLOW DIAGRAMS

DISCUSSION EXERCISE 21:9

---

1. **Discuss** how to adapt the flow diagram given in **question 1** of **Exercise 21:8** to:
   (a) find the sum of all the odd numbers that are less than 10
   (b) find the sum of the first 20 odd numbers
   (c) find the sum of all the two digit even numbers
   Desk check your flow diagrams to make sure that they do what you want them to do.

2. **Discuss** how to adapt the flow diagram given in **question 2** of **Exercise 21:8** to find
   (a) the number of factors of 18
   (b) the factors of any number
   Desk check your flow diagrams.

3. **Discuss** how to adapt the flow diagram given in the **Review** of **Exercise 21:8** to find
   (a) the sum of the cubes of the whole numbers that are less than 6
   (b) the sum of the squares of the whole numbers that are less than 10
   (c) the sum of the squares of the following: 2, 5, 6, 8
   (d) the sum of the cubes of a list of numbers
   Desk check your flow diagrams.

EXERCISE 21:10

Construct flow diagrams for each of the following.
Desk check your flow diagrams with some data to make sure they are correct.

1. A flow diagram which adds 3 to each number in a list and prints out the results.

2. A flow diagram which prints all the odd numbers in a list but not the even numbers.

3. A flow diagram which leaves all the positive numbers unchanged and changes the sign of all the negative numbers; outputs the results.

4. A flow diagram which finds and outputs the whole number square roots of all the numbers less than a given number. (For instance, if 50 is input the output will be 1, 2, 3, 4, 5, 6, 7.)

5. (a) A flow diagram which adds all the numbers in a list and outputs the total.
   (b) A flow diagram which adds all the even numbers in a list and prints out this total.

Review   A flow diagram which calculates and prints out all the one and two digit multiples of a given number.

284

RELATIVE FREQUENCY

The **frequency** of an event is the number of times that event occurs in a number of trials. The **relative frequency** of an event compares the frequency with the number of trials. It is the proportion of times the event occurs in a number of trials.

$$\text{Relative frequency of an event} = \frac{\text{Number of times an event occurs}}{\text{Number of trials}}$$

Worked Example   When a die was tossed 50 times, a one came up 7 times. What is the relative frequency of getting a one?

Answer   Number of trials = 50
Number of ones = 7

Relative frequency of a one = $\frac{7}{50}$ or 0·14.

Worked Example   Adam tossed two coins together a number of times. He recorded the results on the following table.

Event	Tally	f
HH	✚✚✚ ✚✚✚ ✚✚✚	15
HT	✚✚✚ ✚✚✚ ✚✚✚ ✚✚✚ IIII	24
TH	✚✚✚ ✚✚✚ ✚✚✚ ✚✚✚ ✚✚✚ IIII	29
TT	✚✚✚ ✚✚✚ ✚✚✚ III	18

Find (a) the number of times Adam tossed the two coins
(b) the relative frequency of the event "two heads"
(c) the relative frequency of the event "one head and one tail"

Answer   (a) Number of tosses = 15 + 24 + 29 + 18
= 86

(b) "Two heads" occurred 15 times.

Relative frequency of "two heads" = $\frac{15}{86}$

(c) "One head and one tail" occurred 53 times (24 HT and 29 TH).

Relative frequency of "one head and one tail" = $\frac{53}{86}$

285

EXERCISE 22:1

1. This tally chart gives the number of pictures on each of the pages of a newspaper.

Number of pictures	Tally	Frequency
0	卌 卌	10
1	卌 ‖	7
2	卌 ‖‖	9
3	卌 |	6
4	卌 |	6
5	‖‖	4
6	卌 |	6

(a) How many pages were there in this newspaper?
(b) Find the relative frequency of a page having just one picture.

2. The results of a raffle are shown below.

1076	1094	1099	1100	1110	1212	1215	1245	1256	1262	1292	1293	1299	1303	1306
1363	1365	1440	1480	1528	1544	1546	1652	1683	1729	1794	1799	1842	1892	1922
2101	2127	2186	2232	2278	2279	2284	2321	2334	2349	2384	2419	2423	2446	2461
2472	2513	2519	2520	2542	2627	2638	2663	2671	2674	2675	2732	2768	2776	2783
2794	2879	2902	2911	2913	2939	2939	2945	2963	2987	3010	3029	3080	3121	3142
3145	3148	3162	3171	3180	3189	3363	3365	3380	3425	3429	3488	3567	3612	3635
3645	3698	3718	3734	3738	3766	3766	3771	3786	3793	3801	3863	3874	3886	3954
4016	4104	4125	4141	4157	4158	4170	4171	4188	4224	4264	4274	4308	4390	4498
4504	4517	4582	4585	4614	4630	4656	4669	4694	4697					

Find the relative frequency of a winning number
(a) beginning with the digit 2
(b) containing the digit 2

3. A card was drawn from a pack and its suit noted. The card was put back and the pack shuffled. This was done 250 times. The results are shown in the table.

Suit	Spade	Heart	Diamond	Club
Frequency	52	67	61	70

Find the relative frequency of
(a) a spade (b) a club (c) a heart (d) a diamond
What is the sum of these relative frequencies?

4. Two coins were tossed together 200 times. The results are shown.

2 Heads	2 Tails	1 Head, 1 Tail
47	43	110

Find the relative frequency of
  (a) 2 heads   (b) 2 tails   (c) 1 head and 1 tail
What is the sum of these relative frequencies?

Review   A die was rolled 200 times and the results were as shown in this table:

Number on die	1	2	3	4	5	6
Frequency	24	29	32	41	39	35

Find the relative frequency of
  (a) a one   (b) a two   (c) a three   (d) a four
  (e) a five   (f) a six
What is the sum of these relative frequencies?

GAME and INVESTIGATION 22:2

An adaptation of UNDER and OVER SEVEN : a game for one player

The player begins with 20 points. The player tosses two dice and adds together the numbers that come up. Before the player tosses, (s)he nominates whether the total will be "under 7" or "exactly 7" or "over 7".
    If (s)he nominates "exactly 7" and (s)he is right, (s)he gains 4 points.
    If (s)he nominates "under 7" and (s)he is right, (s)he gains 1 point.
    If (s)he nominates "over 7" and (s)he is right, (s)he gains 1 point.
    In all cases, if (s)he is wrong, (s)he loses 1 point.
The game continues in this manner with the player nominating before each toss whether the total will be "under 7" or "exactly 7" or "over 7".
The game finishes when the player has 0 points.

Things to investigate:
Does it always take the same number of tosses before the game finishes. Should it?
Is it wise to never nominate "exactly 7"?
Is there any element of skill in this game?
What if 5 points were gained for correctly nominating "exactly 7"?
What if 2 points were gained for correctly nominating "exactly 7"?
What if 2 points were lost for an incorrect nomination?
What if . . .

ESTIMATING PROBABILITY

DISCUSSION and PRACTICAL EXERCISE 22:3

1. What is the probability of getting a head when a coin is tossed?
   If a coin is tossed 1000 times, how many times do you expect to get a head?
   If a coin is tossed 10 times, how many times do you expect to get a head?
   Discuss.

   Toss a coin 1000 times. Find the relative frequency of a head after 100 tosses, after 200 tosses, . . . after 1000 tosses. You could use a tally chart to record each time a head comes up, or you could work with a partner and have your partner count the number of heads. Summarize your findings on a table such as that shown below.

Number of tosses	100	200	300	400	500	600	700	800	900	1000
Number of heads										
Relative frequency of a head										

   Did the relative frequency of a head get closer to $\frac{1}{2}$, the more trials you did?

   Did you expect it to get quite close to $\frac{1}{2}$? Discuss.
   What if the coin was tossed 5000 times?
   What if the coin was tossed 10000 times? Discuss.

2. What is the probability of getting a 2 when a die is tossed?
   If a die was tossed 240 times, how many times would you expect to get a 2?
   Discuss.

   Toss a die 240 times and collate the results onto a table such as that shown below. It would be a good idea to use a tally chart to collect the data.

Number on die	1	2	3	4	5	6
Frequency						
Relative freq.						

Did you get the number of 2's you expected? Did you expect each of the relative frequencies to be close to $\frac{1}{6}$? Were the relative frequencies all close to $\frac{1}{6}$? Discuss.
If you tossed the die 24000 times, would you expect each of the relative frequencies to be very close to $\frac{1}{6}$? Discuss.

INVESTIGATION 22:4

COMPUTER SIMULATIONS

The computer can be used to simulate the tossing of a coin or a die.

By using the computer, we can avoid actually tossing the coin or die. We can just record the results. We can consider the results of a great many more trials than it would be possible to consider otherwise.

Program 1 can be used to simulate the tossing of a coin.
Program 2 can be used to simulate the tossing of two dice.

Program 1 : Tossing a coin 1000 times; recording the frequency of a head and the frequency of a tail.

```
10      DIM   TALLY (2)
20      FOR C = 1 TO 1000
30      R = RND (2)
40      TALLY (R) = TALLY (R) + 1
50      NEXT C
60      PRINT "OUTCOME       FREQUENCY"
70      PRINT "HEAD", TALLY (1)
80      PRINT "TAIL", TALLY (2)
90      END
```

Program 2 : Tossing two dice together 1000 times; adding the numbers obtained on each toss; recording these sums.

```
10      DIM TALLY (12)
20      FOR C = 1 TO 1000
30      R = RND (6) : S = RND (6)
40      T = R + S
50      TALLY (T) = TALLY (T) + 1
60      NEXT C
70      PRINT " SUM  TWO  DICE    FREQUENCY"
80      FOR T = 2 TO 12
90      PRINT T, TALLY (T)
100     NEXT T
110     END
```

Using Program 1, investigate the long-run relative frequency of getting a head when a coin is tossed.

Using Program 2, investigate the long-run relative frequency of getting a total of 12 when two dice are tossed together.

Investigate how to adapt the above programs to do the following simulations:

• the results when one die is tossed   • the results when two coins are tossed together

If an experiment is repeated a great number of times, the relative frequency of an event occurring can be used as an estimate of the probability of that event occurring. The more often the experiment is repeated, the better the estimate will be.

Relative frequency is used as an estimate of the probability of an event occurring when it is not possible to calculate the probability but it is possible to conduct an experiment to find the relative frequency.

Example To estimate the probability that a telephone number, chosen at random, begins with the digit 3 we could proceed as follows:

Choose a great number of telephone numbers.
Count the numbers that begin with the digit 3.
Find the relative frequency of the chosen telephone numbers beginning with 3.
Use this relative frequency as an estimate of the probability.

For instance, suppose we look at 10000 telephone numbers and find that 960 of them begin with the digit 3. Then the relative frequency of these numbers beginning with a 3 is $\frac{960}{10000}$ or 0·096. We could then estimate the probability of a telephone number, chosen at random, beginning with a 3 to be 0·096 or about 0·1.

DISCUSSION and PRACTICAL EXERCISE 22:5

1. Take one page of your local telephone book.
   (a) Copy this table. Record, on the table, the number of times the digits 0, 1, . . . 9 occur.

Digit	0	1	2	3	4	5	6	7	8	9
Frequency										
Relative freq.										

   (b) Find the relative frequency of each of the digits and complete the last line of the table.
   (c) Use your results to estimate the following probabilities.
       P(0)   P(3)   P(7)   P(9)
   (d) Take another page and repeat (a), (b), and (c).
   (e) Were the estimates of P(0), P(3), P(7), P(9) about the same in both cases? Did you expect them to be? **Discuss**.

2. Select a page of this book which has a lot of numbers on it.
   (a) What would you expect the relative frequency of the digit 4 to be? **Discuss.**
   (b) Find the relative frequency of the digit 4 on the page you selected.
       (Only consider the digits on this page, not the letters.)
   (c) **Discuss** your results with the other students in your group or your class.
   (d) Using the results of your group or class, estimate the probability of a digit on a page of this book being a 4.

3. If a drawing pin is dropped onto the desk it will land either on its side *(fig 1)* or on its back *(fig 2)*.

   fig 1

   Design an experiment to estimate the probability of a dropped drawing pin landing on its side.

   fig 2

   Carry out your experiment.

4. Conduct an experiment of your choice to estimate the probability of an event, using relative frequency as an estimate. You may wish to use one of the following suggestions:
   probability that the next car to pass the school is white
   probability that the next person to use a zebra crossing is male
   probability that the next person to leave the library is wearing glasses

---

INVESTIGATION 22:6

STRAWS and π

Equipment: A small length of drinking straw or a matchstick or a similar object.
A page ruled with horizontal lines that are twice as far apart as the length of the piece of straw. For instance, if the straw is 2cm long, then the lines should be 4cm apart.

Procedure: Drop the straw onto this ruled page. Repeat a great number of times, recording whether or not the straw landed so that it touched one of the lines.

Investigate the relationship between the long-run relative frequency and π.

SUBJECTIVE ESTIMATES of PROBABILITY

Example 1   The probability of getting a head when a coin is tossed is 0·5.
This probability is based on knowing that there are two equally likely outcomes when a coin is tossed and of these, only one is a head.

That is, we use   Probability = $\dfrac{\text{Number of favourable outcomes}}{\text{Number of possible outcomes}}$

Example 2   The probability that Greg will be late for school tomorrow is 0·1.
This estimate of the probability of Greg being late can be based on the relative frequency of Greg being late in the past.

That is, we use   Probability = $\dfrac{\text{Number of times event occurs}}{\text{Number of trials}}$

Example 3   The probability that a cure for cancer will be found within the next year is 0·007.
This probability cannot be based on equally likely outcomes as in Example 1 or on relative frequency as in Example 2. It would probably be based on the current state of cancer research. This is a subjective estimate of probability.

A subjective estimate of probability is not based on equally likely outcomes or on relative frequency.
Subjective estimates of probability have to be made when an experiment cannot be repeated under the same conditions.
Subjective estimates of probability are a way of saying how strongly we believe an event will occur. If we believe the event is likely to happen we will give it a high probability, certainly greater than 0·5. If we believe the event is unlikely to happen we will give it a low probability, certainly less than 0·5.

DISCUSSION EXERCISE 22:7

1.   Which of the following are subjective estimates of probability? Discuss.
The probability of money being obsolete by the year 2090 is 0·008.
There is 0·25 probability of a spade when a card is drawn from a pack.
When two coins are tossed, there is 0·5 probability of getting either two heads or two tails.
The probability of a car going through an amber light at the intersection of John Avenue and James Street is 0·02.
The probability of someone landing on Mars in the 21st century is 0·0001.

2.   Think of some situations where subjective probability would be used. Estimate a probability for each situation. Discuss.

3. Write a short article. In your article, include some of the subjective probabilities you discussed earlier.

   Have another student in your group, or class, comment on your article.

MUTUALLY EXCLUSIVE EVENTS

Example   When this spinner is spun it could stop in the section marked 1 or 2 or 3 or 4 or 5 or 6 or 7 or 8.

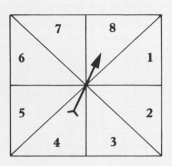

Let the event "stops on an odd number" be called event A.
Let the event "stops on the 2" be called event B.
The events A and B cannot happen at the same time.
We say that event A and event B are mutually exclusive.

Now suppose that event A is "stops on an odd number" and event B is "stops on a multiple of 3." In this case, events A and B can happen at the same time. This would be so if the spinner stopped in the section marked 3 since 3 is both an odd number and a multiple of 3. In this case, the event A and the event B are not mutually exclusive.

Events which cannot happen at the same time are called **mutually exclusive events**.

State whether or not the following events A and B are mutually exclusive.

1. A die is tossed.
    Event A : tossing an even number
    Event B : tossing an odd number

2. Two coins are tossed.
    Event A : two heads
    Event B : one head and one tail

3. A die is cast.
    Event A : a number greater than 4
    Event B : an odd number

4. Two coins are thrown.
    Event A : two heads
    Event B : at least one head

5. A card is drawn from a full pack.
   Event A : a spade
   Event B : an ace

6. A day dawns.
   Event A : it is a fine day
   Event B : it is windy

7. A sheep has lambs.
   Event A : the lambs are twins
   Event B : the lambs are triplets

8. Two students are chosen at random.
   Event A : one student wears glasses
   Event B : one student is tall

9. A counter is drawn from a box containing red, blue and white counters.
   Event A : a red counter
   Event B : not a red counter

Review 1 A die is tossed.
   Event A : a number less than 4
   Event B : the number 4

Review 2 Salina goes shopping.
   Event A : Salina goes shopping with Kate
   Event B : Salina goes shopping with Shannon

DISCUSSION EXERCISE 23:2

1. Think of pairs of events which are mutually exclusive. Discuss.
   Think of pairs of events which are not mutually exclusive. Discuss.

2. A card is drawn from a pack.
   Event A : an ace   **Event B** : the king of spades
   What might **event C** be if the three events A, B and C are mutually exclusive?
   Discuss.
   What might **event C** be if the three events A, B and C are not mutually exclusive?
   Discuss.

The ADDITION PRINCIPLE

Remember: For equally likely outcomes, P(an event occurs) = $\dfrac{\text{Number of favourable outcomes}}{\text{Number of possible outcomes}}$

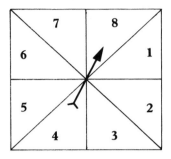

When this spinner is spun it could stop in the section marked
1 or 2 or 3 or 4 or 5 or 6 or 7 or 8. There are eight equally
likely outcomes.
The following example and counter example refer to this
spinner.

Example Let the event "stops on an odd number" be called event A.
Let the event "stops on the 2" be called event B.

Favourable outcomes for event A are 1, 3, 5, 7.
There are four favourable outcomes.
There are eight possible outcomes. $P(A) = \frac{4}{8}$

The only favourable outcome for event B is 2.
There is one favourable outcome.
There are eight possible outcomes. $P(B) = \frac{1}{8}$

Notice that, $P(A) + P(B) = \frac{4}{8} + \frac{1}{8}$

$$= \frac{5}{8}$$

The event "A *or* B" is "stops on an odd number *or* on 2."
Favourable outcomes for A *or* B are 1, 2, 3, 5, 7.
There are five favourable outcomes.
There are eight possible outcomes.

$P(A \textit{ or } B) = \frac{5}{8}$ which is the same as $P(A) + P(B)$

That is, in this example $P(A \textit{ or } B) = P(A) + P(B)$.

This example illustrates the addition principle for probabilities.

Counter Example   Let A be the event "stops on an odd number."
Let B be the event "stops on a multiple of 3."

Favourable outcomes for event A are 1, 3, 5, 7.
There are four favourable outcomes.
There are eight possible outcomes. $P(A) = \frac{4}{8}$

Favourable outcomes for event B are 3, 6.
There are two favourable outcomes.
There are eight possible outcomes. $P(B) = \frac{2}{8}$

Notice that, $P(A) + P(B) = \frac{4}{8} + \frac{2}{8}$

$$= \frac{6}{8}$$

The event "A *or* B" is "stops on an odd number *or* on a multiple of 3."
Favourable outcomes for "A *or* B" are 1, 3, 5, 6, 7.
There are five favourable outcomes.
There are eight possible outcomes.

$$P(A \text{ } or \text{ } B) = \frac{5}{8} \text{ which is not the same as } P(A) + P(B).$$

That is, in this example $P(A \text{ } or \text{ } B) \neq P(A) + P(B)$.   Why not?

The **addition principle** for probability is:

For mutually exclusive events, $P(A \text{ } or \text{ } B) = P(A) + P(B)$

Worked Example   Of 50 counters in a bag, 7 are black and 6 are white. Dana takes one counter at random. Find the probability that Dana's counter is either black or white.

Answer   The events "Black", "White" are mutually exclusive.
$P(\text{Black } or \text{ White}) = P(\text{Black}) + P(\text{White})$

$$= \frac{7}{50} + \frac{6}{50}$$

$$= \frac{13}{50}$$

Worked Example   One of the older Coxon children is to babysit for a neighbour.
$P(\text{Gavin babysits}) = 0 \cdot 2$, $P(\text{Alex babysits}) = 0 \cdot 35$.
Find the probability that either Gavin or Alex babysits.

Answer   Since only one of the Coxon children babysits, Gavin and Alex do not babysit together. The events "Gavin babysits", "Alex babysits" are mutually exclusive.
$P(\text{Gavin } or \text{ Alex}) = P(\text{Gavin}) + P(\text{Alex})$

$$= 0 \cdot 2 + 0 \cdot 35$$

$$= 0 \cdot 55$$

EXERCISE 23:3

Use the Addition Principle P(A *or* B) = P(A) + P(B) to answer the following questions.

1. A die is tossed.
   Find the probability of getting a 3 or an even number.

2. A card is drawn from a pack.
   Find the probability of getting an Ace or a Jack.

3. Two coins are tossed.
   Find the probability of getting two heads or two tails.

4. Two dice are thrown. Find the probability of getting a total of 7 or the same numbers on both dice.

5. The probability that Belen buys "The Mirror" is 0·2 and the probability that she buys "The Sun" is 0·25. (Belen does not buy more than one paper.)
   What is the probability that she buys either "The Mirror" or "The Sun"?

6. In a family of five, the probability that Kirstie is first home is $\frac{5}{12}$ and the probability that Bronwyn is first home is $\frac{1}{12}$.
   Find the probability that either Bronwyn or Kirstie is first home.

7. Sue drives to work in London.
   The probability that she parks on Regent Street is 0·2.
   The probability that she parks on Oxford Street is 0·18.
   What is the probability that she parks on either Regent Street or Oxford Street?

8. Six cats are fed from six different coloured feeding bowls.
   The probability that Cassius is fed from the red bowl is 0·15, the probability that Smokey is fed from the red bowl is 0·25 and the probability that McGiver is fed from the red bowl is 0·4.
   Find the probability that (a) either Cassius or Smokey is fed from the red bowl
   (b) either Smokey or McGiver is fed from the red bowl
   (c) either McGiver or Cassius is fed from the red bowl

9. John answers the phone in his office from 9 a.m. until midday and then from 1 p.m. until 4 p.m. Ruski phones this office each day. The following table shows the probability of Ruski phoning at particular times of the day.

Time	Probability
in the morning before 9 a.m.	**0·15**
from 9 a.m. until midday	**0·4**
from midday until 1 p.m.	**0·15**
in the afternoon after 4 p.m.	**0·05**

(a) Find the probability that Ruski phones between 1 p.m. and 4 p.m.
(b) What is the probability that John answers Ruski's call?

Review 1
A die is tossed.
Find the probability of getting an odd number or a six.

Review 2
The probability that Michaela is last into class is 0·08 and the probability that Stacey is last is 0·21.
Find the probability that the last student into class is either Stacey or Michaela.

Review 3
The caretaker enters the school through one of three doors; the front door, the side door or the hall door. He enters through the front door with probability 0·3 and through the hall door with probability 0·05.
Find the probability that this caretaker enters the school through
(a) the side door
(b) either the front door or the hall door
(c) either the front door or the side door

INVESTIGATION 23:4

ANALYSIS of GAMES

We can often improve our chances of winning a game that involves the throwing of dice or coins. We can do this by being aware of the probability of particular outcomes.

An analysis of "Beat the Shaker" follows.

continued . . .

. . . *from previous page*

Beat the Shaker Two players, A and B, each roll a die. A rolls first, then B. If B gets a higher number than A, then B gets 1 point. If B gets a lower number than A, or the same number, then A gets 1 point. The game continues in this manner, with A always rolling first.

Analysis

1, 1	1, 2	1, 3	1, 4	1, 5	1, 6
2, 1	2, 2	2, 3	2, 4	2, 5	2, 6
3, 1	3, 2	3, 3	3, 4	3, 5	3, 6
4, 1	4, 2	4, 3	4, 4	4, 5	4, 6
5, 1	5, 2	5, 3	5, 4	5, 5	5, 6
6, 1	6, 2	6, 3	6, 4	6, 5	6, 6

The listing above gives the possible outcomes.
A's number is listed first and B's number is listed second.
B gets a point for those outcomes in black.
A gets a point for those outcomes in red.

Since 15 of the 36 possible outcomes give B a point, then the probability of B getting a point is $\frac{15}{36}$ or $\frac{5}{12}$.

Since 21 of the 36 possible outcomes give A a point, then the probability of A getting a point is $\frac{21}{36}$ or $\frac{7}{12}$.

Then, to give yourself the best chance of winning this game, you would go first.

You should also consider the number of tosses. For example, if each player tossed the die 12 times then the expected number of points won by A is $12 \times \frac{7}{12} = 7$

and the expected number of points won by B is $12 \times \frac{5}{12} = 5$

whereas if A and B each tossed the die 60 times
then the expected number of points won by A is $60 \times \frac{7}{12} = 35$

and the expected number of points won by B is $60 \times \frac{5}{12} = 25$

There is a difference of 10 between the expected number of points after 60 tosses which is a lot more than an expected difference of 2 points after 12 tosses. So the greater the number of tosses, the safer A should feel about winning.

Choose a game you often play, that involves dice or coins. Analyse this game.

Invent a game that uses dice or coins. It could be based on "Beat the Shaker". Analyse your game. Play your game with many different opponents. If you made a good analysis you should be able to win more often than you lose.

Some games, if analysed well, involve no element of chance. The following games are of this sort. You can always win these games. Each is a game for two players.
Play these games. Try to develop a winning (or non-losing) strategy.

GAMES 23:5

Counter Game : a game for two players
Materials required : 15 counters set out with 7 in
one row, 5 in another and 3 in
the other.
The Play : Players take turns to remove any number of adjacent counters from any single row.
The winner is the player to remove the last counter.

Grid Game : a game for two players
Materials required : 16 counters and a 4 × 4 grid.
The Play : Players take it in turn to place either 1, 2 or 3 counters on the grid (one counter per square). If 2 or 3 counters are put on in any one turn, then they must form an unbroken line (horizontally, vertically or diagonally).
The loser is the player who places the last counter on the grid.
Note: instead of placing counters on the squares, the squares may be coloured in.

Circle Game : a game for two players
Materials required : The diagram shown, drawn on a
piece of paper.
A blue pen for one player, a red pen
for the other.
The Play : The players take it in turn to colour a circle.
The winner is the first player to have coloured
three connected circles.

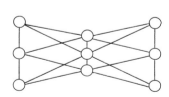

1. Find the mean, median, mode and range of the following data.

    (a) 12, 14, 14, 18, 24, 27
    (b) 3, 5, 6, 6, 7, 8, 9, 11, 12, 13, 15, 19, 24, 24, 25
    (c) 1, 2, 3, 5, 7, 9, 10, 11, 12, 14
    (d) 3, 4, 5, 1, 2, 6, 8, 3, 2, 4, 9, 4, 3, 2, 5, 8, 7, 2

    (e)

x	1	2	3	4	5
f	3	0	5	2	7

2. Write a flow diagram for the following task: Doing a set of maths. questions, checking the answers after each one is done and redoing the questions if necessary until the correct answers are obtained.
Use the following list of instructions. Place each in the correct type of operation or decision box.

    Check the answer
    Stop
    Do the next question
    Do the first question
    Any more questions?
    Start
    Answer correct?
    Do the question again

3.

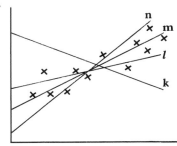

Which of the lines **k**, **l**, **m** or **n**, is a line of best fit for this data?

4. Two coins were thrown together 150 times. Two tails appeared on 42 of these tosses.
Copy and complete: (a) Fraction of "two tails" = $\frac{\cdots}{150}$

               (b) Relative frequency of "two tails" = . . .

5.

Number of cars	1-5	6-10	11-15	16-20	21-25	26-30
frequency	11	4	7	0	1	2

The 25 students in a class decided to all work on a survey on cars. Part of their survey involved each of the students going to a different location for one hour, and counting the number of cars they saw with personalised number plates. The results of this part of the survey are shown in the table above (11 students saw between 1 and 5 cars with personalised number plates, 4 saw between 6 and 10 cars etc.).

Find **(a)** the mean number of cars with personalised number plates
(b) the median class interval
(c) the modal class

6. In which of the following are the events A and B mutually exclusive?

(a) Event A : John goes to the football match
Event B : Jessie goes to the football match

(b) Event A : a diamond is drawn from a pack of cards
Event B : a picture card is drawn from a pack of cards

(c) Event A : a prime number is obtained when a die is tossed
Event B : a six is obtained when a die is tossed

7. **(a)** Copy this histogram. Draw the frequency polygon.
(b) What might the numbers on the horizontal axis represent?
(c) Make up a title for the graph.

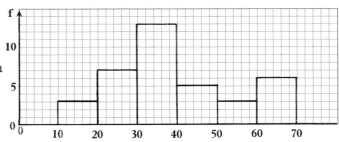

8.

Student	A.B.	D.H.	J.Z.	T.A.	M.P.	C.D.	T.W.	W.T.	E.F.	K.V.	S.T.	M.T.	D.M.	A.D.	B.P.
Time taken (seconds)	50	45	64	57	40	61	60	50	68	53	68	44	59	55	47
Number incorrect	6	5	1	4	6	3	1	4	2	6	1	6	3	5	5

Fifteen students were given 50 calculations to do mentally. The time each student took and the number of calculations each student answered incorrectly are shown in the above table.
Draw a scatter diagram for this data. (Have time on the horizontal axis.) Draw the line of best fit for this data.

9.

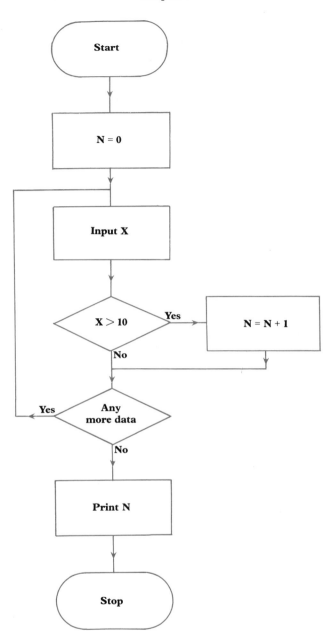

Data: 8, 11, 24, 9, 18, 7, 35, 9·8

Do a desk check for this flow diagram with the given data.
List the output.
What does this flow diagram do?

10. Jenny conducted a survey on the hours of sleep that 100 students had during one week. She collated the results onto the following frequency table.

Hours of sleep	35-40	40-45	45-50	50-55	55-60	60-65	65-70
frequency	1	4	22	29	37	5	2

Jenny then calculated an approximate value for the mean number of hours of sleep. She also found the median class interval and the modal class. What answers should Jenny have given for (a) the mean
 (b) the median class interval
 (c) the modal class

Jenny analysed the data, using her answers to (a), (b), and (c). What might Jenny have written?

11. This table gives the number of letters in the words on the last page of "An Eagle Has Landed."

No. of letters	1	2	3	4	5	6	7	8	9	10	11	12	13
frequency	6	21	34	22	21	7	10	3	0	1	1	0	1

(a) How many words are on this page?
(b) What is the relative frequency of a word having 7 letters?
(c) One word is chosen at random from this page. Estimate the probability of this word having at least 7 letters.
(d) Find the mean, median, mode and range of the data.
(e) Write a sentence or two about the data, referring to your answers to (d).

12. A card is drawn from a full 52-card pack.
Use the addition principle for probabilities to find the probability that the card drawn is either a spade or a red ace.

13. This table shows the armspan and handspan of 12 women.

Armspan (cm)	160	158	161	154	158	150	161	149	157	151	148	161
Handspan (cm)	18	20	17	19	21	19	22	22	23	18	19	21

(a) What sort of correlation would you expect there to be between armspan and handspan?
(b) Plot the data on a scatter diagram. (Plot Armspan on the horizontal axis.) Draw on a line of best fit, if you think there is one.
(c) If you think it is sensible to do so, estimate the handspan of a woman who has an armspan of 159 centimetres.

14. Sometimes Paul drives to work, sometimes he catches the bus and the rest of the time he travels by tube.
The probability that he takes the tube is 0·34.
The probability that he takes the bus is 0·26.

Find the probability that Paul
   (a) drives to work
   (b) either catches the bus or the tube
   (c) either drives or takes the bus
   (d) either drives or takes the tube

15. The following data gives the time (to the nearest minute) for a number of people to complete a "village to village run." Data is given for those aged under 30 and for those aged 30 or more.

Under 30	32	43	51	35	39	42	45	54	38	62	39	34
	41	55	39	44	34	58	64	43	47	46	49	32
	41	52	39	48	52	44	38	34	39	40	61	50
	55	37	42	52	53	54	37	49	38			
30 or older	43	41	38	51	52	54	49	53	54	39	45	48
	55	58	57	43	39	47	51	49	54	50	42	38
	40	58	54	50	48	51	38	42	34	47	52	54
	36	42	58	53	47	49	54	55	56			

   (a) Use tally charts to sort each of these sets of data into the categories 30– , 35– , 40– , 45– , 50– , 55– , 60–65.
   (b) Draw up frequency tables with class intervals 30– , 35– , etc. for each set of data.
   (c) On the same set of axes, draw the frequency polygons for the "under 30" data and for the "30 or older" data.
   (d) Use the frequency polygons to compare the data. Write a few sentences noting any differences or similarities.

16. Construct a flow diagram which increases all the odd numbers input by 1 and leaves the even numbers unchanged.
Do a desk check of your flow diagram using the following numbers as input:
   3, 15, 6, 0.

17. Take a newspaper or magazine and count the number of advertisements on each page.

    (a) Copy the following table. Collate your results onto this table.

No. of advertisements	0	1	2	3	4	5	6	7	8 or more
Frequency									
Relative freq.									

    (b) Find the relative frequency of the number of advertisements and complete the last line of the table.

    (c) Estimate the probability of a page, chosen at random, having 5 advertisements.

    (d) If you repeated (a) to (c) again, with a different newspaper or magazine, would you expect the estimate of the probability of a page having 5 advertisements to be the same?

18. Design an experiment to estimate the probability of a paper clip, dropped from a height, landing across parallel lines drawn on a piece of paper.

19. Would you expect there to be correlation between the height of a student and the amount of sleep a student has?
    Make an hypothesis about this.
    Conduct a survey to test your hypothesis. Design and use a questionnaire to collect the data. Use a scatter diagram to help in your analysis of the data.

INDEX

SUPPLEMENT for LEVEL 7

CONTENTS

MEASUREMENT ACCURACY

DISCUSSION EXERCISE 25:1

Draw a square of side 10cm.
Draw in both diagonals.

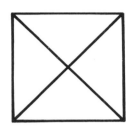

Measure the length of one diagonal, to the nearest mm.
Measure the length of the other diagonal, to the nearest mm.

Discuss your answers with the rest of your group or your class or your neighbour.
Discuss possible reasons for getting different answers.

"No measurement is exact". **Discuss** this statement.

A student estimated the length of a corridor to be 20 metres. How might the student have estimated this? **Discuss.**

When the student measured the length of this corridor he got an answer which was quite different from his estimate. What might have gone wrong? **Discuss.**

Think of a situation where someone you know (maybe yourself) has measured inaccurately and this has mattered. **Discuss.**

The accuracy of a measurement depends on how accurately the measuring instrument used can be read and on how accurately this is actually read.

DISCUSSION EXERCISE 25:2

1.

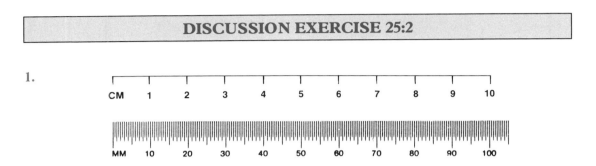

Measure the length of a small object, such as a paper clip, using both of the measuring instruments shown above.
Did everyone in your group get the same measurement using the ruler with cm divisions?
Did everyone in your group get the same measurement using the ruler with mm divisions?
Discuss.

Measure the length of another small object using the ruler with mm divisions. Measure again. Did you get the same answer both times? Would it have been easy (or was it easy) to get different answers?
Discuss possible reasons for getting different answers.
Discuss ways of measuring as accurately as possible.

2. The ruler is one instrument used to measure length. What other measuring instruments are used for length? Discuss.

3. Mass, capacity, time are other things that need to be measured. What measuring instruments are used for these? Discuss.

4.

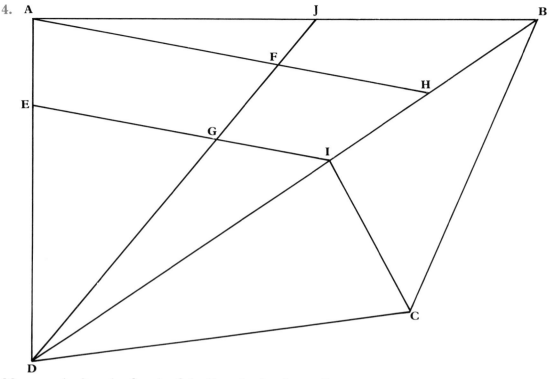

Measure the length of each of the lines in the above diagram.

Compare your measurements with those of the rest of your group or class or neighbour. If your measurements differ from those of other students, how can you decide whose measurement is most accurate? **Discuss.**

PRACTICAL EXERCISE 25:3

Athletics events which are now timed electronically were not always timed with such precision.

Research one of the following: Olympic Games
Horse Racing
Yacht Racing
Speedway

Pay particular attention to the way in which measurements, in the topic you choose, have increased in accuracy throughout the years.

Write a project on your research.

EFFECT of MEASUREMENT ERRORS

Sometimes an error in measurement is very important and sometimes it is quite unimportant. It depends on the size of the error and the particular situation.

DISCUSSION EXERCISE 25:4

1. Anna measured a length to be 4cm shorter than it actually was. How important would this error be in the following situations? **Discuss.**

   Situation 1   Anna was measuring the length of her room, to enable her to calculate the cost of buying carpet for the room.
   Situation 2   Anna was measuring the length of a card, to enable her to purchase a box of the right size for these cards.

   List some other situations where an error in the measurement of length would be important and others where it would be unimportant. **Discuss.**

2. Abe was unaware that his watch was 5 minutes slow. How important is this in the following situations? **Discuss.**

   Situation 1   Abe has to catch the 0805 train.
   Situation 2   Abe is going to spend 20 minutes on his aerobics.

   List some other situations where an error in the measurement of time would be important and others where it would be unimportant. **Discuss.**

3. **Discuss** the effect of measurement errors in these situations.

   Situation 1   A customer asks for 3·8m of dress fabric. The shop assistant measures incorrectly and gives the customer 3·6m.
   Situation 2   A customer asks for 20·5m of curtain fabric. The shop assistant measures incorrectly and gives the customer 20·6m.

4. **Discuss** the effect of measurement errors in these situations.

   Situation 1   Natasha asked for 100 grams of caviar. She was given 150 grams.
   Situation 2   Ben was baking a chocolate cake. The recipe said 200g of butter was needed. Ben measured incorrectly and used just 190g of butter.

CHOOSING the DEGREE of ACCURACY

All measurements are approximate. For instance, a length could be measured to the nearest mm or nearest cm or nearest m or nearest km. Whether we choose to give the length to the nearest mm or cm or m or km depends on how accurate we need the measure to be.

DISCUSSION EXERCISE 25:5

1. A fashion designer cuts the pattern pieces for a dress for his daughter.
   How inaccurate can the pattern pieces be cut and still have the dress fitting satisfactorily? Discuss.

2. To build a house, what measurements are needed?
   How accurate do these have to be? Do some need to be more accurate than others? Discuss.

3. Do the lengths of some sports fields and tracks need to be known more accurately than others? Discuss.

4. Can you think of any circumstances in which it would be necessary to have road distances given more accurately than shown by signposts? Discuss.

   FAREHAM 13

5. Think of things you or your family would be likely to buy by the length. Would you buy these things by the metre or centimetre or millimetre? Discuss.

6. Think of things you or your family would be likely to buy by weight or volume.
   Discuss whether you would buy by the gram or kilogram or tonne or millilitre or litre.

7. Discuss the importance of manufactured goods being of the weight claimed (or the volume claimed) on the label.

8. The spring balance and the electronic pan balance are two weighing instruments.
   What things would you weigh using an electronic pan balance? Discuss.

   Three instruments used to measure length are the ruler, callipers and the micrometer screw gauge.
   In what situations would it be appropriate to use each of these? Discuss.

   What are the burette and measuring cylinder used to measure? In what situations would it be more appropriate to use a burette? Discuss.

   Discuss instruments for measuring time. Discuss situations in which it would be more appropriate to use one of the instruments rather than another.

EXERCISE 25:6

1.

$$l \quad ml \quad \text{tonne} \quad \text{kg} \quad \text{g}$$
$$\text{km} \quad \text{m} \quad \text{cm} \quad \text{mm}$$

Which unit of measurement would you use for each of the following? Choose from those given in the box.

(a) distance between two towns

(b) distance between your chair and the classroom door

(c) weight of a chocolate

(d) length of a corridor

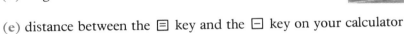

(e) distance between the ⊟ key and the ⊟ key on your calculator

(f) the width of a river

(g) the weight of a loaded lorry

(h) the amount of cough medicine in a bottle

(i) the thickness of a pane of glass in a window

(j) the weight of a bicycle

(k) the capacity of the petrol tank of a car

2. Write down at least two things you would measure to each of the following degrees of accuracy.

(a) to the nearest hour

(b) to the nearest 5 min.

(c) to the nearest min.

(d) to the nearest sec.

(e) to the nearest $\frac{1}{10}$ of a sec.

Review   Write down two things, other than those in **question 1** that you would measure to each of the following degrees of accuracy.

(a) to the nearest m

(b) to the nearest *l*

(c) to the nearest mm

(d) to the nearest g

(e) to the nearest kg

(f) to the nearest *ml*

PRACTICAL EXERCISE 25:7

1. Choose the degree of accuracy needed to measure a variety of lengths around your school.
   Decide whether you need to use a trundle wheel or metre tape or ruler with cm and/or mm divisions or a micrometer screw gauge.

   Measure these lengths as accurately as you can with the measuring instruments you choose.

   Be sure to measure long distances such as the length of a school field and very short lengths such as the thickness of a door hinge.

 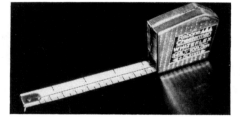 

2. Design an experiment, such as measuring reaction time, to measure small intervals of time.
   Choose the degree of accuracy you will use.

3. Choose five objects to weigh.
   Choose the degree of accuracy you will use.
   Compare your results with those of the other members of your group.

4. Choose five jars or bottles such as a tomato sauce bottle etc.
   Find the capacity of these.
   Choose the degree of accuracy you will use.
   Compare your results with those of the other members of your group.

INVESTIGATION 25:8

DEVICES to measure TIME

The first of the modern day timing devices was the pendulum clock. This was invented in the 17th century.
Before this, many other devices were used to measure time. Some of the devices used to measure a small interval of time were: The Water Clock
Sinking Bowl Clock
Candle Clock

These worked on the following principles.

The Candle Clock
Marks were made at equal distances down the side of a candle.
How close do you think these marks might be if it took 5 minutes to burn the length of candle between two adjacent marks?

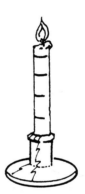

The Water Clock
A container, such as that shown, was filled with water.
The water dripped out of a hole at the bottom.
Marks were made on the inside of the container. Equal intervals of time were read off by watching the level drop from one mark to the next.
Do you think the marks should be equally spaced on the container shown?

Sinking Bowl Clock
A small bowl, with a hole in the bottom, was placed in a large container of water. The time it took for the bowl to sink measured a particular interval of time.

Investigate the accuracy of the Water Clock, the Sinking Bowl Clock and the Candle Clock.

Design and make a timing device to measure a short interval of time, perhaps 2 minutes or 5 minutes.
You may like to base your design on one of the timing devices above or you may like to design quite a different sort of device.
Experiment to make your timing device as accurate as possible.

COMPOUND MEASURES: SPEED

Tina ran 100m in 25 seconds.
James ran 200m in 48 seconds.
How fast did Tina run? How fast did James run? **Discuss.**

In chemistry, Dale and Andrea both made salt solutions.
Dale used 10g of salt to 50*ml* of water; Andrea used 20g of salt to 80*ml* of water.

In each of the above, two measurements are made.
What two measurements are made to find speed?
What two measurements are made to make the salt solution?

Discuss other things that you do that involve compound measures; that is, things that involve a combination of two measurements.

Think of things around the school that involve compound measures.
Think of things in the grounds, in the canteen, in the laboratory and in the workshop.
Discuss.

Tina's speed for the 100m was 4 metres per second i.e. 4m/s.
Dale's salt solution was 10g per 50*ml* or 0·2g/*ml*.

That is, Tina's speed was measured as 4m/s; Dale's salt solution was measured as 0·2g/*ml*.

How might the things around the school, that you discussed above, be measured?
Discuss.

SPEED

If it takes a car 1 hour to travel 90km, we say its average speed is 90km per hour or 90km/h.

That is, if the car had travelled at a speed of exactly 90km/h all the way, it would have taken 1 hour to travel the 90km.

This is unlikely to happen. Some of the journey would have been travelled at a speed greater than 90km/h and some of the journey would have been travelled at a slower speed. We cannot say anything about the speed during parts of the journey. We can only say that the average speed is 90km/h since it took 1 hour to travel the 90km.

$$\text{average speed} = \frac{\text{distance travelled}}{\text{time taken}}$$

Speed is usually measured in kilometres per hour (km/h)
or metres per second (m/s)
or miles per hour (mph)

Worked Example Yvonne cycles a distance of 48km in $2\frac{1}{2}$ hours. Find Yvonne's average speed.

Answer average speed = $\frac{\text{distance}}{\text{time}}$

$$= \frac{48}{2 \cdot 5}$$

$$= 19 \cdot 2 \text{km/h}$$

Worked Example A bus travels the 14km from Llangurig to Rhayader in 18 minutes. Find the average speed of this bus.

Answer We will give the average speed in km/h. To do this we need the distance in km (which it is) and the time in hours.

18 min = $\frac{18}{60}$ hours

$\qquad$ = 0·3 hours

average speed = $\frac{\text{distance}}{\text{time}}$

$$= \frac{14}{0 \cdot 3}$$

$$= 47 \text{km/h (to 2 s.f.)}$$

Worked Example   Ali ran the 800m in 2 min 48 sec. What was Ali's average speed, in metres per second?

Answer   2 min 48 sec = 168 sec

average speed = $\frac{\text{distance}}{\text{time}}$

= $\frac{800}{168}$

= 4·8m/s (to 1 d.p.)

The formula   average speed = $\frac{\text{distance}}{\text{time}}$ may be rewritten as

distance = average speed × time   or   **time = $\frac{\text{distance}}{\text{average speed}}$**

Worked Example   Catherine walks at an average speed of 1·4m/s for 2·6km. How long does this take Catherine?

Answer   Since the speed is given in m/s, we will use metres for the distance and seconds for the time.

2·6km = 2600m

time = $\frac{\text{distance}}{\text{average speed}}$

= $\frac{2600}{1·4}$

= 1857 sec (to the nearest second)

This is, Catherine walks for 30 minutes 57 sec, or nearly 31 minutes.

Worked Example   **A train travels at an average speed of 108km/h for 2 hours 13 min. How far has the train travelled?**

Answer   2 hours 13 min = $2\frac{13}{60}$ hours

= 2·22 hours (3 s.f.)

It is better not to round until the final step of the answer.

We will use $2\frac{13}{60}$ rather than 2·22 in the distance calculation.

distance = average speed × time

= $108 × 2\frac{13}{60}$

= 239·4km   **Key** 108 ⊠ [2 + 13 ÷ 60] =

EXERCISE 25:10

Where rounding is necessary in this exercise, round to 1 decimal place.

1. Find the average jogging speed, in km/h, of the following students.

   (a) Amanda jogs 18km in 3 hours.

   (b) Amy jogs 8km in 1 hour 15 minutes.

   (c) Kayla jogs 9km in $1\frac{1}{2}$ hours.

2. Lex walks 8km in 1 hour 40 minutes.

   Find Lex's average speed.

3.

Distance travelled	Time taken	Average speed
100km	1 hr 30 min	
100km	1 hr 45 min	
100km	1 hr 20 min	
100km	1 hr 25 min	

This table shows the time taken for four different cars to travel 100km from Oxford to Birmingham.

Copy and complete this table.

4. A student runs the 100m in 28 secs.
   What is this student's average speed in m/s?

5. Another student runs the 400m in 1 min 15 sec.
   What is this student's average speed, in metres per second, for the 400m?

6. A runner sets out at midday to run to the next village, a distance of 12km. She wants to arrive at this village at 1330 hours.
   At what average speed should she run?

7.

Time	11:00	12:00	12:30	13:00
Speedometer reading (km)	46825	46897	46897	46938

This table shows the speedometer reading on Julian's car at certain times during his journey north.

(a) At what average speed did Julian travel between 11:00 and 12:00?

(b) At what average speed did he travel between 12:30 and 13:00?

(c) What distance did Julian travel between 12:00 and 12:30?
Explain your answer.

8. An albatross is cruising at an average speed of 90km/h.
What distance does the albatross cruise in
(a) 2 hours
(b) three-quarters of an hour

9. Annabel ran a road race at an average speed of 6km/h. She completed this race in 2 hours 15 minutes.
How long was this road race?

10.

Average Speed (km/h)	Time taken (hrs & min)	Time taken (hrs)	Distance (km)
80	2 hr 30 min		
70	4 hr 15 min		
90	1 hr 45 min		
60	2 hr 12 min		
50	1 hr 36 min		

Copy and complete this table.

11. A train is travelling at 120km/h.
How far does this train travel between 0720 hours and 0800 hours?

12. A bus travels the 200km between Bristol and Plymouth at an average speed of 80km/h.
How long does the bus take for this journey?

13. The table given below shows the maximum speed of some very fast animals. It also shows the distance for which they are able to run at that speed.

Animal	Top speed in metres per second	Distance in metres
cheetah	28	500m
racehorse	18	300m
antelope	15·5	6000m
deer	12·5	32000m

Calculate the time for which each of these animals is able to run at maximum speed. (Give the answers to the nearest second.)

Review

	Aberdeen					
Brighton	991	**Brighton**				
Bristol	846	253	**Bristol**			
Cardiff	877	307	74	**Cardiff**		
Dover	1025	135	320	375	**Dover**	
Exeter	967	291	135	195	451	**Exeter**
London	898	85	195	249	122	325

This distance chart gives the distances in kilometres, between some places in Great Britain.

Give the answers to the following questions to the nearest whole number.

(a) How long would it take to travel from London to Exeter at an average speed of 100km/h? (Answer in hours and minutes.)

(b) Anna leaves Bristol at 9:20a.m. and arrives at Dover at 12:50p.m. What was Anna's average speed?

(c) Steven drove from Brighton to Bristol, then from Bristol to Exeter. If this journey took Steve 5 hours, what was his average speed?

(d) Susan drove from Brighton at an average speed of 80km/h for just over $3\frac{1}{2}$ hours. Where was Susan going to — Bristol or Exeter?

Supplement page 15

DISCUSSION EXERCISE 25:11

1. Jane's top running speed is 15km/h.
   Jessie's top running speed is 10m/sec.

   To find whether Jane or Jessie is the fastest, both running speeds must be given in either km/h or m/sec. **Discuss** how this could be done.

2. Rachel counted the number of seconds it took to travel past a train that had stopped. She also noted the speed, in km/h, at which her car was travelling.
   Rachel then worked out the length of the train.

   How did she do this? **Discuss.**

3. What other lengths or distances could be worked out using the method Rachel used in **question 2**? **Discuss.**

PRACTICAL EXERCISE 25:12

1. Design an experiment to find the average jogging or running or cycling speed for each student in your group. You will need to measure both distance and time as accurately as possible. Discuss how you will do this with the equipment you have available.

    Conduct the experiment you have designed.

2. What is walking? What is jogging? What is running?
    As a group, define the rules for "normal walking" and for "fastest possible walking."

    Design and carry out an experiment to find the difference between "fastest walking speed" and "normal walking speed" for each student in your group or class.

3. Discuss how you could estimate the average speed for students who walk to school, for those who cycle to school and for those who travel to school by car or bus or train.
    Do some of these estimates.

4. Use your library or local RAC or AA or automobile club to research the maximum speeds of cars. You could also get information from pamphlets on new cars.
    You could consider just present day cars or cars throughout this century. You could consider just British cars or foreign cars. You could consider just one type of car such as the racing car.

5. Do a project on the speeds of animals and birds.

INVESTIGATION 25:13

SPEED versus COST

"The faster a car travels, the more petrol per km it uses."
Do you think this statement is true?

Using the current price of petrol, and the petrol consumption at various speeds, investigate "speed versus cost" for one make and model of car.

COMPOUND MEASURES: DENSITY

Some parts of the New Forest are denser than others. What do we mean by "denser"?
Discuss.

"Yoghurt is denser than milk."
"Roast lamb is denser than a pork pie."
Discuss these statements.

Discuss how the following statements might be completed.
    "___ is denser than air."
    "Water is denser than ___."
    "Nails are denser than ___."
    "___ is denser than hair."

Do you think cornflakes are denser than sugar?
Imagine this box is filled to the top with sugar.
Imagine an identical box filled to the top with cornflakes.

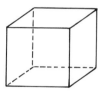

Is the volume of both boxes the same?
Which box is heavier — the box of sugar or the box of cornflakes?
Is the mass of the empty boxes the same?
What can you say about the mass of the cornflakes and the mass of the sugar in the boxes?

What can you say about the ratios $\dfrac{\text{mass of cornflakes}}{\text{volume of cornflakes}}$, $\dfrac{\text{mass of sugar}}{\text{volume of sugar}}$? **Discuss.**

Density compares mass with volume. $\boxed{\textbf{density} = \dfrac{\textbf{mass}}{\textbf{volume}}}$

The unit of measurement for density is g/cm³ or kg/m³.

If mass is measured in grams, volume is measured in cubic centimetres.
Density is then given in grams per cubic centimetre.
That is, density is given in g/cm³.

If mass is measured in kilograms, volume is measured in cubic metres.
Density is then given in kilograms per cubic metre.
That is, density is given in kg/m³.

Worked Example A 20cm³ piece of steel has a mass of 150g.
What is the density of this piece of steel?

Answer density = $\frac{\text{mass}}{\text{volume}}$

$= \frac{150}{20}$

$= 7{\cdot}5\text{g/cm}^3$

Worked Example A 200cm³ piece of metal has a mass of 1·2kg.
Find the density of this metal.

Answer Since the volume is given in cubic centimetres, we need the mass in grams for the density calculation.

1·2kg = 1200g   density = $\frac{\text{mass}}{\text{volume}}$

$= \frac{1200}{200}$

$= 6\text{g/cm}^3$

The formula for density can be written in one of the following ways.

density = $\frac{\text{mass}}{\text{volume}}$ mass = density × volume   volume = $\frac{\text{mass}}{\text{density}}$

If we are finding density we use **density = $\frac{\text{mass}}{\text{volume}}$.**

If we are finding mass we use **mass = density × volume.**

If we are finding volume we use **volume = $\frac{\text{mass}}{\text{density}}$.**

Worked Example It is known that the density of cork is 0·25g/cm³. The mass of a piece of this cork is measured as 165g. What is its volume?

Answer volume = $\frac{\text{mass}}{\text{density}}$

$= \frac{165}{0{\cdot}25}$

$= 660\text{cm}^3$

Volumes of liquids are usually given in *ml* rather than cubic centimetres.
The relationship is 1*ml* = 1cm³

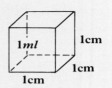

Worked Example   The label on the outside of a bottle of turpentine is shown. How much do the contents of this bottle weigh if the density of the turpentine is 0·86g/cm³?

Answer   700*ml* = 700cm³

mass = density × volume
      = 0·86 × 700
      = 602g

That is, the weight of the turpentine in the bottle is 602g.

EXERCISE 25:15

1. A 30cm³ piece of lead has a mass of 345g.
   What is the density of this lead?

2. The mass of a 1200*ml* block of ice is 1104 grams.
   Find the density of the ice.

3. A piece of cork weighs 10kg. Its volume is 0·04m³.
   Find the density of this cork.

4. Two models are cast from metal.
   One model is made from 40cm³ of brass. This model weighs 340g.
   The other model is made from 50cm³ of iron. This model weighs 375g.

   Find the densities of the two metals used in the models.

5. A stone weighs 4·4kg.

   (a) What is the mass of this stone in grams?

   (b) Find the volume (in cm³) of this stone if its density is 2·2g/cm³.

6. The density of mercury is 14·6g/cm³.
   How many *ml* of mercury weighs 73 grams?

7. A statue is made from clay of density 1·4g/cm³.
   Another statue is carved from wood of density 0·8g/cm³.

   Both statues are weighed to find their masses.
   The wooden one is found to have a mass of 4500g. The clay
   one has a mass of 7700g.

   Which statue has the greater volume?

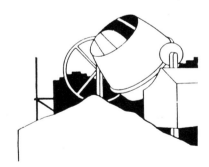

8. The density of glass in an ornament is 2·5g/cm³.
   Michaela finds the volume of this ornament to be 45cm³.
   She then calculates its mass. What answer should she get?

9. Water has a density of 1g/cm³.
   How much does 1·5*l* of water weigh?

Review 1   The volume of a pane of glass is 1000cm³. This pane weighs 2·4kg.

   (a) What is the mass of the pane of glass in grams?

   (b) Find the density of this glass.

Review 2   Joanne is mixing and pouring concrete.
   Altogether she mixes and pours 2·4m³.
   How much does this 2·4m³ of concrete weigh
   if its density is 2500kg/m³?

Review 3   A piece of Cheddar cheese has a mass of 750g.
   A piece of Edam cheese has a mass of 720g.

   The density of the Cheddar cheese is 1·8g/cm³ while that of the Edam cheese
   is 1·7g/cm³.

   Which piece of cheese has the greater volume?

INVESTIGATION 25:16

FINDING DENSITIES

It is claimed that Archimedes was in the bath
when he realised how the volume of any object
could be worked out.
How can you work out volumes using a
measuring jar partly filled with water?
Investigate.

How can you find the density of any object?
Investigate.

OTHER COMPOUND MEASURES

Ratio is often used to solve problems with compound measures.

Worked Example   Cornflour is used to thicken a mixture, at the rate of 30g/*l*.
How much cornflour is needed to thicken 400*ml*?

Answer   Ratio of cornflour to mixture = 30g : 1*l*
= 30g : 1000*ml*
If x is the amount of cornflour needed to thicken 400*ml*,
then x : 400 = 30 : 1000

$$\frac{x}{400} = \frac{30}{1000}$$
$$x = 12$$

That is, 12g of cornflour is needed.

Worked Example   15 litres of water flows from a hose in 20 seconds.
Give this rate of flow in *l*/sec.

Answer   If x is the number of litres of water that flows in 1 second,
then x : 1 = 15 : 20

$$\frac{x}{1} = \frac{15}{20}$$
$$x = 0 \cdot 75$$

That is, the rate of flow is 0·75*l*/sec.

EXERCISE 25:17

1. Aaron's car uses oil at the rate of 500*ml*/2000km.
   How much oil does Aaron's car use on a journey of 500km?

2. Grain was spilling from a hopper at the rate of 2kg/sec.
   How long did it take for 1 tonne to spill?

3. The flour output from a mill was 20 tonne/hour.
   What was the output every 15 minutes?

4. Gravy is made by mixing gravy powder with water at the rate of 50g/*l*.
   How much water is needed with 20g of gravy powder?

5. Shalome mixes a spray for her plants. She mixes 50g of spray powder with 10*l* of water.
   The instructions on the packet of powder were given in g/*l*. What were these instructions?

6. James applies 6kg of fertilizer to a 200 square metre lawn.
   Find the rate of application of this fertilizer in g/m².

7. Gayle used 5 litres of paint to paint an area of 80m².
   Give the quantity of paint that Gayle used in m²/*l*.

8. Every hour, an ice cream manufacturer makes 120 litres of ice cream.
   Give this in *l*/min.

Review 1   Jake made a breakfast drink by mixing flavouring powder with water at the rate of 50g/*l*.
   How much flavouring powder does Jake use if he uses 400*ml* of water?

Review 2   A car travels 300km on 20*l* of petrol.
   Give the petrol consumption rate of this car in km/*l*.

PRACTICAL EXERCISE 25:18

Design and carry out an experiment to measure a compound measure other than speed or density.

You could consider measuring pulse rate or breathing rate or flow rate of water from a tap.

Number from Previous Levels

Revision Exercise

1. (a) mm (b) m (c) l (d) t (e) mg (f) km   2. C   3. (b) 55   4. $\frac{15}{40}$ 6. 6·7cm or
67mm   7. (a) 87·2 (b) 7·03 (c) 0·205   8. (a) 3 (b) 0 (c) 0 (d) 9   9. (a) 0·4
(b) 0·05 (c) 20 (d) 4   10. (a) 2500 (b) 50 (c) 28·41 (d) 13400 (e) 0·345 (f) 0·034
(g) 230   11. $\frac{1}{2}$, $\frac{5}{9}$, $\frac{2}{3}$, $\frac{3}{4}$, $\frac{4}{5}$, $\frac{6}{7}$ 12. (a) 50000mm = 50m (b) 1250m (c) 3km
(d) 4km (e) Little Wadd Farm   13. (a) 17 (b) 16800 (c) 94 (d) 64 (e) 19488 (f) 26
(g) 27   14. 2·09, 2·146, 2·4, 2·6, 2·614, 2·64, 3·064, 3·46, 3·6, 3·61   15. 31 bicycles and 13
tricycles   16. a, d, e   17. −1·8 at A, −1·3 at B, −1 at C, −0·6 at D   18. D   19. (a) 4 : 3
(b) 15cm   20. (a) $\frac{3}{5}$ (b) $\frac{4}{25}$ (c) $\frac{7}{100}$ (d) $\frac{6}{125}$ 21. £237·16   22. (a) 1 : 3 (b) 16 : 75
(c) 26 : 7   23. 1840, 1916, 1992, 2000   24. £16·50   26. 1·2l 27. (a) True (b) True
(c) False   28. There is more than one answer. One possible answer is four 1sts, seven 2nds,
three 3rds.   29. They are all the same as $\frac{6}{15}$.   30. No   31. £12600   32. (a) 3 (b) 9
(c) 15 (d) 1·5   33. (a) 374 (b) 29·1% (c) 41·5% (d) 16 more tested ; an increase of 4·5%
(e) 35·3   34. 1005 hours   35. 504   36. (a) 50ml (b) about $1\frac{3}{4}$ pints (c) about 1000
(d) about 9 pints (e) 1800 grams

Chapter 1   Problem Solving

Exercise 1:1

1. 11   2. 3   3. Eade boy   4. $3\frac{1}{2}$ hours   5. Tuesday   6. 20 along each side and 1 at each
corner if the path is one slab wide. The path could be three slabs wide; the 84 slabs would then
be sufficient to border a square with side the same length as 4 slabs.   7. Coopers at 17,
Andersons at 19, Taylors at 21   8. 65   9. A–Megan, B–Rebecca, C–Annabel, D–Heather,
E–Lisa   10. at least 3   **Review 1** Jake–collie, Paz–terrier, Churchill–labrador,
Millie–spaniel   **Review 2** 60

Chapter 2   Calculation

Exercise 2:2

1. a, c, d, g, i, j will have answers less than 200. b, e, f, h, k will have answers greater than 200.
2. b, e, f, h, i have answers less than 0·4. a, c, d, g, j will have answers greater than 0·4.
3. (a) 16 (b) 0·16 (c) 100 (d) 1000 (e) 200000 (f) 18 (g) 0·5 (h) 2000 (i) 0·8
(j) 60 (k) 200 (l) 0·04 (m) 4 (n) 0·16 (o) 0·005 (p) 50 (q) 0·027 (r) 300
4. 240m   5. £16   6. £0·27   **Review 1** (a) 200 (b) 1·8 (c) 18 (d) 200
Review 2 £200

Exercise 2:3

1. D   2. £6·40   3. 176km   4. £27·12   5. (a) just over 53 litres   (b) about 375km
(c) Yes (d) about 21km   6. (a) 157·5 metres   (b) 105   (c) £47·25   (d) 9 hours
Review 13

Puzzle 2:5

Reduced by 23 pence.

Exercise 2:8

1. (a) ⬛1⬛ should be keyed instead of the first ⬛=⬛
(b) ⬛1⬛ should be keyed before ⬛=⬛   (c) another ⬛1⬛ should be keyed instead of the first ⬛=⬛
(d) needs ⬛[⬛ keyed before the 4 and ⬛]⬛ after the 2 (or the second ⬛×⬛ replaced by ⬛÷⬛)
(e) needs ⬛1⬛ keyed after the 1   2. (a) 3 (b) 6 (c) 7 (d) 16 (e) 4 (f) 7 (g) 3
(h) 3 (i) 2 (j) 1·5 (k) 1 (l) 2 (m) 3   3. (a) 3 (b) 6 (c) 7 (d) 16 (e) 4 (f) 7
(g) 3 (h) 3 (i) 2 (j) 1·5 (k) 1 (l) 2 (m) 3   4. (a) 4·5 (b) 3·22 (c) 4·15 (d) 2·03
(e) 13 (f) 0·994 (g) 1·45 (h) 0·916 (i) 2·34 (j) 6·72   5. (a) 3 m/s^2 (b) 1·19m/s^2
(c) 4·3m/s^2 (2s.f.)   6. (a) 8m (b) 6·864m (c) 29·512m   7. (a) 1·263m (b) 30·663m
8. 4·8m/s^2 (2s.f.)   Review 1 (a) 4·5 (b) 3 (c) 2·1   Review 2 (a) 2·5 (b) 2·0 (c) 19

Exercise 2:13

1. (a) $2 \times 2 \times 7$ (b) $3 \times 3 \times 7$ (c) $2 \times 2 \times 2 \times 2 \times 2 \times 2 \times 2$ (d) $2 \times 3 \times 5 \times 7$
(e) $3 \times 3 \times 5 \times 5$ (f) 17 (g) $2 \times 2 \times 2 \times 2 \times 3 \times 3$ (h) $2 \times 3 \times 3 \times 7$ (i) $2 \times 7 \times 11$
(j) $2 \times 3 \times 31$ 2. (a) 16 (b) 2 (c) 14 (d) 20 (e) 15 (f) 36 (g) 1 (h) 2 (i) 6
3. (a) 96 (b) 480 (c) 42 (d) 1700 (e) 450 (f) 504 (g) 119 (h) 720 (i) 2160
4. Yes, January 21st   Review (a) $78 = 2 \times 3 \times 13$, $240 = 2 \times 2 \times 2 \times 2 \times 3 \times 5$,
$420 = 2 \times 2 \times 3 \times 5 \times 7$ (b) 6 (c) 1680

Chapter 3   Error in Measurement

Exercise 3:2

1. greatest number = 1704, least number = 1695   2. greatest number = 262449,
least number = 262350   3. (a) 7mm (b) 5mm (c) 2mm (d) 1mm (e) 15mm
(f) 18mm (g) 8mm (h) 1mm (i) 25mm   4. a, b, c, f, g   5. c, i   6. a, e, g, h
Review 1   greatest number = 844, least number = 835   Review 2 b, d, e

Exercise 3:4

1. C   2. B   3. C   4. A   5. (a) 0·5km (b) 0·05 sec (c) 0·005*l* (d) 0·5kg (e) 0·5kg
(f) 0·005 sec (g) 0·05cm (h) 0·005km (i) 0·5 sec (j) 0·005*l*   6. (a) 500m (b) 50m
(c) 50m (d) 5m (e) 500m   Review 1 B   Review 2 (a) 0·5 g (b) 0·05kg (c) 0·005g
(d) 0·5kg

Chapter 4   Number Review

Page 50

1. b, d   2. (a) 2000   (b) 80   3. 15   4. greatest number = 144, least number = 135
5. (a) $\boxed{[}$ needed before 18 and $\boxed{]}$ needed after 24 **or** $\boxed{=}$ needed after 24
(b) another $\boxed{]}$ needed after the first $\boxed{]}$ (c) the second $\boxed{\text{Min}}$ should be $\boxed{\text{MR}}$ 6. e, g, h
7. 6   8. (a) 11·75   (b) 2   9. (a) 26·55km   (b) 26·45km   10. (a) 2·79   (b) 24·6   (c) 8·75
11. (a) £129·50   (b) 72   (c) £19·05   (d) 13   12. B   13. Jimmy owns Jess,
John owns Julip, Justin owns Jip   14. C   15. 1·1 m/s² (to 1d.p.)   16. 0·05m
17. (a) $24 = 2 \times 2 \times 2 \times 3$, $45 = 3 \times 3 \times 5$, $68 = 2 \times 2 \times 17$, $120 = 2 \times 2 \times 2 \times 3 \times 5$ (b) 15
(c) 408

Algebra from Previous Levels

Page 57   **Revision Exercise**

1. (a) 4   (b) 4   (c) 27   (d) 15   (e) 14   2. 56664   3. (a) a^2 (b) 2a   (c) n   (d) $4x^2$
(e) 2n   (f) 10ab   (g) 4a – n   4. a cuboid (box)   5. 20   6. (a) 16   (b) 2   (c) 64
(d) 8·5 (to 1d.p.)   (e) 31·9 (to 1d.p.)   (f) 2   7. (a) 12n – 21   (b) 16n – 15   8. 2n – 3
9. (a) 7·5   (b) 13   (c) 3·375   (d) 3   (e) 3·5   10. (a) 3h + 16 = 5h – 2   (b) 9
11. (b) (0, 0), (20, 25), (40, 50), (80, 100)   (d) Tamara - 95%, Timothy - 35%, Tewfik - 56%
13.

14. 6   15. (a) $3x – 16° = x + 40°$; x = 28°
(b) $3x + 2x + x + 30° = 180°$; x = 25°
16. (a) divide by 10 ; 0·05, 0·005, 0·0005
(b) multiply by 2 ; 48, 96, 192   (c) add 3 ; 15, 18, 21
(d) three times the square of the number that gives the
position of the term ; 75, 108, 147
(e) add the two previous terms ; 13, 21, 34
17. 2·3 (to 1d.p.)   18. 181
19. (a) 4n + 3 = 2n + 12 ; n = 4·5   (b) 18cm
20. 3·3 (to 1d.p.)   21. £406
22. One possible program is: 10   FOR N = 5 TO 104
                              20   PRINT 4 * N
                              30   NEXT N
                              40   END

23. (a)

x	–2	–1	0	1	2
y	7	4	3	4	7

(b)

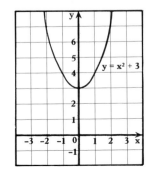

Chapter 5   Sequences

Exercise 5:3

1. **(a)** **(i)** 6 **(ii)** 9 **(iii)** n + 1 **(b)** $t_n = n + 1$ **(c)** 26 **(d)** 36   2. **(a)** 9 **(b)** $t_n = 2n + 1$
(c) 41   3. **(a)** 5, 8, 11, . . . **(b)** 14 **(c)** 3n + 2 **(d)** 11 **(e)** 74   4. **(a)** $t_n = 3n$ **(b)** $t_n = n + 3$
(c) $t_n = 4n + 2$ **(d)** $t_n = 4n + 1$ **(e)** $t_n = 4n - 1$ **(f)** $t_n = 5n - 4$ **(g)** $t_n = -3n + 55$
(h) $t_n = -2n + 6$ **(i)** $t_n = 4n - 9$ **(j)** $t_n = -2n$ **(k)** $t_n = -3n + 3$ 5. **(a)** $t_n = 3n + 1$; t_{33}
(b) $t_n = 5n - 3$; t_{40} **(c)** $t_n = -2n + 9$; t_{12} **(d)** $t_n = -4n + 64$; t_{21} Review 1 **(a)** 10 **(b)** 8, 10
(c) $t_n = 2n + 2$ **(d)** 54 **(e)** 45 Review 2 **(a)** 6n – 4 **(b)** 122 **(c)** 16

Exercise 5:7

1. £75   2. 6   3. **(a)** 120, 130, 140 **(b)** 440 metres   4. **(a)** 332·1, 332·7, 333·3, 333·9, . . .
(b) 342·9 metres per second   5. Her parents were right. She would be 83.   6. £1100 profit
Review 21·75cm

Puzzles 5:8

1. 12cm   2. 23

Chapter 6   Indices. Reciprocals

Exercise 6:3

1. **(a)** 5^9 **(b)** 5^7 **(c)** 5^8 **(d)** 5^{17} **(e)** 5^3 **(f)** 5^4 **(g)** 5^{12} **(h)** 5^4 **(i)** 5^6 **(j)** 5^{16} **(k)** 5^6
2. **(a)** $2^7 = 128$ **(b)** $3^5 = 243$ **(c)** $5^2 = 25$ **(d)** $2^7 = 128$ **(e)** $4^2 = 16$ **(f)** $2^4 = 16$ **(g)** $7^1 = 7$
(h) $5^2 = 25$ 3. None   4. b, c, d, e, f are all correct   5. **(a)** x^9 **(b)** a^{12} **(c)** p^8 **(d)** x^{14}
(e) b^{a+x} **(f)** b^{a+c} **(g)** a^{x-b} **(h)** a^{xy} **(i)** x^{6a} **(j)** p^{12x} **(k)** x^{2p} **(l)** b^{2a} **(m)** a^8 **(n)** x^3
6. **(a)** x^4y^6 **(b)** $a^{12}b^4$ **(c)** $x^{10}y^5z^{15}$ **(d)** $16\,a^8b^{12}$ **(e)** $27\,p^9q^{15}$ **(f)** $16\,a^{10}x^8$ **(g)** $32x^5y^{15}z^{15}$
7. **(a)** 3^2 **(b)** 5^9 **(c)** 2^2 Review 1 d is correct   Review 2 **(a)** a^7 **(b)** p^{12} **(c)** a^6 **(d)** y^4
(e) x^{15} **(f)** $9a^8$ **(g)** $8\,x^9y^{12}$ Review 3 2^4

Exercise 6:6

1. **(a)** $\frac{3}{2}$ **(b)** $\frac{4}{3}$ **(c)** $\frac{10}{3}$ **(d)** $\frac{7}{8}$ **(e)** $\frac{4}{5}$ **(f)** 6 **(g)** $\frac{1}{7}$ **(h)** $\frac{1}{8}$ **(i)** $\frac{10}{7}$ **(j)** $\frac{10}{13}$
2. **(a)** $\frac{a}{c}$ **(b)** $\frac{c}{a}$ **(c)** $\frac{x}{z}$ **(d)** $\frac{z}{x}$ **(e)** $\frac{x}{a}$ **(f)** $\frac{a}{x}$ **(g)** $\frac{1}{x}$ **(h)** $\frac{1}{d}$ **(i)** $\frac{1}{2z}$ **(j)** $\frac{1}{5x}$
(k) $\frac{4}{x}$ **(l)** $\frac{x}{2}$ 3. **(a)** 7·1 **(b)** 0·14 **(c)** 3·3 **(d)** 0·1 **(e)** 0·04 **(f)** 0·019
Review 1 **(a)** $\frac{4}{3}$ **(b)** $\frac{1}{9}$ **(c)** 10 **(d)** $\frac{1}{k}$ **(e)** $\frac{1}{3k}$ **(f)** $\frac{3k}{a}$ Review 2 **(a)** 1·67 **(b)** 0·05
(c) 0·86

Exercise 6:8

1. **(a)** $\frac{2}{9}$ or $0·\dot{2}$ **(b)** $\frac{2}{5}$ or 0·4 **(c)** $2·\dot{7}$ **(d)** 1·5 **(e)** 2 **(f)** $\frac{2}{3}$ **(g)** – 0·24 **(h)** – 0·2
2. **(a)** 4·8 hours or 4 hrs 48 min **(b)** $4·1\dot{6}$ hours or 4 hours 10 min **(c)** 4·4 sec **(d)** 27·5 sec
3. **(a)** 600cm³ **(b)** 40cm³   4. 3 min   5. 1·97 ohms (2d.p.)   Review 1 **(a)** $\frac{3}{8}$ or 0·375
(b) 0·5   Review 2 5 amps

Answers

Chapter 7   Inequalities. Polynomial Equations

Exercise 7:3

1. (a) $n \geq -2$ (b) $n \leq 4$ (c) $n < 1$ (d) $n \geq 2\cdot5$ (e) $-3 \leq n < 4$ (f) $-3 \leq n \leq 5$
(g) $1 < n \leq 4$ (h) $2 < n < 6\cdot8$ (i) $n \leq 1\frac{1}{2}$ (j) $n > 1\cdot4$ (k) $-1\frac{1}{2} < n < 2$
(l) $-3 \leq n < 2\cdot5$ (m) $n \geq 14$ (n) $-2\cdot5 < n \leq 2\cdot5$ (o) $n < 15$ (p) $n > -7$ (q) $-9 \leq n \leq -5$
(r) $n \leq 0$ (s) $-4 < n < 0$

2. (a), (b), (c), (d), (e), (f), (g), (h)

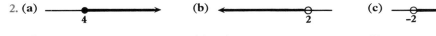

3. (a) $4, 5, 6, \ldots$ (b) $\ldots, -1, 0, 1$ (c) $-1, 0, 1, \ldots$ (d) $\ldots, -2, -1, 0$ (e) $1, 2, 3, 4$
(f) $-1, 0, 1$ (g) $-1, 0, 1$ (h) $-1, 0, 1, 2, 3$

Review 1 (a), (b), (c)

Review 2 (a) $-4, -3, -2, -1, 0, 1, 2$ (b) $\ldots, 0, 1, 2$ (c) $-2, -1, 0, \ldots$

Exercise 7:4

1. C   2. (a) D   (b) A   (c) B   3. B   4. (a) $1, 2, 3$ (b) $-4, -3, -2, -1, 0, 1$ (c) $2, 3, 4, 5, 6$
(d) $\ldots, 0, 1, 2$ (e) $-4, -3, -2, \ldots$ (f) $\ldots, -2, -1, 0$ (g) $2, 3, 4, \ldots$ (h) $0, 1, 2, \ldots$
(i) $\ldots, -1, 0, 1$ (j) $-1, 0, 1, 2, 3$ (k) $\ldots, 0, 1, 2$ (l) $1, 2$ Review (a) $-1, 0, 1, \ldots$
(b) $-2, -1, 0, 1, 2, 3$

Exercise 7:6

1. (a) $3\cdot2$ and $-3\cdot2$ (b) $2\cdot3$ and $-4\cdot3$ (c) $1\cdot3$ and $5\cdot7$ (d) 4 and -1 (e) 0 and 3 (f) $-1\cdot5$
(g) $1\cdot8$ (h) $-2\cdot7$ and $-0\cdot3$ and $3\cdot0$ (i) 0 and 2 and -3 2. (a) B   (b) B   (c) A   3. $x = 15m$,
$a = 15\cdot664m$, $n = 14\cdot349m$ Review $2\cdot8$ and $0\cdot7$

Chapter 8   Simultaneous Equations

Exercise 8:3

1. $x = 4$, $y = 1$ 2. $a = 1$, $b = 2$ 3. $x = 3$, $y = -2$ 4. $p = 2$, $q = -0\cdot5$ 5. $l = -1$, $m = 4$
6. $x = 4$, $y = 1\cdot5$ 7. $a = -2$, $b = -1$ 8. $x = 3$, $y = -2\cdot5$ Review 1. $x = 2$, $y = -3$
Review 2. $p = 3$, $q = -4$

Answers

1. **(a)** a = 2, d = 1 **(b)** x = 6, y = –1 **(c)** p = 3, q = –1 **(d)** x = –6, y = 4 **(e)** a = –1,
b = –0·5 **(f)** x = 5, y = –3 **(g)** a = –1, b = 2 **(h)** x = 0·5, y = –3 **(i)** p = 0·5, q = –2
(j) x = –2, y = –3 **(k)** x = –2·5, y = –1 3. **(a)** x = –2, y = 3 **(b)** x = –3, y = –1 **(c)** x = 1,
y = –2 **(d)** x = 0·5, y = 4 **(e)** x = 5, y = –3 **(f)** a = 2, b = 3 **(g)** x = 3, y = 5 **(h)** a = 1,
b = 5 Review **(a)** a = –3, b = 3 **(b)** x = 5, y = 2 **(c)** p = 1·5, q = –4

Page 99

Exercise 8:8

1. **(a)** x = 2, y = 3 **(b)** x = 6, y = 3 **(c)** x = 1, y = 1 **(d)** x = –2, y = –1
2. **(a)** x = 1, y = –2 **(b)** x = –2, y = –3 **(c)** x = 2, y = 7 **(d)** x = 1, y = 1
(e) x = 0·5, y = 3 Review **(a)** x = 2, y = –3 **(b)** x = 3, y = 5

Page 100

Exercise 8:10

1. 1500 before publication, 3500 after publication 2. R.J. share – £3, F.T. share – £4
3. 58, 37 4. 10 5. £2 6. 80 7. £170 8. 18, 15 9. 16 10. 12 Review 8

Chapter 9   Line Graphs

Page 104

Exercise 9:2

1. **(a)** £15 **(b)** £10 **(c)** the second cheapest **(d)** dearest £7·50, second most expensive £6,
second cheapest £4·50, cheapest £4 **(e)** Ann–second cheapest, Aaron–cheapest 2. **(a)** 26°C
(b) 6°C **(c)** 28 seconds **(d)** 5°C **(e)** 2 min 28 sec 3. **(a)** No **(b)** Jess **(c)** Jasper
(d) 1 minute **(e)** hot **(f)** cold 4. **(a)** June **(b)** July and August **(c)** £3000 **(d)** £51000
(f) £4000 5. **(a)** 30*l* **(b)** 1200km **(c)** twice **(d)** 60*l* **(e)** $\frac{1}{2}$ **(f)** 80*l* **(g)** Yes
(h) 15km/*l* **(i)** 6·7 litres per 100km Review **(a)** March 7th **(b)** morning **(c)** 38°C
(d) 9 times **(e)** 38·5°C **(f)** 6 a.m. on March 4th **(g)** Yes

Page 109

Exercise 9:6

1. 60p 5. £45 Review **(a)** 3·2 hectares **(b)** 20 acres

Page 111

Exercise 9:9

1. A–plane, B–train, C–car from Southampton, D–car from Fareham, E–ship, F–car in garage
at Fareham 2. **(a)** 9km **(b)** 3 hours **(c)** 6km **(d)** 6km/h 3. **(a)** 12km/h **(b)** 18km
(c) 9km/h **(d)** 30km **(e)** 3 hours **(f)** 10km/h 4. **(a)** C **(b)** 30km **(c)** D and A
(d) 50 min **(e)** 2 hours 30 min **(f)** 140km **(g)** 56km/h 5. **(a)** B **(b)** Yes **(c)** after they
have been travelling for 10 minutes **(d)** 20km Review **(a)** 32 min **(b)** 1·6km **(c)** 8·27 a.m.
(d) Salina **(e)** 2·2km **(f)** 100 metres per minute (to 3s.f.)

Page 116

Exercise 9:10

1. 1413 2. 55m 3. 10 sec 4. 100m Review 0823

318

Chapter 11   Algebra Review

1. (a) D (b) C   2. (a) 3^{11} (b) 3^6 (c) 3^8 (d) 3^{10} 3. (a) 15 (b) $\frac{5}{4}$ (c) $\frac{1}{7}$ (d) $\frac{x}{b}$
(e) $\frac{1}{2z}$ 4. (a) 10 matches to form 3 squares, 13 matches to form 14 squares
(b) 4, 7, 10, 13, 16   (c) $t_n = 3n + 1$ (d) 262   5. (a) Jason   (b) return journey by 5km/h
6. (a) . . ., 2, 3, 4   (b) –1, 0, 1, 2, 3, 4   (c) 0, 1, 2, . . .   7. (a) x = –2, y = –3   (b) x = 2,
y = 0·5   8. 1·2, –1·7   9. (a) the Saturday of the 1st week   (b) 6   (c) 3·5°C (to 1d.p.)
10. (a) 1, 3, 5, 7, 9   (b) 181   (c) The 61st term.   11. x = 2, y = –1   12. 3   13. 0700 hours
14. (a) 1740   (b) 5 minutes   (c) 15km/h   (d) 24km/hr   (e) 16km/h   15. £80   16. (a) 2·9
(b) 0·12   (c) 0·11   (d) 0·024   17. e + *l* = 140, 75e +80*l* = 11100;   20 paid before 1st May
18. (a) a^{x+b} (b) a^{x-b} (c) a^{xb} (d) a^{x+b-z} (e) a^6 (f) a^6b^8 (g) $9a^8b^2$
19. (a) $x^2 + 2x = 40$ (b) 5·4 metres   20. (a) $t_n = 7n - 2$ (b) $t_n = -3n + 31$ (c) $t_n = -2n$
(d) $t_n = 3n^2$ (e) $t_n = n^3 + 1$ (f) $t_n = \frac{n+1}{n+3}$ 21. –5, –4, –3, –2, –1, 0, 1, 2, 3   22. (a) 0·6

(b) 4·6   23. Ben leaves home later than Angela, walking more slowly than Angela. He misses
the bus, then runs home. He then travels to school by car, arriving at school earlier than Angela.
(If the car travelled along the same route near the school that Angela walked, it didn't stop to pick
Angela up.)

Shape and Space from Previous Levels

Revision Exercise

1. (a) 1   (b) infinite number   (c) 1   2. (a) 8   (b) 12   (c) 18   3. (a) g   (b) n   (c) b, m
(d) c, i   (e) a, *l*   4. (a) h, k, e, f, *l*, n, a   (b) d and g ; e and f   (c) 360°   (d) 180°
5. (a) C   (b) C   6. (a) Area = 13·5cm², Perimeter = 18cm   (b) Area = 112mm²,
Perimeter = 58mm   (c) Area = 78·5m², Perimeter = 31·4m   7. A′(1, –3), B′(4, –5), C′(6, 2),
D′(–1, 0)   8. (a) pentagon   (b) cube   (c) parallelogram   (d) sphere   9. (a) x = 95°,
y = 48°, z = 37°   (b) x = 60°, y = 49°, z = 70°   10. C   11. Bearing of A from P is 052° ;
bearing of B from P is 063° ; bearing of C from P is 131° ; bearing of D from P is 240° ;
bearing of E from P is 328°   12. (a) B and D ; F and G   (b) E   (c) C, E   (d) A, B, D, F, G
(e) D and E ; B and C ; C, D and E ; B, C and D ; B, C, D and E   13. (a) 2·4m³   (b) 157cm³
14. (a) 3   (b) (4, 1)   15. List 1 shapes all have equal sides ; List 2 shapes have perpendicular
diagonals (these shapes also have 4 sides ; these shapes also have two pairs of adjacent equal sides)
16. 285°   17. (2, 4), (6, 0), (2, 0), (2, –4), (–2, 0)   18. (a) 46°   (b) 20°   (c) 53°   (d) 145°
19. (b) about 5km

20.

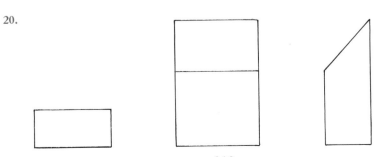

21. **(b)** Triangle 1 to Triangle 2   22. 160°   24.

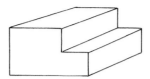

25. **(a)** fig (i) and fig (iii)   **(b)** Yes, possible in fig (iii)
26. **(a)** 2312cm³   **(b)** Yes   27. 56mm   28. FD   200
                                                     RT   120
                                                     FD   200
                                                     RT   60
                                                     FD   200

Chapter 12   3–D Coordinates

Page 146   **Exercise 12:2**

1. **(a)** C **(b)** R **(c)** E **(d)** T **(e)** B **(f)** D   2. G (5, 0, 0), H (5, 4, 0), I (5, 4, 2),
J (0, 0, 3), K (5, 0, 2), L (0, 5, 3), M (3, 4, 2), N (3, 5, 3)   3. A (0, 0, 2), B (0, 2, 2),
C (2, 2, 2), D (2, 0, 2), F (0, 2, 0), G (2, 2, 0), H (2, 0, 0)   4. A (1, 2, 2), C (4, 6, 2),
D (4, 2, 2), E (1, 2, 0), F (1, 6, 0), G (4, 6, 0)   5. **(a)** A (2, –3, 0), B (2, 3, 0), C (–2, 3, 0),
D (–2, –3, 0), T (0, 0, 7) **(b)** (3, 3, –3), (–3, 3, –3), (–3, –3, –3), (3, –3, 3), (3, 3, 3), (–3, 3, 3),
(–3, –3, 3)   **Review** A (3, 2, 4), B (3, 7, 4), D (6, 2, 4), F (3, 7, 0), G (6, 7, 0), H (6, 2, 0)

Chapter 13   Locus

Page 155   **Exercise 13:4**

1. circle, centre A, radius 3cm   2. a pair of parallel lines, each 25mm from AB   3. the
perpendicular bisector (mediator) of the line joining C and D   4. the bisector of the acute angle
PQR   5. the line parallel to the lines AB and CD and equidistant from both of them
6. **(a)** circle, centre B, radius 2cm   **(b)** the bisector (from A to BC) of the angle BAC
(c) the perpendicular bisector (mediator) of the line AC   **Review (a)** the perpendicular bisector
(mediator) of the line joining D and B   **(b)** the bisector (from A to DC) of the angle DAB
(c) circle, centre S, radius the length of the chain (maybe part of a circle depending on the length
of the chain)

Page 159   **Exercise 13:7**

1. to the left of the perpendicular bisector (mediator) of the line joining A and B   2. the interior
of a circle, centre C, radius 2cm   3. below the line which is parallel to AB and CD and
equidistant from them   4. between the pair of lines that are parallel to EF and distance 15mm
from EF   5. between GH and the bisector of the angle GHI

15. (a)

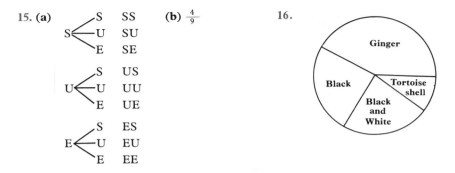

S —┌ S   SS
  ├ U   SU
  └ E   SE

U —┌ S   US
  ├ U   UU
  └ E   UE

E —┌ S   ES
  ├ U   EU
  └ E   EE

(b) $\frac{4}{9}$

16.

17. (a) H1, H2, H3, H4, H5, H6, T1, T2, T3, T4, T5, T6   **(b)** $\frac{1}{4}$

18. Group 1, Group 3, Group 5   **19. (a)** Yes   **(b)** Any network with the same number of arcs from each node as in the networks in (a) will represent the given roads.

Chapter 19   Mean, Median, Mode, Range.
Frequency Tables and Graphs

Page 242   **Exercise 19:3**

1. (a) mean = 7, median = 7, mode = 7   **(b)** mean = 5·9 (1d.p.), median = 5·5, modes are 2, 5 and 7   **(c)** mean = 6·27, median = 6·3, no mode   **(d)** mean = 63·3 (1d.p.), median = 72·5, mode = 76   **(e)** mean = 0·48, median = 0·45, mode = 0·3   **(f)** mean = 1·48, median = 1·45, mode = 1·3   **2. (a)** 10   **(b)** 9   **(c)** 3·7   **(d)** 68   **(e)** 0·8   **(f)** 1·8   **3. (a)** 1·60m   **(b)** 1·60m
4. (a) range = 49, mean = 71·3, median = 71·5, mode = 63 and 74   **Review (a)** Cardiff
(b) Andover   **(c)** Stirling   **(d)** Coventry

Page 245   **Exercise 19:4**

1. (a) 2·5   **(b)** 38   **(c)** 16   **(d)** 7·6 (1 d.p.)   **2. (a)** 3   **(b)** 40   **(c)** 11 and 18   **(d)** 9
3. (a) 2·5   **(b)** 40   **(c)** 18   **(d)** 8   **4. (a)** 4   **(b)** 50   **(c)** 10   **(d)** 8
5. (a) mean = 2·2 (1d.p.), median = 1, mode = 1, range = 4   **6. (a)** mean = 29·6 (1d.p.), median = 30, mode = 31, range = 6   **Review (a)** mean = 2·0 (1d.p.), median = 2   **(b)** 8
(c) 1

Page 248   **Exercise 19:6**

1. (a) 2   **(b)** 9·9 days (to 1d.p.)   **(c)** 1–3 days   **(d)** 7–9 days   **2. (a)** 26·7   **(b)** 29
Review (a) 22·3   **(b)** 21–25   **(c)** 21–25

Page 250   **Exercise 19:7**

1. (a) 1·45kg   **(b)** 5·09kg   **(c)** 5–6kg   **(d)** 4–5kg   **2. (a)** 32min   **(b)** 52·0min (1d.p.)
3. (a) 2·1km (1 d.p.)   **(b)** 0·5–1·0km   **(c)** 2·0–2·5km   **4. (a)** 124·5m   **(b)** 156·2m (1 d.p.)
Review (a) 3·2m   **(b)** 4·02m   **(c)** 4·0–4·5m   **(d)** 4·0–4·5m

Exercise 19:11

1.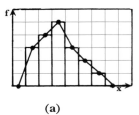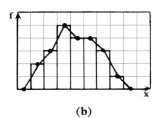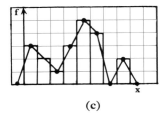

            (a)   **(b)**   **(c)**

2. **(a)** 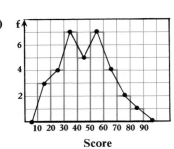 **(b)**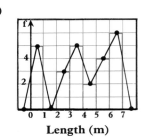

3. **(a)**

Score	15–19	20–24	25–29	30–34	35–39	40–44	45–49
Tally	⊤⊦⊦⊦	⊤⊦⊦⊦ ‖‖	⊤⊦⊦⊦ ⊤⊦⊦⊦	⊤⊦⊦⊦ ‖‖	⊤⊦⊦⊦ ‖‖‖	⊤⊦⊦⊦ ‖	‖‖‖
f	5	8	10	8	9	6	4

(b)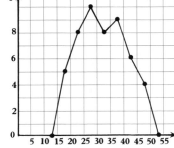

328

4. (a)

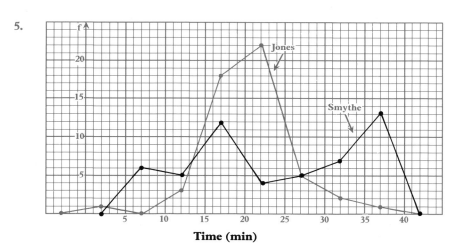

% Saving

5.

Time (min)

Review 1 (a)

Number of mistakes	0–4	5–9	10–14	15–19	20–24	25–29
Tally	卌 卌 卌 |||	卌 卌 ||||	卌 ||	||	|||		
f	18	14	7	2	3	1

(b)

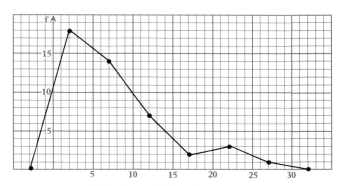

Number of Mistakes

Answers

Review 2

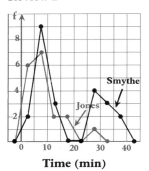

Time (min)

Chapter 20 Scatter Diagrams

Page 263 — Exercise 20:4

1. (a)

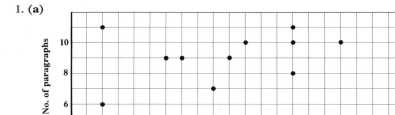

2. (a), (b)   (c) 69   (d) 82

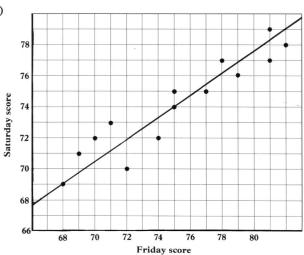

3. **(b), (c)**

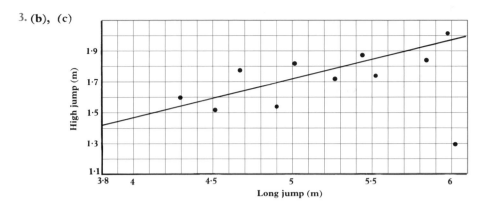

The point (6·03, 1·30) has been ignored in drawing the line of best fit.

4. **(a)**

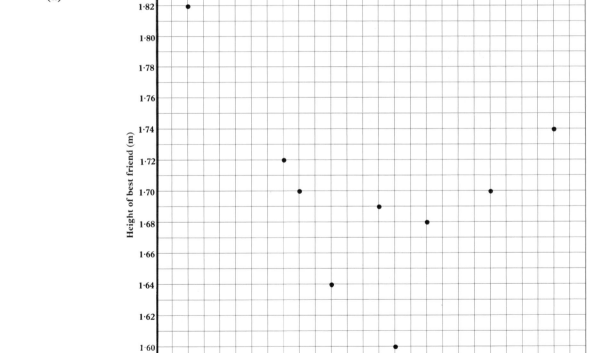

(b) No. Since there
is no correlation
a line of best fit cannot be drawn.

5. (a), (c)

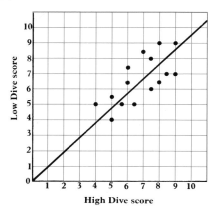

Review (a), (b)

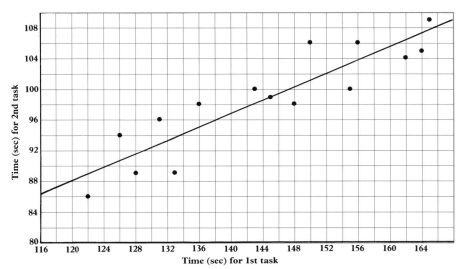

138 seconds   102 seconds

Chapter 21   Flow Diagrams

Page 274   **Exercise 21:4**

1. 4, 8, 12, 16, 20, 24 Multiplies each number by 4.   **2.** 2, 4, 6, 8, 10, 12 Leaves the even numbers unchanged but adds 1 to each odd number.   **3.** 36, 44, 22, 6 Writes down the even numbers.   **Review** 20, 35, 95, 120 Writes down the numbers that are divisible by 5.

Page 277   **Exercise 21:5**

1. 8, 10, 16   **2.** 6, 4, 6, 6, 4   **3.** 5, 7, 9, 3   **Review** 1, 0, 0, 1, 1, 0

Exercise 21:8

1. 36; finds the sum of the odd numbers that are less than 12   2. 1, 2, 3, 6, 9, 18; finds the factors of a number   3. 8; finds the mean of a list of numbers   4. 2, 3, 3, 4, 4, 5; finds the greatest whole number that is less than the square root of a number   **Review** 55; finds the sum of the squares of the whole numbers that are less than 6

Exercise 21:10

Possible flow diagrams are given below. Others are possible.

1.

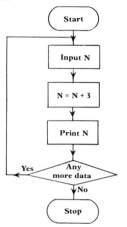

2.

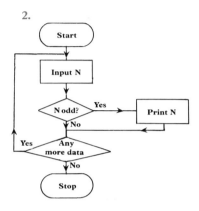

3.

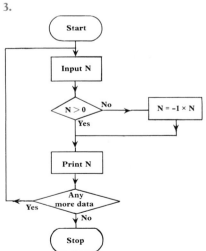

4.

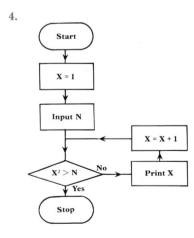

Review

5. (a)   (b)

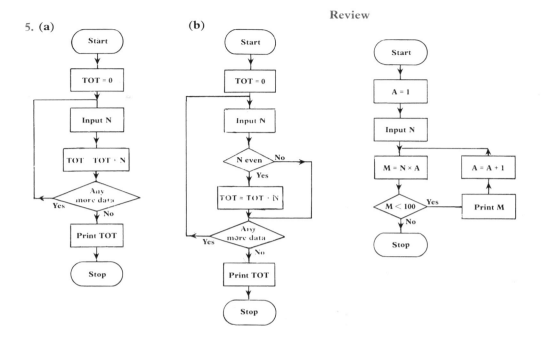

Chapter 22   Estimating Probability

Page 286   Exercise 22:1

1. (a) 48   (b) $\frac{7}{48}$ 2. (a) $\frac{4}{13}$ (b) $\frac{1}{2}$ 3. (a) $\frac{26}{125}$ (b) $\frac{7}{25}$ (c) $\frac{67}{250}$ (d) $\frac{61}{250}$ Sum = 1

4. (a) $\frac{47}{200}$ (b) $\frac{43}{200}$ (c) $\frac{11}{20}$ Sum = 1   Review (a) $\frac{3}{25}$ (b) $\frac{29}{200}$ (c) $\frac{4}{25}$ (d) $\frac{41}{200}$

(e) $\frac{39}{200}$ (f) $\frac{7}{40}$ Sum = 1

Chapter 23   Calculating Probability

Page 295   Exercise 23:1

1. mututally exclusive   2. mutually exclusive   3. not mutually exclusive   4. not mutually
exclusive   5. not mutually exclusive   6. not mutually exclusive   7. mutually exclusive
8. not mutually exclusive   9. mutually exclusive   Review 1 mutually exclusive
Review 2 not mutually exclusive

Page 299   Exercise 23:3

1. $\frac{2}{3}$ 2. $\frac{2}{13}$ 3. $\frac{1}{2}$ 4. $\frac{1}{3}$ 5. 0·45   6. $\frac{1}{2}$ 7. 0·38   8. (a) 0·4   (b) 0·65

(c) 0·55   9. (a) 0·25   (b) 0·65   Review 1 $\frac{2}{3}$ Review 2 0·29   Review 3 (a) 0·65

(b) 0·35   (c) 0·95

Chapter 24   Data Handling Review

Page 303

1. **(a)** mean = 18·2 (1d.p.), median = 16, mode = 14, range = 15   **(b)** mean = 12·5 (1d.p.),
median = 11, mode = 6 and 24, range = 22   **(c)** mean = 7·4, median = 8, no mode, range = 13
(d) mean = 4·3 (1d.p.), median = 4, mode = 2, range = 8,   **(e)** mean = 3·6 (1d.p.),
median = 4, mode = 5, range = 4

2.

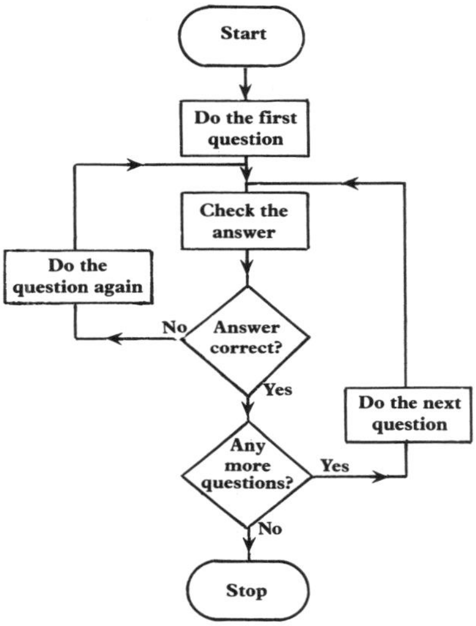

3. line m   4. **(a)** $\frac{42}{150}$ **(b)** 0·28 ($\frac{7}{25}$)   5. **(a)** 9·4 **(b)** 6-10   **(c)** 1-5   6. c

7. **(a)**

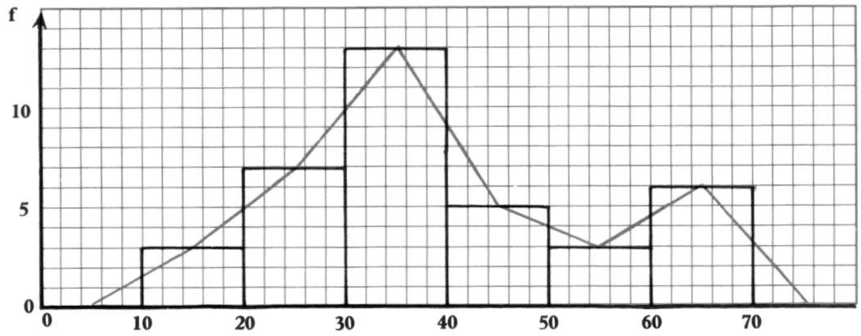

8.

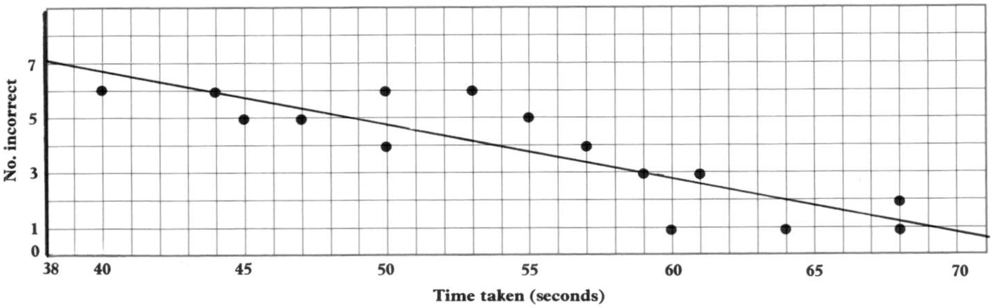

335

9. The output is 4. The flow diagram counts the number of numbers in a list that are greater than 10.

10. **(a)** 53·5 **(b)** 50-55 **(c)** 55-60

11. **(a)** 127 **(b)** $\frac{10}{127}$ or 0·08 (1d.p.) **(c)** $\frac{16}{127}$ or 0·13 (1d.p.) **(d)** mean = 4·0 (1d.p.),

median = 4, mode = 3, range = 12   12. $\frac{15}{52}$

13. **(b)**   **(c)** not sensible

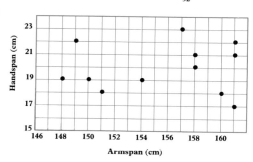

Armspan (cm)

14. **(a)** 0·4 **(b)** 0·6 **(c)** 0·66 **(d)** 0·74

15. **(b)**

Under 30

Time (min)	30–	35–	40–	45–	50–	55–	60–65
f		5	11	9	6	8	3	3

30 or over

Time (min)	30–	35–	40–	45–	50–	55–	60–65
f		1	6	7	9	15	7	0

(c)

f

Time (min)

16.

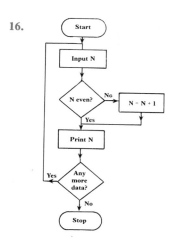